D1602087

and the SEAWORTHY DOUBLE-ENDER

Colin Archer

and the SEAWORTHY DOUBLE-ENDER

By

JOHN LEATHER

INTERNATIONAL MARINE PUBLISHING
COMPANY
Camden, Maine 04843

OTHER BOOKS BY JOHN LEATHER

Gaff Rig
The Northseamen
Clinker Boatbuilding
Panorama of Gaff Rig (with Roger Smith)
World Warships in Review
Modern Development in Yacht Design (with David Cannell)
Spritsails and Lugsails
The Sailor's Coast

Library of Congress Catalog Card Number 78-55782
International Standard Book Number 0-87742-086-6
Typeset by A & B Typesetters, Inc., Concord, New Hampshire
Printed and bound by The Alpine Press, South Braintree, Massachusetts

Published by International Marine Publishing Company
21 Elm Street, Camden, Maine 04843

CONTENTS

ACKNOWLEDGMENTS

During the preparation of this book, I have been fortunate to have had assistance from several Norwegian friends in assembling information and assisting with translation. For an Englishman even to attempt a book on a Norwegian personality, he *needs* to have good friends who speak the language. My thanks are particularly due to Oddbjorn Jonassen of Bergen; Lieutenant J. Berggrav, Royal Norwegian Navy; Jeppe Jul Nielsen of Snaroya; F.O. Thomsson; and Else Marie Thorstvedt of the Norsk Sjofartsmuseum, Oslo. My colleague, David T. Grant, Senior Principal Surveyor for Norway of Lloyd's Register of Shipping, assisted with introductions to the Norsk Sjofartsmuseum, which, with the Norske Folkemuseum of Oslo, provided some of the illustrations. Help with illustrations of redningskoites was received from Uffa Fox Ltd and Norske Selskab Til Skibbrudnes Redning. Others who assisted with illustrations and material on yachts designed in the Colin Archer tradition include Carl H. Vilas, Mrs. Jay Wells, David Cox, the Colin Archer Club of Stockholm, Jan Wilsgaard of Gothenburg, and Erling Brunborg.

Designers who have contributed plans and material on their designs that were influenced by Colin Archer's work include John Atkin, William Garden, Nelson Zimmer, Alan H. Buchanan, Manuel Campos, German Frers (Senior), and the Westsail Corporation.

I am grateful to William W. Robinson, Editor of *Yachting,* for permission to reprint from the writings of Erling Tambs, and to the editors of *Motor Boat and Yachting* and the *Yachting Monthly* for assistance with extracts on Colin Archer craft.

I should not forget my introduction to the redningskoites over 30 years ago, at the invitation of Major Dowes Martin, then owner of the *Risor II.*

This book is the inspiration of Roger C. Taylor, President of International Marine, and the original text has been ably rearranged by their editor, Peter H. Spectre, with whom the author has enjoyed a cordial and refreshingly constructive working relationship.

To these and others, my thanks. I hope readers will enjoy the results of the four years of research and writing that have gone into this appreciation of Colin Archer's work and influence.

JOHN LEATHER
COWES, ISLE OF WIGHT
ENGLAND

PART I

COLIN ARCHER AND HIS DESIGNS

Colin Archer about 1905. (Courtesy of Yachting Monthly*)*

1

COLIN ARCHER

To understand and appreciate the work of a small-craft designer, it helps to know his background and experience, which initially may be very different from the work for which he subsequently became noted—a circumstance that typified Colin Archer's early years. Archer had a varied career as a young man; little of it was connected with the design, construction, or use of small sailing craft.

Colin Archer, though born in Norway, came from a Scottish family. His father, William Archer, was from Perthshire in Scotland. Several generations of Archers had been members of the glover's guild of Perth. The Archer family was reputed to have been descended from an Englishman who had served in Cromwell's army in Scotland during the mid-seventeenth century.

Archer's mother, Julia Walker, came from a farm in the Fifeshire village of Leslie. Her family originally came from the Hebrides, on the Scottish west coast; they moved to Leslie during the sixteenth century to farm and later to operate a tannery. Religious people, several Walkers were ministers in the Presbyterian Church.

As a young man, William Archer became a partner in the firm of Charles Archer and Son, timber merchants located in Newborough, a Fifeshire town on the Firth of Tay. They imported timber from Scandinavia. During a business trip to Norway in 1819, William Archer visited Larvik (then named Laurvig), a small town at the head of Larvik Fjord, which is a small fjord on the southern coast, near the approaches to Oslofjord. This quiet yet thriving maritime community appealed to the young Scot, and the impression of attractive tranquility remained with him long after his return to Newborough.

The economic depression that followed the Napoleonic Wars almost ruined the timber trade. William Archer came to feel that there was little opportunity left for him in Scotland, so in the summer of 1825 he decided to emigrate to Norway with his family, which then numbered seven children—Catherine, Charles, John, David, William, Archibald, and Thomas. He intended to become a lobster merchant and shipper and, because of his previous favorable impression, chose Larvik as his base of operations.

At that time, shipping lobsters from Norway to Britain, particularly the south of England, was a thriving trade. Norwegian fishermen sold their lobster catches to merchants, who shipped them abroad in vessels fitted with tanks in their holds or, more often, with "wet wells"—watertight compartments in the hull with holes through the bottom and sides to allow the circulation of sea water.

The Archer family bought a house with several acres of land on a rocky promontory that jutted into Larvik Fjord. It was known as Tolderodden and included cultivated gardens and trees. The wooden house had a high, pitched roof and faced south toward the entrance of the fjord. The house was renovated and the family moved in. It was a happy place, filled with children; between 1826 and 1836, five more were born—Mary, Alexander, Jane Ann, Colin, and James.

William Archer became a lobster merchant. In later years, he also became a director of a company handling timber that had been floated down from the forests in streams to be made into rafts, which were towed away to customers or for shipment in cargo vessels. In addition, he became British consul at Larvik, since British ships called there to load or discharge cargo.

Colin Archer was born on July 22, 1832. His childhood world of Larvik was a community of shipowners, seafarers, shipbuilders, chandlers, and others associated with that area's then considerable coasting and overseas trade. Craft calling at the port or based there included small square-rigged ships, schooners, ketches, cutters, and local hybrid types. From the beginning, Colin Archer was surrounded by and fascinated with many aspects of seagoing life.

Colin Archer apparently was ten years old by the time he went to the local elementary school. This is understandable, as state education was then unknown and private schools were costly. His fees were temporarily waived, to be paid later, since his father at the time was poor. A year later, Colin Archer passed to the middle school, where he remained until early in 1849, when his formal schooling was over at age 16. During that short period, he showed mathematical ability, which probably was the foundation of his later understanding of naval architecture.

Colin's older brothers also left school at an early age and were sent to Scotland to live with relatives and learn a trade. They were being prepared to go to Australia—then one of the most common destinations for children of large Scottish families who sought a new life and living. For some reason—possibly because he was one of the youngest—Colin at first did not follow his older brothers. He stayed home in Larvik and was employed by Michael Treschow, who owned a small shipyard at Jordfalden, a creek on the west side of Larvik Fjord, two miles seaward of Tolderodden. At the yard, ships to carry ore from mines also owned by Treschow were built and repaired. Young Colin Archer worked there for 18 months as a ship carpenter; there is no record of his commencing a formal apprenticeship, though he probably did the work of an apprentice. During that time he attended evening classes in navigation.

In 1850, Colin's father decided it was time for him to join his brothers in Australia. Actually, he was to get there in a roundabout way, as he was first to join his brother Tom, who was in California, having left Australia in 1849 to join the Gold Rush. Colin took passage across the Atlantic, crossed the Isthmus at Panama to the Pacific coast, and traveled by ship north to San Francisco. He spent two years in the gold fields, as both a carpenter (he had brought his tools from Larvik) and a prospector. In about May, 1852, he sailed for the Sandwich Islands (now Hawaii), where his brother Archibald had a plantation on the island of Kauai. After a brief stay, he took passage for Australia, where he joined his brothers who had settled there.

The Archer brothers—Thomas, Charles, David, and William—were sheep farmers in New South Wales. Colin went to work with them in 1853 and was to remain until 1861.

Larvik, Norway, Colin Archer's home. The Archer family house, Tolderodden, is at the extreme right below the church on a small promontory. Most of Archer's craft were constructed here.

He participated in the work of the sheep station and made long trips on horseback into the bush to survey the runs of sheep and explore the country for improved feeding and watering areas. At one point, he sailed a small ketch the brothers bought to run supplies to parts of the station more easily accessible by water. This duty was short, however, as the boat was sold when other means of supply were developed. Colin became supervisor of one of the Archer sheep stations when his brother Charles left to return to Norway in 1857 to be with his father, whose health was deteriorating.

In 1861, the Archer brothers received news from Tolderodden that their father was failing rapidly. Colin left on September 10, 1861, to join his father and brother. On arrival in London, worse news was awaiting him—his brother Charles had died suddenly at age 50 after receiving a head injury a few months previously while skiing. Colin Archer sadly hurried home to Norway and a new destiny.

On arrival at Tolderodden, Colin Archer became nominal head of the Archer household. His father died in 1862. As family wealth had accrued from the Australian ventures, he was able for a time to lead the life of a man of leisure and indulge in occasional travel. Three years of this passed, and he began to miss the activity of his earlier years abroad. He was an avid boat sailor, and his interest in the sea and ships had remained undimmed since his days of working in Treschow's shipyard. Ideas of a maritime occupation recurred, but he realized that his family responsibilities dictated that whatever he did would have to be carried out from Larvik.

Colin Archer in middle age.

Colin Archer decided to make a career of designing and building small craft. As he had no formal training in ship or boat design or construction, he commenced the study of naval architecture on his own. Then in 1865-66, he began the construction of small craft on the shore of a shallow inlet called The Bugt that led off the fjord in front of his house.

By 1867, Archer's boatbuilding venture needed a more permanent site, so he had two building berths constructed at the rear of the house, on the northwestern shore of the promontory facing Larvik. Here, through the years, almost all but the largest of Colin Archer's designs were built by the few shipwrights he employed. (The largest ships, such as the *Fram*, which will be discussed in a later chapter, were built at a yard in Raekevik Bay, on the east shore of Larvik Fjord, below the town.)

In 1868, Colin Archer married Karen Sophie Wiborg from Kragero, a nearby small town. There was plenty of space on the grounds of Tolderodden, so he decided to build a new, smaller house for himself and his bride. Named Lilleodden, the house had a small room on the ground floor where Archer was to develop all of his subsequent designs and theories of naval architecture.

Colin Archer's designs and the craft he built from them will be discussed fully in later chapters, but suffice it to say that much of his day was spent at the drafting table in the study, the remainder discussing the construction of craft in the boatbuilding sheds with the foreman and dealing with general office work arising from the business. By 1879, Archer's technical ability had developed considerably and his reputation as a designer spread beyond southern Norway. That year he was elected a member of the Institution of Naval Architects, then a considerable honor for a non-British designer and builder of small craft. In 1886, Archer was further honored with the Cross of the Order of St. Olaf, conferred on him by the King of Norway. He also received the Silver Medal of the Royal Geographic Society.

Colin Archer enjoyed leisure, particularly time during the long summer days for day-sailing, picnics, and walks. He carried on a lively correspondence covering a wide variety of topics, from English poetry to ship design, with relatives, friends, and correspondents of all ages from many countries, much of it expressing his kindly, ordered personality. Like others in his family, Colin Archer was bilingual in Norwegian and English; most of his letters, however, were in Norwegian. He was fond of poetry in both Norwegian and English, and sometimes wrote verse. But Archer didn't confine his non-business time to purely personal affairs. He invested considerable time and effort in community work; for instance, during 1889-90 he was chairman of the Larvik municipality board and for some time was a member of the harbor board. He brought to both his clear thought and direct speech.

By the late 1890s, Colin Archer was a nationally known figure. The success of his rescue ship designs, and the design and construction of the polar ship *Fram,* had brought recognition, but the accolades did not affect his quiet manner and humble approach to his work and its associated problems. Humility and clarity of thought were qualities he retained throughout his life. He was at the peak of his career as a designer. Pilot, rescue, and fishing vessels as well as yachts were being built to his designs at Tolderodden and in several other yards, and he was still making innovations—for instance, shortly after the turn of the century he developed several types of motor craft.

In 1909, when Colin Archer was seventy-eight years old, his assistant, Axel Harman, died and Archer decided to retire. It took two years, however, for new construction from his designs to be completed. It was only after the last vessel was launched that Archer settled down to retired life at Tolderodden, to correspondence and the company of relatives and friends. He could look back on a life of

The rescue ship Langesund II *(RS 15) under construction in Archer's Tolderodden yard in 1901. Colin Archer (left foreground) is discussing a plan, probably with Axel Harman, his draftsman and assistant.*

achievement, despite the unevenness of his early days, which had nevertheless provided the funds for the establishment of his career as a designer and builder. Perhaps most important to him was having won the respect and esteem of thousands of fishermen, pilots, rescue ship crews, yachtsmen, and other seafarers on the coasts of Norway, the Baltic countries, and beyond.

After retirement, Colin Archer maintained his interest in the design and construction of small craft, besides engaging in a variety of other activities. During 1911, for instance, he visited the youngest of his two daughters who was living in Egypt with her husband, Judge Halvard Heggen. He was accompanied by his eldest daughter and her husband. He remained an avid sailor and cruised the waters near his home, and at least once made a lengthy cruise, when he set off in a pilot cutter he had built some years before on a cruise across the Skagerrak to the Skaw, at the tip of Denmark's Jutland peninsula, with a crew consisting of his daughter and a seasick nephew.

Colin Archer remained in good health until almost the end of his life and keenly followed the voyages of craft he had designed or built. As he grew older, however, he found he had to curtail his activities. In 1920 he resigned as District Foreman of the Rescue Society, as this required attendance at meetings in Christiania (now Oslo). But the Society insisted he remain linked to it in an honorary capacity, and, in January, 1921, knowing his health was rapidly failing, they presented him with a special diploma for his work on the rescue boats. A few weeks later, on February 8, 1921, Colin Archer died, aged 89.

He was buried in a secluded spot among the rounded granite rocks on the grounds of Tolderodden, close to the graves of others of his family. Seamen gathered at his funeral—pilots, fishermen, and captains of the rescue ships—as did councillors, committeemen, and government ministers. Many small-craft builders, yachtsmen, and yacht designers were there. Johan Anker, then Norway's leading yacht designer, representing the Royal Norwegian Yacht Club, said of Colin Archer: "As long as there are sailing craft on our waters, so long will his memory live."

Anker's words proved true, but none could then foresee how Colin Archer's designs and ideals of seaworthiness would continue to inspire designers and yacht sailors for succeeding generations.

2

PILOT BOATS

Larvik's position close to the entrance of Oslofjord, with its large numbers of inward and outward bound ships, made Colin Archer gradually familiar with the work and personalities of the local pilots, whose small, sloop-rigged boats cruised outside the Skjaergaard or skerries, a fringe of rocks that lies off much of the Norwegian coast. These pilots hailed from many small villages in the area and spent much of their life seeking ships in the Skagerrak, the channel between southern Norway and Denmark. The Skagerrak is not only the approach to Oslofjord, but also to the Baltic Sea. The approaches to the Norwegian coast are subject to some vicious seas, and the pilot boats, which were necessarily small, needed to be able craft.

In the mid-nineteenth century, the pilot boats of that district were almost all of a type known as the Hvalerbaat, developed from a type of local fishing craft. Until the Hvalerbaat's era, the fishermen of southern Norway had used open rowing and sailing boats for centuries. This limited the choice of fishing grounds and in bad weather frequently resulted in capsized boats and lost men. Such incidents inevitably drew the well-meaning attentions of people outside the fishing communities, and proposals for decked and more able craft were made by Commander P.A. Solling (1758-1827) of Kristiansand, an officer of what was then the Dano-Norwegian Navy.

Solling attempted to induce fishing boat owners to adopt a decked type of sailing boat, but, as is usual with such attempts, the fishermen resented interference from an outsider. During 1799, Solling visited England to study the design and construction of various small fishing craft. He returned to Norway and initiated the design and construction of a decked, sailing fishing craft, built of oak for durability and having well-secured internal ballast. He spent much time demonstrating this boat to fishermen, and gradually some ordered similar craft. The boats proved themselves as capable—and eventually Solling's improved fishing boat superseded the open boats in southern Norway.

During the early nineteenth century, these decked and ballasted sailing boats evolved into a distinct type, which became known as the Hvalerbaat, or Whale Island boat, after a group of islands to the east of Larvik Fjord,

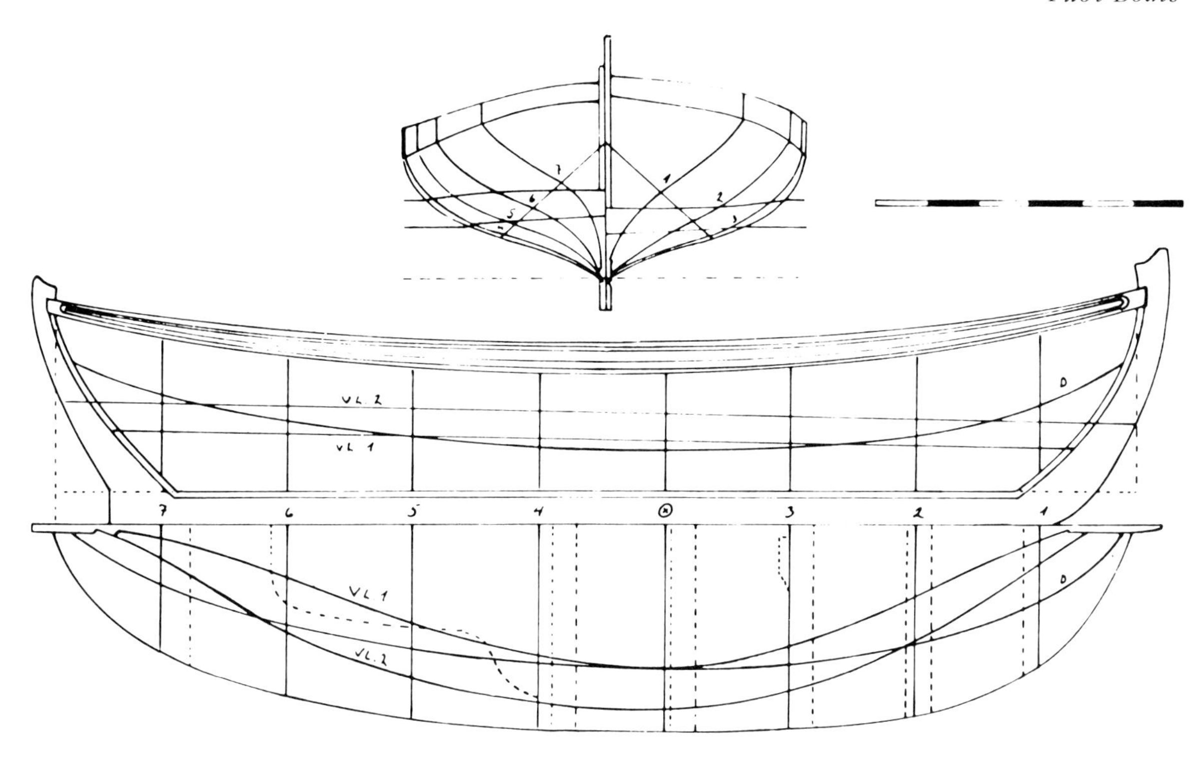

Lines of a pointed-stern sailing boat of the east coast of Norway, recorded by Fredrik Chapman, 1768. This hull has the basic characteristics of the Hvalerbaats from which Colin Archer developed his pilot boat designs.

close to the Swedish coast. The Hvalerbaat was also adopted by pilots of the area, and with the rapid expansion of trade into and from the Baltic after the Napoleonic wars, many pilot boats were in service and pilotage became competitive.

By the 1860s, a typical Hvalerbaat was 28 feet long, by 10 feet beam, by 3 feet draft. They were lightly built, with lapstrake hull planking. Frequent icing of exposed surfaces during the winter caused the loss of many. The owners, both fishermen and pilots, were poor men, and they kept their boats as long as possible. As a result, many were in poor repair and inadequately rigged and equipped. Accommodation was crude on Hvalerbaats. There was a small cabin, without standing headroom, that had wooden bunks and an old tub, which was lined with clay and stones and served as a stove. Frequently the decks leaked from the boat's excessive working, and the crews slept on old sails or nets for mattresses. Many of the men had no oilskins, and the harsh conditions of their lives led to considerable drunkenness and further loss of life.

The hull form of the Hvalerbaat was full forward but it had a long run, ending in a pointed stern. The flaring bow sections above water made the boats pound in a sea and slowed them considerably. The internal stone ballast was usually inadequately secured (despite Commander Solling's advice to the contrary), and, if it broke adrift in bad weather, the boat was often lost.

In the spring and the summer, the life of a pilot was tolerable, but in winter it was harsh. C. Schollert wrote of a contemporary pilot's winter seafaring:

> Imagine the pilot on a stormy winter's night, pitch dark, snowing and freezing. Within the harbour, and for some distance outside, he makes his way through the ice floes. No sooner is he in the open and on his course, than the seas begin to wash over his boat; but not to pass right away; a film of ice is left on the

"Hard Alee." The helmsman of a pilot boat puts her about in rough seas. (From a painting by Christian Krohg)

boat's side and deck, ever becoming thicker. As with the boat, so with the pilot; he, too, becomes iron clad. There is nothing for it, however, but to carry on, straining his eyes and ears for the vessel needing his help. Having come upon her, he brings up as nearly as possible alongside, but cannot board her owing to the heavy sea running; so, with the life line carried for such emergencies fastened around his waist, he is dragged through the waves on to the ship's deck. He goes straight to the helm, and, once his hand is on it, a weight is lifted from the minds of all on board. There he stands looking out for every breaker, every rocky islet and point. At last, steering the ship through the breaking sea, white with foam, he gains the harbour.

By the mid-nineteenth century, many of the boats of these pilots had been improved in design by the various local builders, but the occasional losses of pilot boats and men from them turned Colin Archer's interest to the Hvalerbaat. After observing them carefully, he commenced a design study for the improvement of the type. His attention to pilot-boat design was to last for many years and bring fame to his name. His work on them established his reputation as a designer.

Colin Archer explained his ideas for improvement in hull shape and construction to those cautiously conservative pilots considering ordering a new boat. Most pilots rejected his suggestions, and progress was slow. Colin found the best way to impress the pilots was to emphasize the possible advantages of a new

A Norwegian pilot cutter under sail. Note the small jib and topsail yard.

style of craft—one that would be a larger and better sea boat, safer to work, strongly built of more durable materials, and with comfortable accommodations. His most persuasive argument was economics: a new type could have greater speed to reach an incoming ship before rivals and ability to carry sail longer and ride out worse weather when seeking an inward-bound ship. To achieve all this, Archer's proposals included reduced beam and increased depth and draft, features that were ultimately embodied in the first order for a pilot boat placed with his yard in 1872. The success of the first boat generated orders for more, and Colin Archer's pilot-boat design gradually became established on the Norwegian coast.

The Hvalerbaats, like most Norwegian small craft, were lapstrake planked, construction which required no caulking and could be built with comparatively few heavy frames or a larger number of light ones. The lapstrake planking increased hull resistance and suffered damage if the boat laid alongside a ship when in a seaway, so, after building seven lapstrake-planked pilot-boat hulls, Colin Archer prevailed on pilots to let him use carvel planking on closely spaced, sawn frames.

During 1873 a pilot boat Colin had designed for the Josefsen family of Nevlunghavn won first prize at the regatta held off Jumfruland for pilot and fishing boats. In 1882, Archer described one of his pilot boats of this type in Dixon Kemp's *Manual of Yacht and Boat Sailing*, where the lines and sail plan were shown:

> I doubt if English boats of the same size are as handy with a small crew in all kinds of weather. A pilot and his "boy" (technically so called—he may be an "old boy") will go to sea in one of these boats and

stay there (perhaps for a week) till he finds a vessel. When this happens, perhaps somewhere between the Naze and the Skaw, the boat goes close alongside, the pilot jumps on board, and the "boy" is left to bring the boat home the best way he can. The sail is a sprit, and, notwithstanding the formidable dimensions, one man is supposed to be equal to all contingencies. There are no shrouds—only the forestay. They balance on a wind with the foresail and mainsail, but generally carry a jib or two for sailing free, and often a jibheaded topsail hoisted on a long pole.

These boats will live a long time in a seaway and keep pretty dry (they are decked); but their great "forte" is their extreme quickness in answering their helm, a necessary quality when ships have to be boarded from them in a gale of wind; and they will work to windward through surprisingly narrow places, and at a good rate too. These boats are all oak except the timbers—thirteen to fourteen strakes 1¼ inch boards—clinker built, with juniper treenails with heads, placed about 4½ inches apart. They look clumsy, chiefly from their upper works spreading so much. If this feature—which, however, gives them an enormous reserve of buoyancy—were altered, they might be made to look well enough, though peculiar. The boats carry about one-third to one-fourth of their total weight in ballast, generally consisting of iron ore, which is plentiful in the neighbourhood of Laurvig.

Length extreme	33 feet
Length on waterline	30.2 feet
Breadth extreme	11.6 feet
Breadth on waterline	10 feet
Draught of water	4.2 feet
Displacement	7.5 tons
Area midship section	15 square feet
Area load waterplane	198 square feet
Meta centre height	4.45 feet
Centre of buoyancy aft centre length of load water line	5 feet
Midship section forward of centre of length of load water line	0.4 feet
Area of mainsail	500 square feet
Luff of mainsail	24 feet
Leech of mainsail	22 feet
Head of mainsail	14 feet
Foot of mainsail	14 feet
Whole length of mast about	33 feet
Diameter at deck	11 inches
Diameter at top	4½ inches

Colin Archer wrote further of his pilot-boat designs: "This type of boat gives perhaps the best idea of my work. Those I have built for pleasure sailing only are nearly all modifications of the same type, being designed more for good sea-going qualities than for speed. The modern pilot boat is very like a redningskoite [life boat] (except the internal fittings) but smaller, being generally 38 to 40 feet overall."

Colin Archer rightly considered the extreme flare and forward breadth at the sheer of the pilot boats to be detrimental to speed and, in extreme conditions, to seaworthiness. He progressively evolved designs in which both flare and breadth were reduced. In addition, an external cast iron keel of about half the total weight of ballast carried was bolted under the straight wood keel to improve stability and the power to carry sail. By the mid-1870s Archer-built pilot boats carried between one-third and one-fourth of their total displacement in an external iron keel, the internal ballast being iron ore, trimmed in the bilges and ceiled over. It was also during this period that Archer commenced designing pilot boats on the "wave form" theory of hull balance, to obtain improved sailing and handling characteristics (see the section in the Appendix dealing with Colin Archer's ideas concerning the wave form theory).

By the 1880s, thanks to Colin Archer's efforts, the Norwegian pilot boats had improved in design and condition. Schollert wrote of a number of them putting to sea in summer weather:

It is a lovely sight to watch the whole fleet stand out to sea under a stiff breeze. Among the boats are some of the best sailers along the coast. They are so burnished up that they actually shine, and the rigging has been as carefully overhauled as if they were racing craft. Under the press of sail carried they heel over down to their gunwales, and their lee bows are hidden by the wave of foam churned up. The pilot's family watches the race from the harbour and a smile of satisfaction flits from face to face as a boat forges ahead to windward. It is their father's boat. Such a race is as interesting and fascinating to pilots as a regatta to yachtsmen. But in this case not only honour, but also solid advantage hangs on the result.

Archer's pilot boats came to be recognized by Norwegian seafarers as combining seaworthiness, windward ability, speed within their size and limitations, and comfortable accommodations. At the Arendal festival and regatta in 1886, the first five craft to finish the pilot-boat race were designs from his board, built in his yard.

By 1887, Colin Archer's yard had built 21 pilot boats of gradually improving hull form and rig—the last eight were carvel planked and the last seven had iron ballast keels. As the qualities of Archer's pilot boats became known, orders came in from pilots in other ports, such as Arendal and Aalesund. The success of the pilot boat designed for the Josephsen family led six Nevlunghavn pilots to order new, powerful cutters, which were in turn admired by pilots from neighboring countries engaged in Baltic shipping. This led to orders for one pilot boat each for owners in Denmark and Sweden; after that came an order from the Norwegian Nordland. All this time, development of the model had been progressing, with the external iron keel growing larger, the beam decreasing, and the seakeeping qualities improving—the boats reaching their peak performance in strong winds and big seas.

There was an extensive export of timber from southeast Norway to America and the Baltic countries, and all inward- and outward-bound ships needed pilots, so demand for pilot boats was steady. In fact, until 1914 there was an ever-growing number of ships trading to and from the Baltic, which provided work for Norwegian pilots. Colin Archer benefited from the steady demand once his reputation as a designer became established, but this did not mean that he automatically made money. Innovators and owners of small boatyards share a common liability to lose money on their work, and Colin Archer, who was both, was no exception. Most of his pilot boats were built at a loss, some probably knowingly to induce pilots to order craft of his design to prove to them the correctness of his theories, to which Colin adhered with almost religious conviction. Eventually, the performance of his craft convinced pilots of his ability, and despite criticism from builders of the old Hvalerbaat and from conservative seamen, Colin became accepted as a friend by most of the pilot community. Mention of his name was cheered by pilots at the presentation of prizes after the Arendal regatta, and in 1889 when the Faerder Pilots Association was formed—named for the group of small rocky islands at the entrance to Oslofjord—Colin Archer became one of the members of the Association's original management committee.

As time went on, the competitive nature of pilot work and the desire for improved seaworthiness increased the size of the pilot boats on the southeast coast of Norway. By about 1895, they averaged 39 feet in hull length by 14 feet beam at the deck by 6 feet draft and displaced about 14 tons, with an iron keel of two to three tons weight and further internal ballast. Hull planking was oak, to withstand winter ice, on sawn pine frames.

Before looking at three representative Archer pilot boats, a few words about how they were used: Norwegian pilot boats were sailed with a small crew in all weather. They were tumbled and knocked about, and were often laid alongside ships to board or recover a pilot at sea. This use dictated short, tucked-up ends, cut away below water for maneuvering. Most of the pilot boats were rigged as cutters, but a few were rigged as ketches. Those rigged as cutters had a mast that was stepped well aft, which resulted in a short boom, which in turn made a large staysail necessary. Long bowsprits were a nuisance at sea or in harbor, but with the mast well aft, a craft of this form rode more easily than if the mast were farther forward, in the English cutter fashion, which would make her pitch more heavily.

During Colin Archer's time, each pilot usually owned his own cutter and had a crew of two "boys" (who were usually men) to sail her after he had boarded an inbound ship and to bring her out to take him off an outbound vessel. Sometimes in winter two pilots combined their services and used one cutter. These cutters never adopted the system of using a boarding boat, which was common among most pilots elsewhere, but the cutter was run alongside the ship to be boarded and the pilot jumped either on board or onto a rope ladder, a maneuver requiring skillful handling and a very cool head by everybody. Even so, there were fatalities.

Now let's look at some designs. One boat, designed in 1899, demonstrates typically the extent to which Colin Archer had been able to persuade the pilots to depart from the original Hvalerbaat model and suggests a

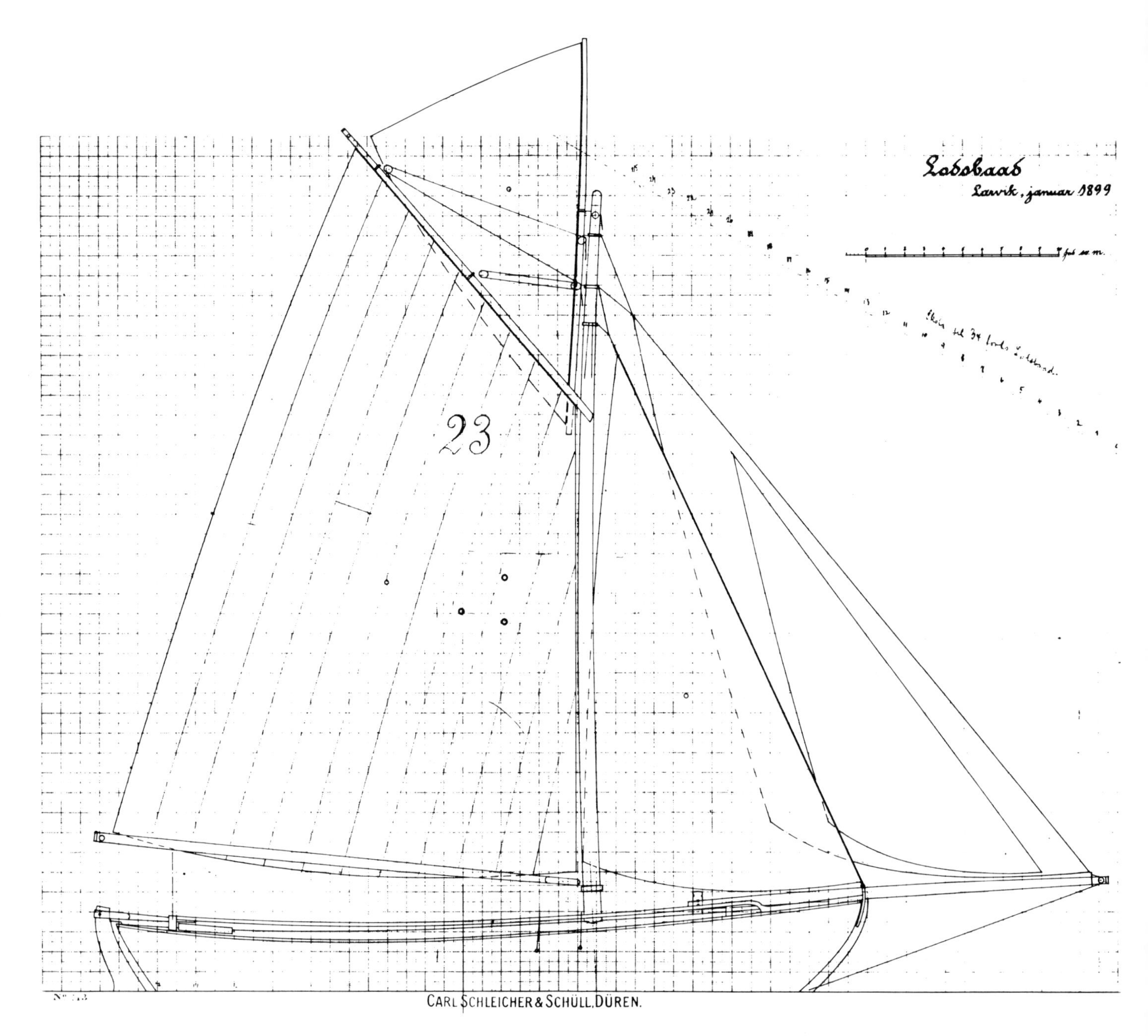

Above and opposite: *Plans of a pilot cutter designed by Colin Archer in 1899. Note the mast sprung forward. (Courtesy of Norsk Sjofartsmuseum)*

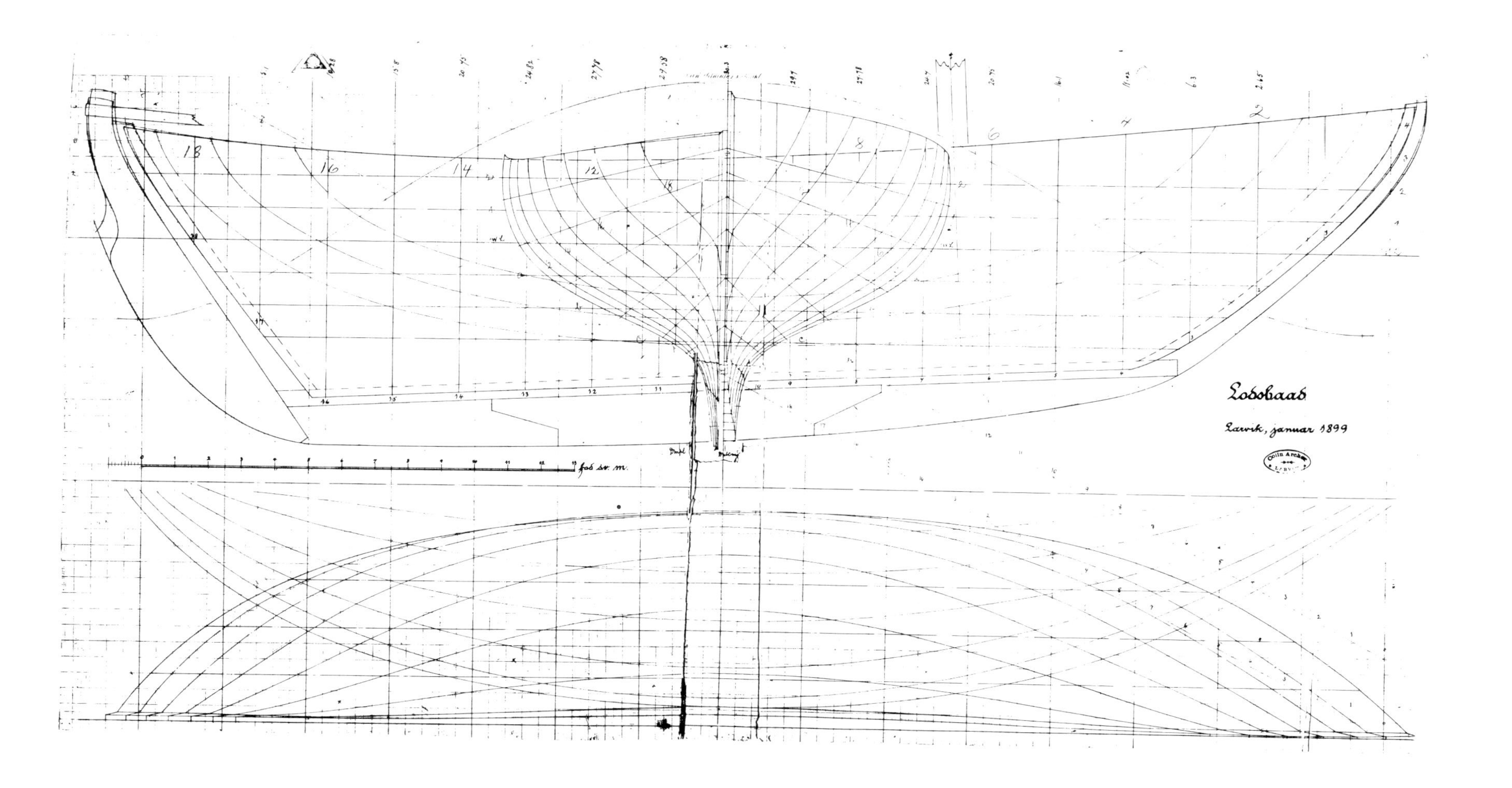

Losbaad
Larvik, januar 1899
fod sv. m.

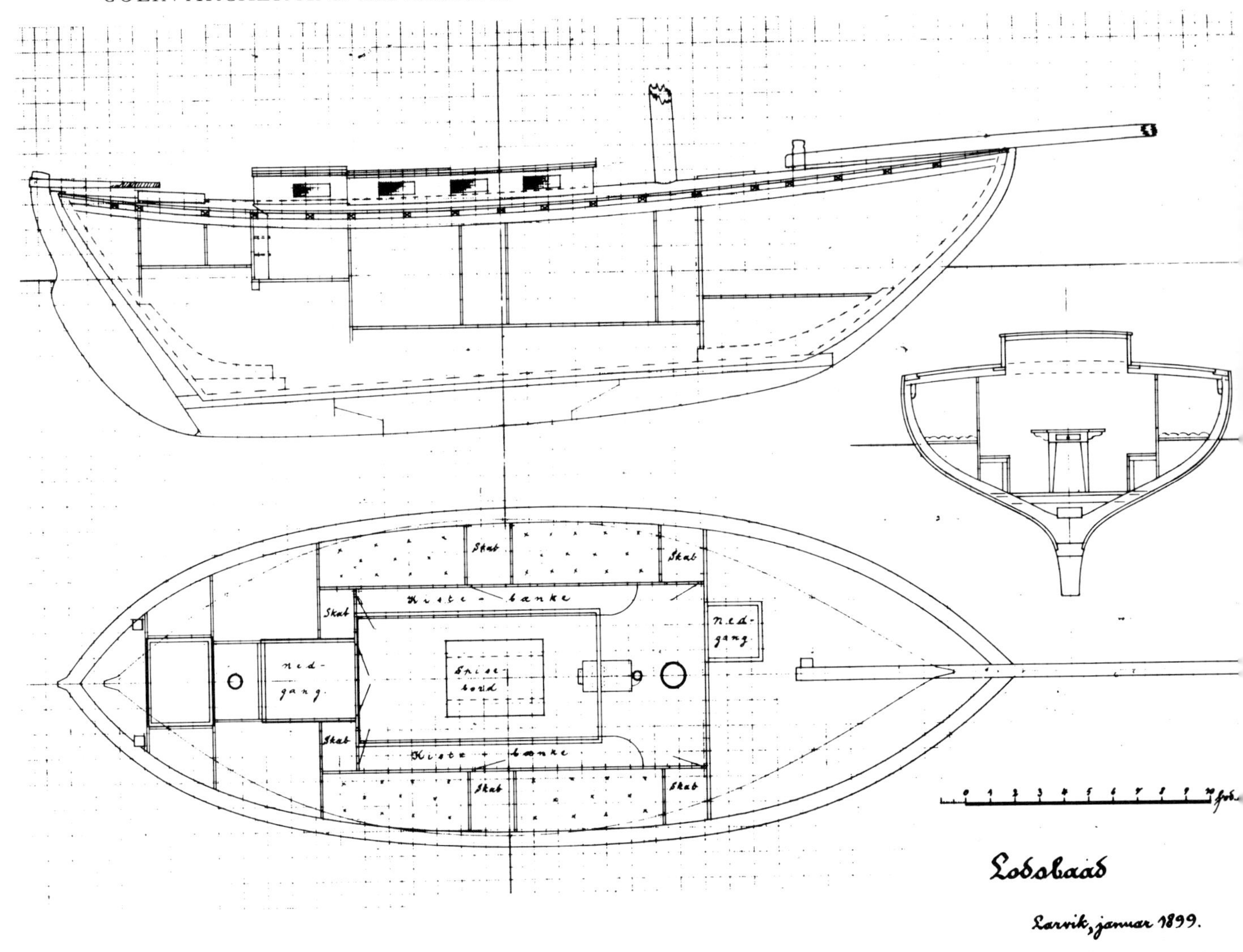

General arrangement of pilot cutter, 1899. (Courtesy of Norsk Sjofartsmuseum)

weatherly craft with excellent seakeeping qualities. Her dimensions were 39 feet, 4 inches long on deck; 34 feet, 7½ inches, waterline length; 13 feet, 6 inches, beam; and 6 feet, 3 inches, draft. The rig was that of a typical Archer cutter with a relatively large mainsail and staysail. There was a small companionway to the amidships cabin, which had bunks for four, each with an enclosed and shuttered front to ensure that the occupant would not be thrown out if he were sleeping on the weather side in a breeze. The use of a low cabin top in many pilot boats and yachts is typical of Archer's designs, as are the small, rectangular ports.

The drafting style of these plans is typical of much of Colin Archer's work, or that of his assistant and draftsman, Axel Harman. The lines plans are well arranged with adequate sections, waterlines, buttocks, and diagonals, and often have curves of areas drawn on them. In contrast, the sail and general arrangement plans are simple and show little detail. Few of Archer's construction plans have survived—he seems to have relied for structural detail on written specifications, to be read in

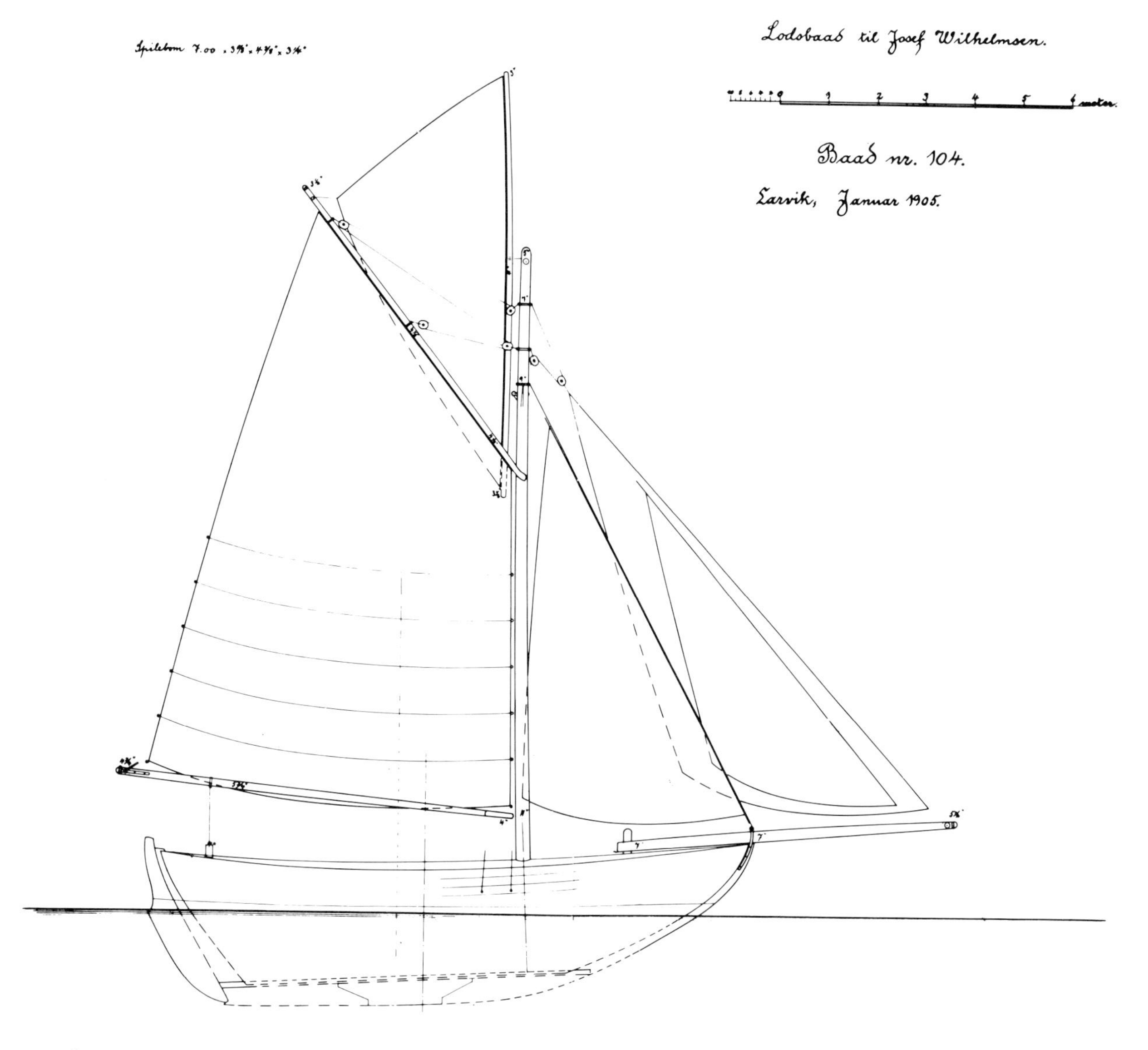

Sail plan of a pilot cutter designed for Joseph Wilhelmsen in 1905. (Courtesy of Norsk Sjofartsmuseum)

conjunction with a construction plan with few annotations. Many of Archer's plans were drawn on graph paper, which is a most unusual medium for naval architects.

Another pilot cutter designed by Archer in 1905 for Joseph Wilhelmsen shows further refinement of the form, and almost yacht-like sections and bow profile. The beam gives the sections considerable flare and a very easy bilge. The craft had a ballast keel of two tons. The vital dimensions were 40 feet length on deck; 34 feet, 9 inches, waterline length; 13 feet, 9 inches, beam; and 6 feet, 1 inch, draft. The accommodations were similar to the 39-foot boat discussed previously. The general arrangement plan shows a plunger bilge pump set in the bridge deck, in front of the helmsman. The mainsail is shorter in the foot than that of the earlier cutter, reflecting the trend of yacht rigs. Five rows of reef points are shown, proof of the variety of weather in which these cutters worked.

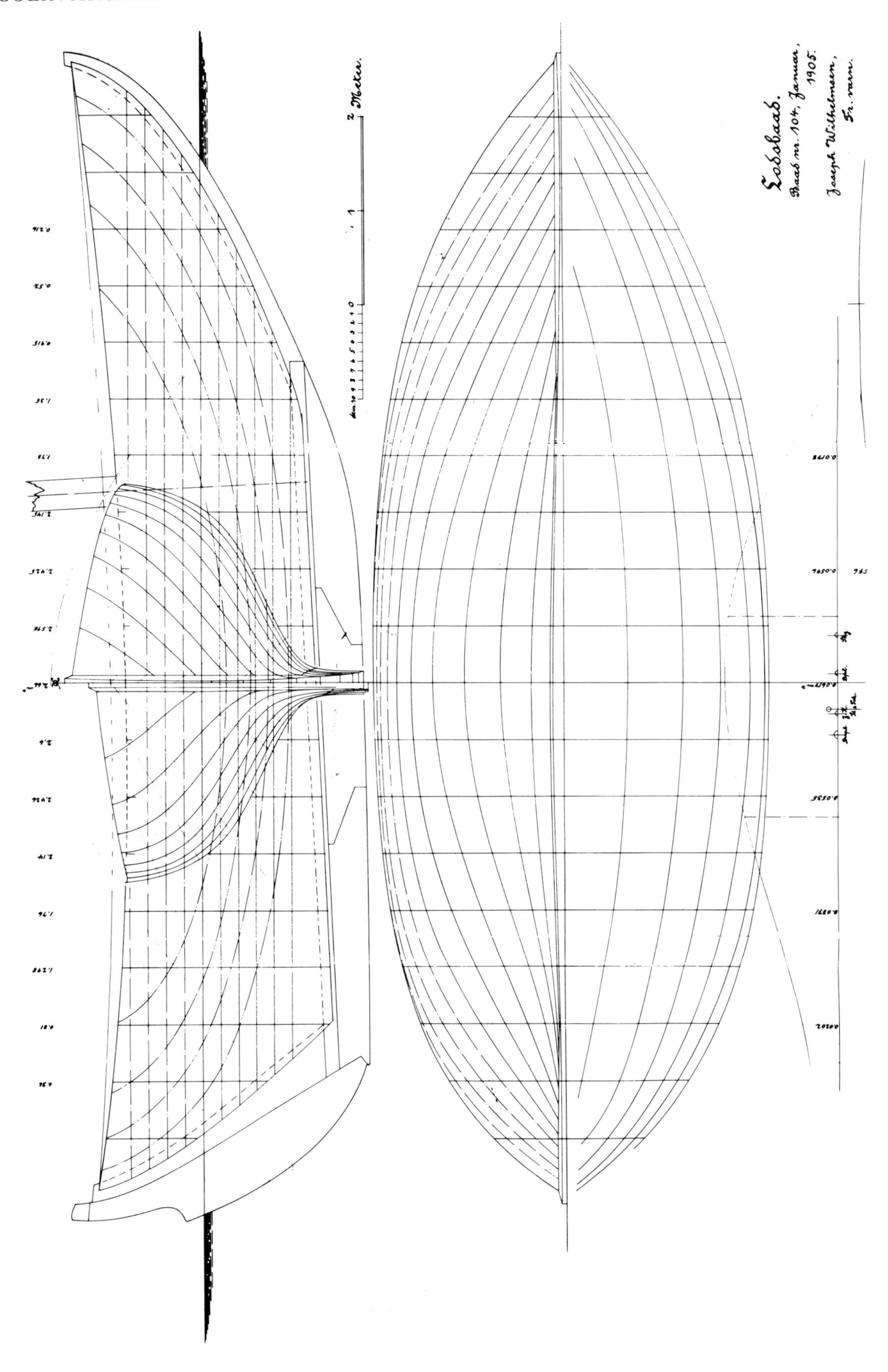
Losbaad.
Baad nr. 104, Januar, 1905.
Joseph Wilhelmsen,
Fr. varn.
2 Meter

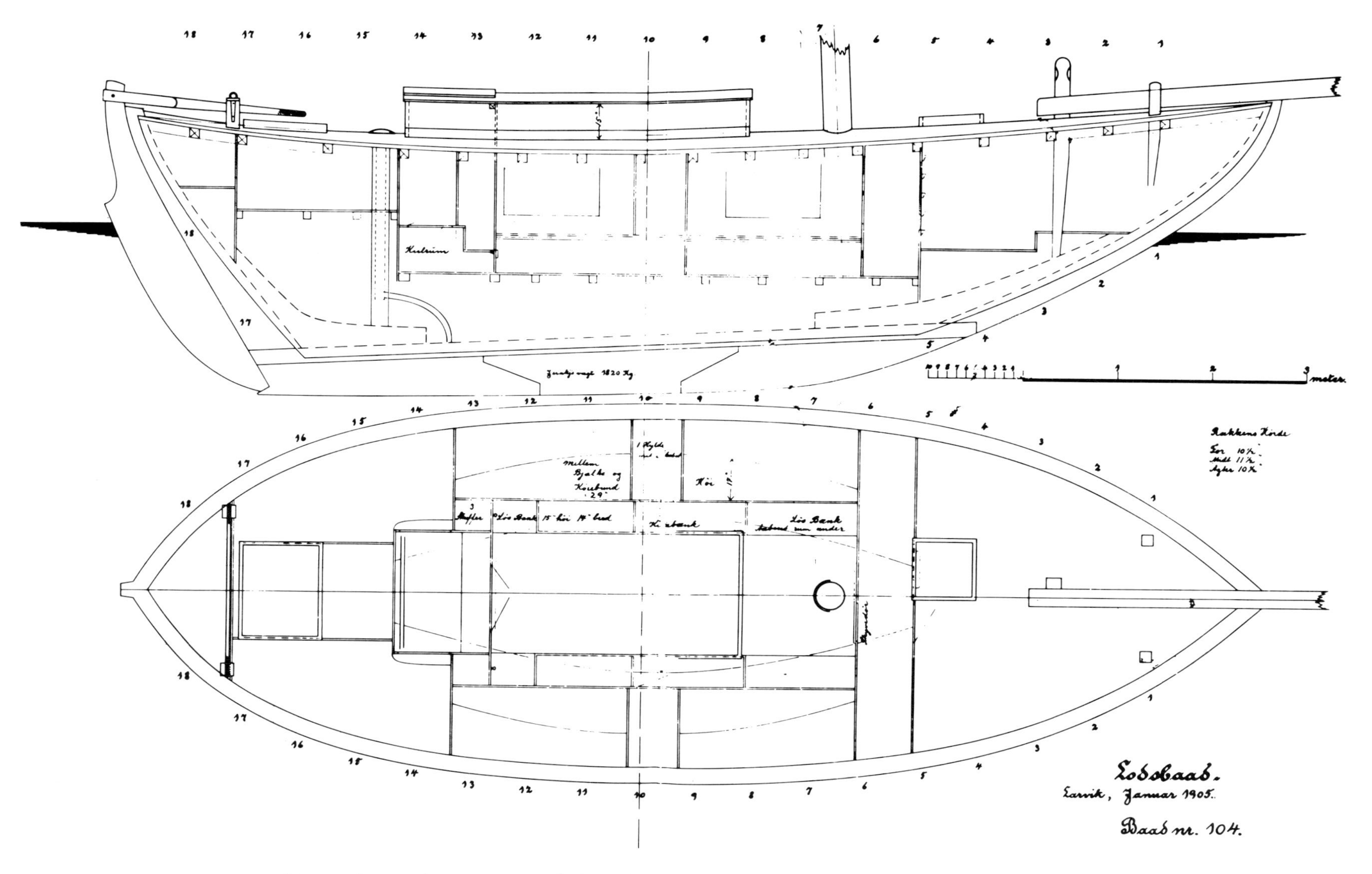

Lines and general arrangement of the Wilhelmsen pilot cutter (Courtesy of Norsk Sjofartsmuseum)

A third pilot cutter, designed about 1909, the year Colin Archer retired, reverted to almost the form, arrangement, and rig of the boat of 1899, probably due to the owner's preference. Her dimensions were 39 feet long on deck; 14 feet, beam; and 5 feet, 10 inches, draft. She displaced about 17 tons and had a 2¾-ton iron ballast keel.

These three designs represent the late development of the sailing pilot boat in Norway, though the type Archer had improved and established continued to be built by others after the introduction of auxiliary motors. By the late 1920s, the sailing pilots had been superseded by powered craft, and many were sold for use as yachts, for which they needed little conversion. Some of their notable voyagings are told in later chapters of this book.

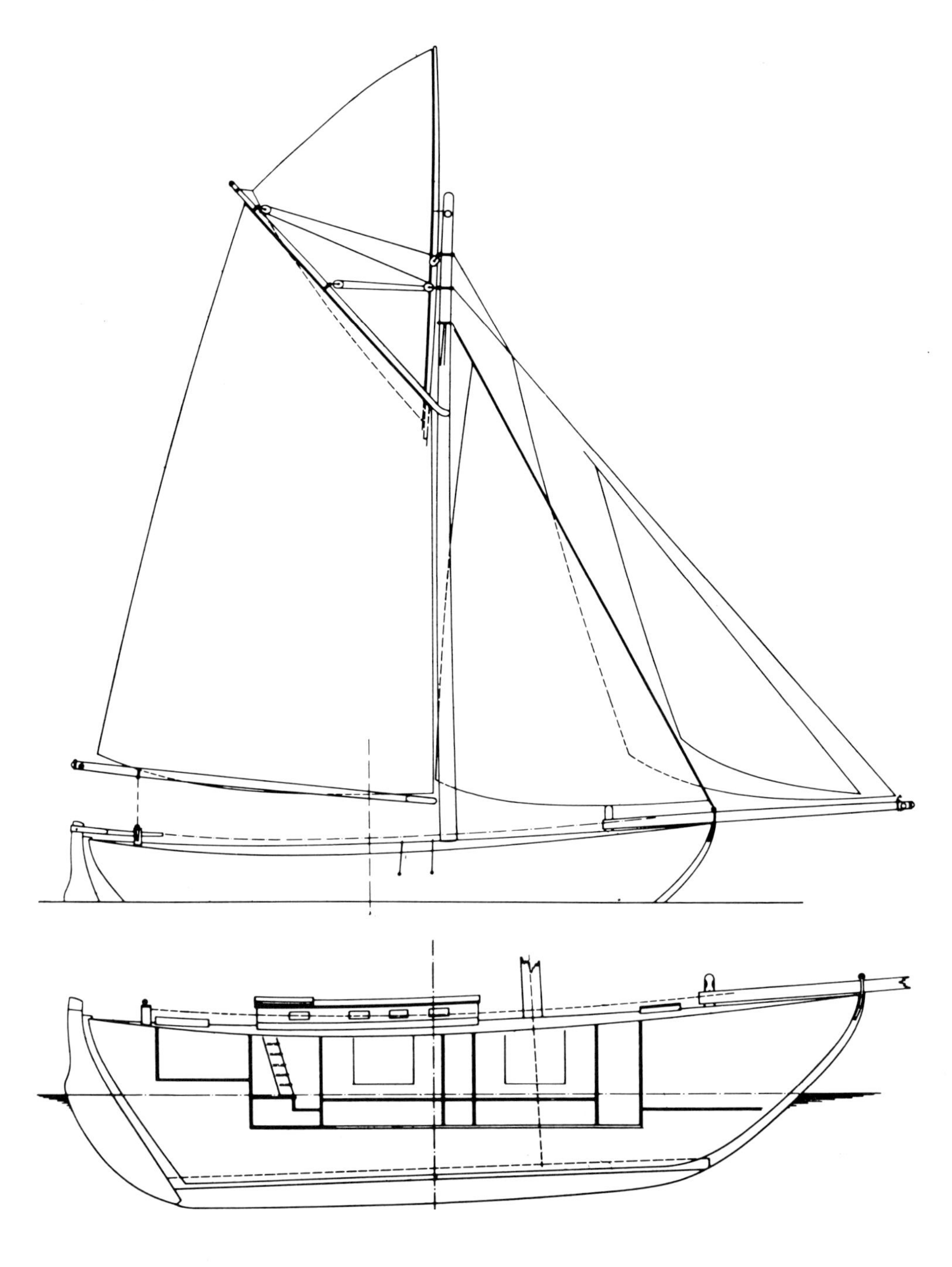

Above and opposite: *Sail plan, cabin plan, and lines of a pilot cutter designed in 1905 by Colin Archer (Courtesy of Norsk Sjofartsmuseum)*

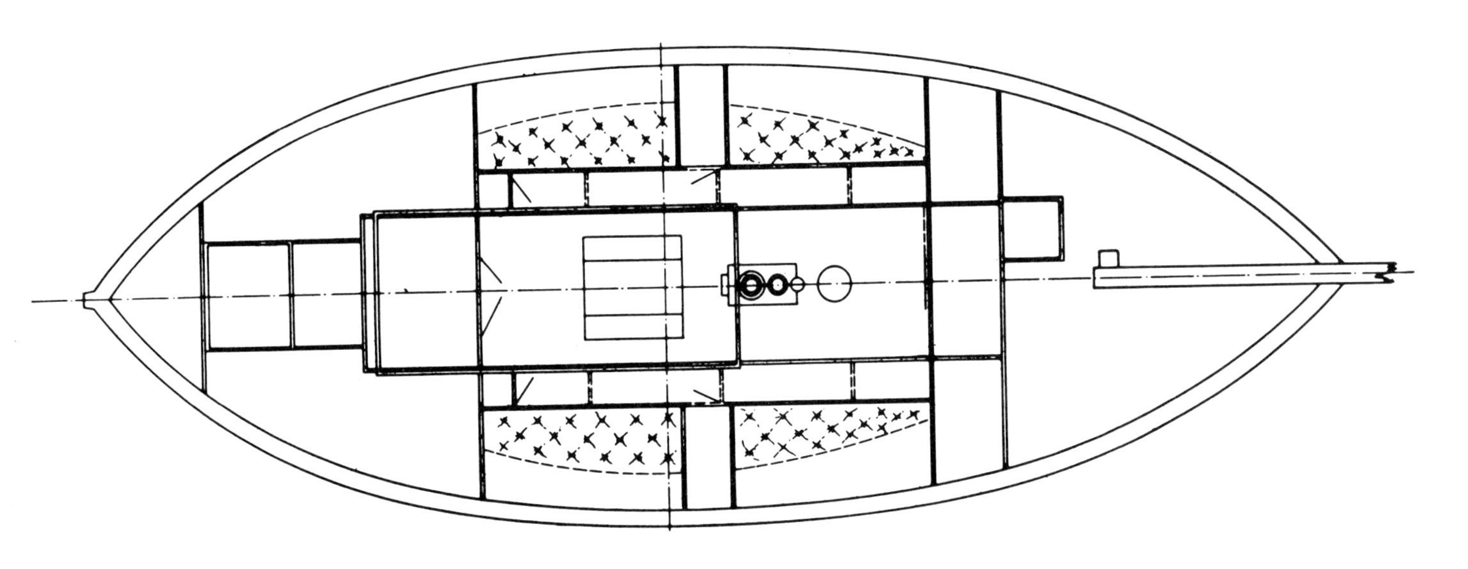

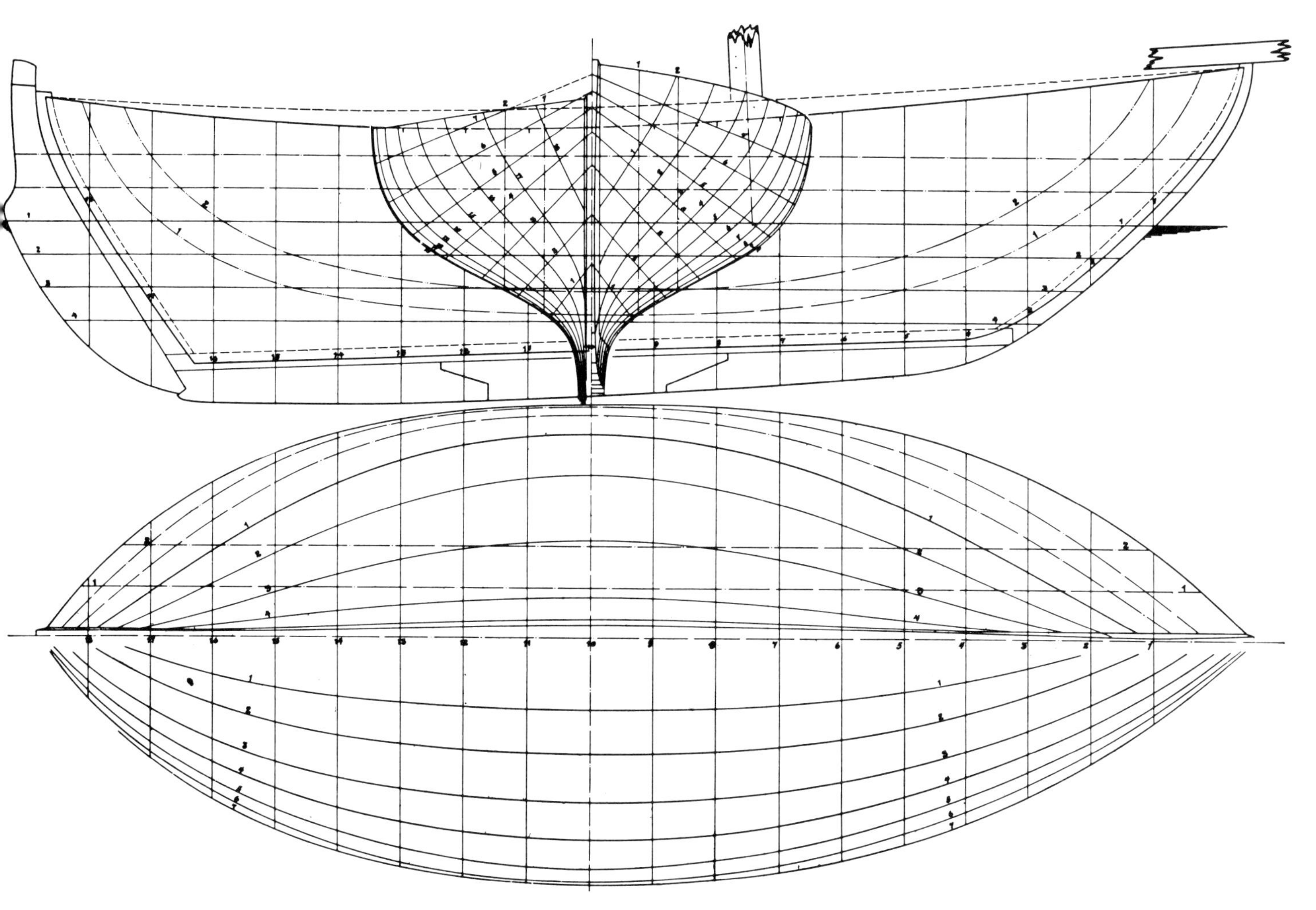

3

YACHTS

Until the beginning of the twentieth century, the Scandinavian countries had little wealth or leisure for yachting in the developed manner it enjoyed before that time in Britain, Germany, and the United States. Small boats and pilot and fishing vessels were occasionally raced for pleasure, and probably the other types of working craft then in use took part in the few races organized locally on a holiday. But yachts were very few before 1870, though there is evidence that around 1863 a builder named Knudson of Larkollen built a pointed-stern, half-decked racing boat named *Garibaldi.*

A regatta was held at Hjeltefjorden, near Bergen, Norway, in August, 1865, in which cutters with sprit mainsails and open boats with squaresails competed. Yacht races were also held at Aarhus, in Denmark, during August, 1866, and the large class included two spritsail-rigged cutters, two gaff cutters, and the clipper-bowed Norwegian *Vikingen*, a 50-footer owned by A.B. Bull. These yachts started from buoys with headsails lowered, as had been the fashion in English yacht racing until the 1860s. Similar races were held off Svendborg, Denmark, in July of the following year, when about 13 Swedish and Danish yachts competed. A rally of sailing boats rigged with sprit and gaff mainsails gathered off Stavanger, Norway, in 1868, but none seem to have been purely pleasure craft or yachts.

Despite the dearth of organized yachting on his part of the coast, Colin Archer always was fond of boat sailing, which he called his "weakness," and he probably owned a succession of small sailing craft.

In 1866-67 Colin Archer had a sailing boat built for his own use, and it is believed she was constructed at Tolderodden, where she was moored. She was named *Maggie,* and a surviving plan has on it "Scottish fishing boat designed by J. and A. Watson, Boatbuilder, Arbroath, 1866." This and her hull form make it almost certain that this was a design Colin Archer obtained from the fishing port of Arbroath, on the coast of Angus, north of Dundee on the east coast of Scotland, and which he modified slightly in the after lines. For this boat he designed a schooner rig, which made her even more unusual.

The lines of the *Maggie* are those of a contemporary east coast of Scotland fishing boat known as a "fifie," then being built in lengths varying from 35 to 50 feet and rigged with two lugsails, which in some ports were set on masts disposed in schooner fashion. The *Maggie* had a long, straight keel, slightly raked stem, and a pointed stern. The sternpost was gently raked and rounded. Archer seems to have slightly altered the after waterlines and buttocks. All her ballast was carried inside. She was decked and had a long cockpit from about one-third abaft the stem to the stern. The hull with its flat sheer was unremarkable and had no Norwegian characteristics, but the rig was in contrast to Colin Archer's subsequent work, as it was based on the American pilot-schooner style. It had a well-raked foremast, and the mainmast was stepped through a wide thwart in the cockpit. The short gaffs were almost horizontal, and the foresail was boomless, sheeting abaft the mainmast. The main boom extended beyond the stern, and each sail had two sets of reef points. A staysail and jib set on a long running bowsprit were drawn on the plans, but a photograph indicates she also set a large jib sheeted by the foremast, in true American style.

About 1870, Colin designed and had built what was (certainly incorrectly) described as the first Norwegian craft built as a yacht, owning her in partnership with a lawyer named Gron. His developing occupation of designing and building improved pilot craft led to the close study of sailing craft performance, and his bilingualism enabled him to read English-language yachting books and periodicals, particularly the English weekly, *The Field,* then the leading magazine with technical comment on yacht design and construction, and other aspects of the sport. Archer was thus aware of the advances in hull form and rig of the fastest yachts of the time. He recognized that the sport would eventually become established in Norway, so he commenced project designs for yachts. The cutter *Marina* for Hans H. Holm is an example of such work. The *Marina* is believed to have been his first commission for a yacht. She was launched in 1875.

The same year Colin Archer designed the cutter yacht *Havskum* (*Sea Foam*) with dimensions of 27 feet overall by 8-foot beam by 2 foot, 3 inch draft aft and 1 foot, 9 inch draft forward. She was a clinker-planked cutter with a hull form whose profile vaguely resembled a shallow-draft English cutter but had the beam, deck plan, sections, and low freeboard of a contemporary American sloop-yacht. The tumbled-in topsides may have been influenced by reading of the celebrated American schooner *Sappho* and her kind. The *Havskum* carried all her ballast in the bilge. Her cutter rig had a loose-footed mainsail, a small yard topsail, and, unusually, a large staysail tacked to a short iron bumkin at the stemhead. The small jib was set on a short bowsprit, which followed the line of the sheer.

The *Havskum* was another most unlikely design and emphasizes how at that time Colin Archer was heavily influenced in his ideas of yachts by what he read in English and perhaps American books and journals. A similar cutter, *Bolgen* (*The Wave*), was also built at the same time, and the type attracted interest on the coast, though why these craft carried such a restricted draft is a mystery.

None of Colin Archer's yachts was large—a favorite size was between 30 and 40 feet long. Most were designed as cruisers that were occasionally raced, rather than as specialized racing craft.

Colin Archer's yacht design work gained success almost immediately. Gothenburg held an international regatta in 1871, and, in the racing classes, yachts designed by Colin Archer attracted attention. The *Maggie* won a prize, and the *Thor* was mentioned as a fast boat. During 1872, Colin published a pamphlet, with drawings, entitled *Directions for Designing Yachts and Boats*, in which he explained the principles of yacht design in a manner and language that amateurs could understand. He did this with a view toward encouraging interest in yacht sailing in Norway. He knew that once established, sailing for pleasure was bound to flourish on a long, indented coastline like Norway's, which offered sheltered waters in many places. Colin Archer promoted yachting for the pleasure of the sport rather than for financial gain; he made little money from his yacht designs. Yet working on yachts did help him in his development of other types and vice versa—the design and construction of yachts and their racing advanced Archer's interest in scientific aspects of the design of sailing craft and improvement in their windward performance and sea-keeping ability. Other Archer-designed craft proved to be fast. A pilot boat he designed and built for Vilhelm Josefsen, mentioned in the previous chapter, won a race in 1873.

Yachting soon gained a hold in Norway. By the 1880s, regattas were being held regularly at many places along the Norwegian coast, particularly in the approaches to Oslo, at Arendal, Moss, and Larvik. In 1883, Colin Archer was one of the founding members of the Koneglig Norsk Seilforening (the Royal Norwegian Yacht Club). In 1900, he was elected Commodore, an honor he treasured.

Also in 1883, Colin Archer's work with yachts received significant recognition. He received a commission to design a new one-design class for the Royal Swedish Yacht Club. A number of boats were to be built, the best boats for racing he could conceive, and these were to be drawn for by club members in a lottery. This was a method for promoting new designs and sailing that the club continued for many years. Five boats were built for the club by Archer—the *Vinga, Valborg, Viola, Ellida,* and *Hervor.*

However, Archer's favorite type of yacht seems to have been the double-ender with a gaff-cutter rig, boats of a form refined from his designs for improved working boats. Of the 32 yachts designed and built by Colin Archer listed in the 1914 edition of *Lloyds Register of Yachts,* most were of this type. Yachts designed and built purely for racing did not interest him greatly, nor was there then demand for such craft in Norway. Besides, it is doubtful that his shipwrights then had the skills and necessary experience in fine yacht work—their expertise was the ability to produce sound craft with good pilot-boat finish at a reasonable price.

Notable yachts Colin designed included the *Odd* of 1887 for Whil. Wolff; the *Venus* of 1890, designed and built for W.F. Meyer of Bergen; and the 11.45-ton *Maagen,* launched in 1890 for W. Stibolt of Drammen. But the 11.20-ton cutter *Storegut* was the best of them. Launched in the spring of 1890 for Whil. Wolff and later sailed by Fred Olsen of the Norwegian shipping family, she was a very fast boat. With dimensions of 35 feet by 11 feet by 6.3 feet depth, she carried a large sail area on a pole-masted cutter rig.

It is interesting that in an age when British and American yachts of all sizes carried long, fidded topmasts, most Scandinavian yachts, including the *Storegut,* retained the heavier pole mast with a yard topsail set above it. Many boats with that rig were built for owners in southern Norway and some for yachtsmen in other Scandinavian countries, particularly Denmark and Sweden.

The *Storegut* was probably Archer's most successful yacht, one of the 23 successively owned by Whil. Wolff. Her best race was at Kiel in 1895, when a great regatta and naval review marked the opening of the Kiel Canal. On one day of the regatta the wind blew so hard that most of the racing yachts would not risk their masts in starting or were forced to give up in the gale-force squalls. However, the little *Storegut* won her class handsomely, and Fred Olsen received the Hohenzollern Cup from the German Emperor. Her performance attracted considerable comment and comparison with the much larger, heavily canvassed racers that remained at their buoys that day. German sports magazines were particularly enthusiastic over the skoite type's seaworthiness.

Owners of modest-sized, seaworthy yachts like the *Storegut* enjoyed good cruising and

The yacht Storegut, *designed and built in 1890 by Colin Archer for Fred Olsen, a Norwegian shipowner. The* Storegut *was a notably fast craft of her type.*

racing at moderate expense, unlike many of their English and American contemporaries, who generally lavished vast sums on craft that were outdated after a season or two. Yachts of this type were built of good materials—the 35-foot, 5-inch cutter *Fantom,* launched from Archer's yard in 1890, is still sailing in English waters as the *Velsia,* owned by Messrs. Cox, Braine and Godsal. The *Venus,* referred to above, won many of the races for her class when new and was a strong rival of the *Mignon* and *Storegut.* She is still sailing in Norway, having been re-rigged to her original sail plan. The *Mignon* was in the Mediterranean a few years ago, and the clipper-bowed cutter *Titania,* which Colin Archer built in 1895 for Chris. Mostue of Christiania, was racing annually until recently and is now owned at Asker, near Oslo.

Colin Archer's yachts did not all show Scandinavian-traditional influence. The cutter *Lady* represents Archer's designs for yachts that were influenced by British practice during the period 1885 to 1895. This 4.23-tonner, built in 1895, had the then-fashionable clipper bow and cutter rig, but with the Scandinavian pole mast and a topsail set with the topsail yard not quite peaked vertically, as

The pointed-stern Velsia *is typical of the majority of Colin Archer's cruising yachts in that she evolved from his working craft. Built in 1890, the* Velsia *still cruises under English ownership. (Courtesy of D.P. Cox)*

was then the British and American practice. The heel of the yard protruded forward of the masthead. The clew was spread by a jackyard, but the gaff was too long for the head of the mainsail. The low cabin house with rectangular windows was Archer's own concept, as was the swept-up, rounded, counter stern, a more seaworthy after end than the long, low counters then common on yachts of orthodox design. With the spinnaker boom stowed vertically alongside the mast and the hands in dark guernseys, white trousers, and sun hats,

The 4.23-ton cutter yacht Lady *was a Colin Archer design of 1895 that featured the then-fashionable clipper bow and cutter rig.*

the *Lady* was obviously prepared for racing.

During 1897, Colin Archer built a rater for racing at the Stockholm Jubilee regatta that summer. This long-ended, fast, and lightly built boat with a fin keel was almost identical to the scores of similar ½-, 1-, 2½-, and 5-raters turned out in Britain under the Length and Sail Area rating rule. Like most of her contemporaries, she set a high-peaked standing-lug mainsail and a staysail tacked to the stemhead. She may have been from a British design, as in 1902 Archer built the round-bowed cutter *Figaro* for shipowner Fred Olsen, from a design by George L. Watson of Glasgow, then a leading international designer. She was one of the biggest boats built by Archer with a 40-foot, 3-inch waterline length; 10-foot, 10-inch beam; and 7-foot, 6-inch depth. (That was a busy year for the Archer yard. The 43-foot-waterline-length cutter *Utowana,* which Archer designed, was also launched. She had a 14-foot beam and

7-foot, 10-inch depth and was owned by Wilhelm Kloed. *See* page 36.)

Colin Archer was always interested in small daysailers, in which he got afloat most often. One of his designs for the traditional "snekke" type, the *Concordia,* is still sailing in Norway. With a clinker-planked hull, a pointed stern, a boomless sprit mainsail, and a staysail tacked to the stemhead, the snekke resembles a miniature of the pilot boats Colin Archer set out to refine in the 1860s.

In 1898, Colin Archer designed a 37-foot, 4-inch-waterline cruising and racing cutter-yacht for Johan Thorne that exhibited the influence of the English cutter in her above-water profile and rig. Dimensions were 53 feet, 8 inches length on deck; 37 feet, 4 inches waterline length; 12 feet, 5 inches beam; and 6 feet, 9 inches draft. She had a 11,000-pound lead keel. The underwater profile was as conservative as any contemporary cruising yacht, but the body sections showed the flare and easy bilge of Colin Archer's working craft, faired into the hollow flare of the clipper bow and the rounded lift of the counter. The clipper bow was by then outdated in English cutter yachts, and the counter stern had rather more rake than those of her English counterparts, due to the generous freeboard of the yacht. The rig of Archer's boat for Thorne followed English practice for a racing cutter of the early 1890s—a loose-footed mainsail, with a jib-headed or a jackyard topsail, to suit wind strength, set above it on the housing topmast. She had a staysail and three sizes of jibs, which were carried on a traveller, and a jib topsail set at the end of the bowsprit, which was supported by a bobstay. She had a spinnaker, which was set on a 34-foot spinnaker boom. The mast was supported by a single running backstay on each side. Colin Archer appeared to have been unfamiliar with the need for a shifting backstay to support the topmast head, which this boat would certainly need when carrying the large topsail off the wind in a breeze.

On deck, Thorne's yacht had some of the features of the pilot and rescue craft—a low cabin house and a steering cockpit divided from the main cockpit, which opened onto the two-berth after cabin. Forward was a double-berth cabin with a head opening off it. The forecastle had a hatch to the foredeck and two berths for the professional crew, a contrast to the canvas pipe-cots of English yacht forecastles. She looks like a well-conceived craft, with a healthier beam and displacement than her English contemporaries. She was no doubt fast for her size.

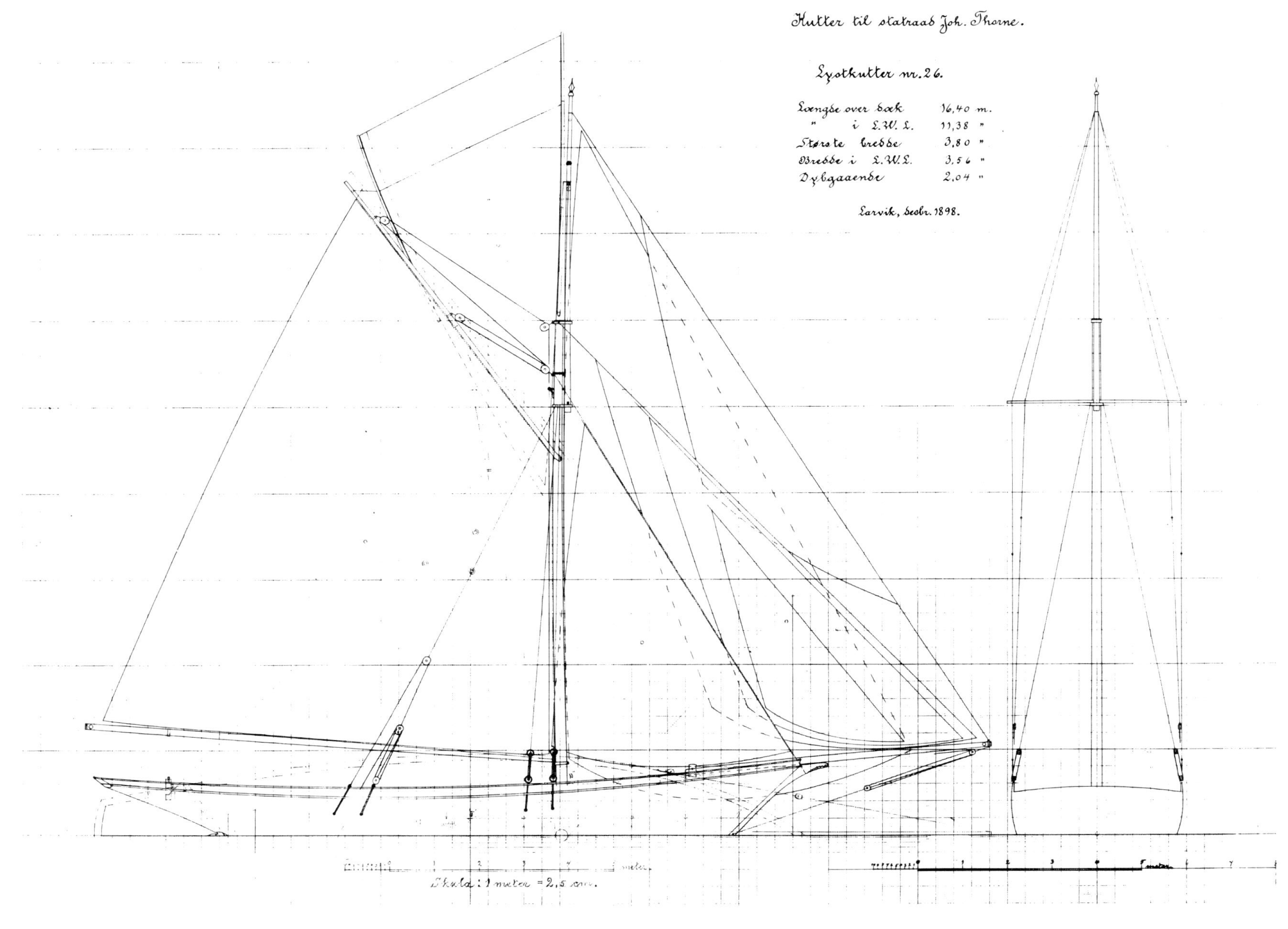

Above and next two pages: *Plans of a clipper-bowed yacht designed by Colin Archer for Johan Thorne in 1898. (Courtesy of Norsk Sjofartsmuseum)*

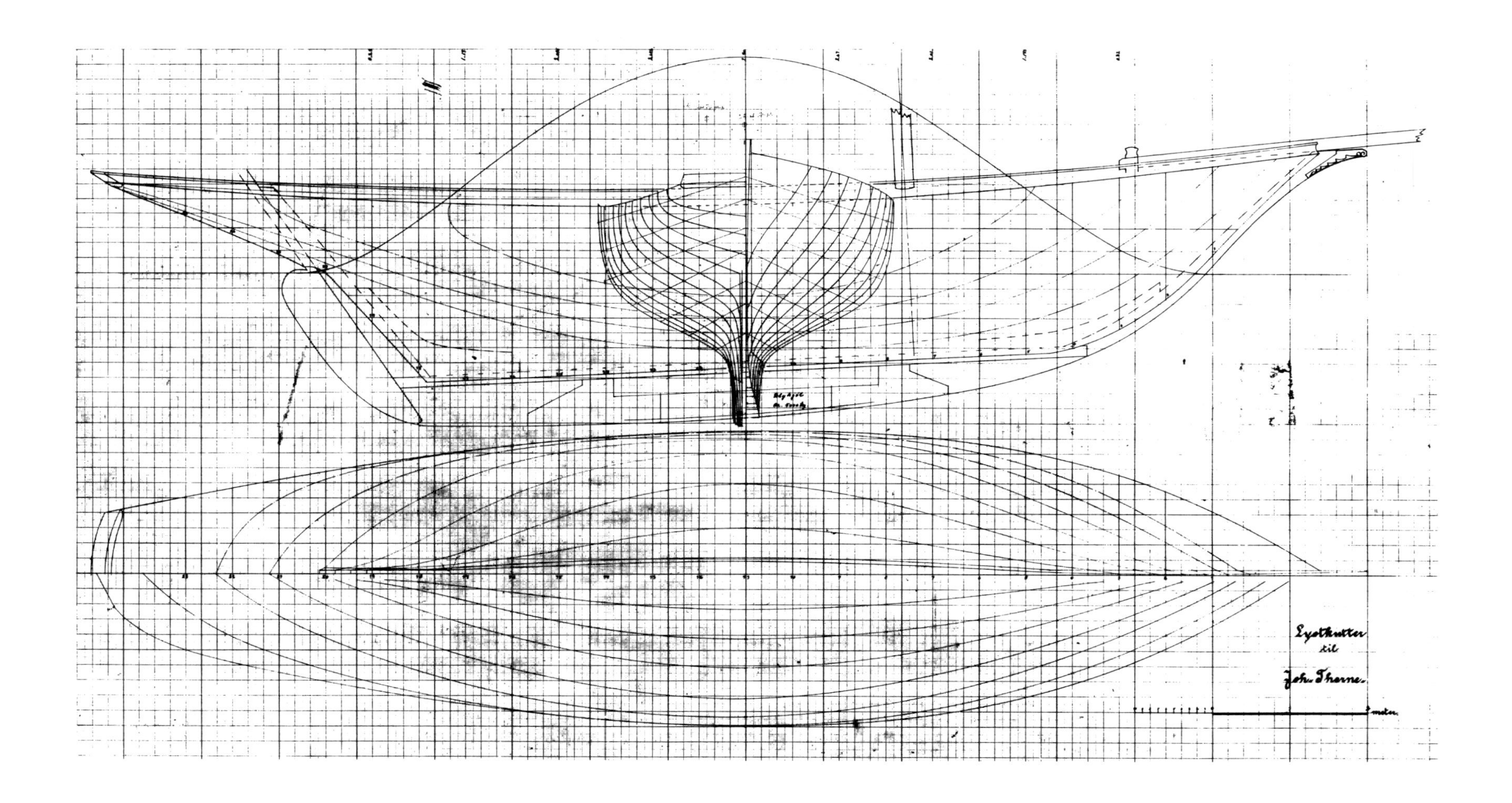
Lystkutter
til
Joh. Thorne.
meter

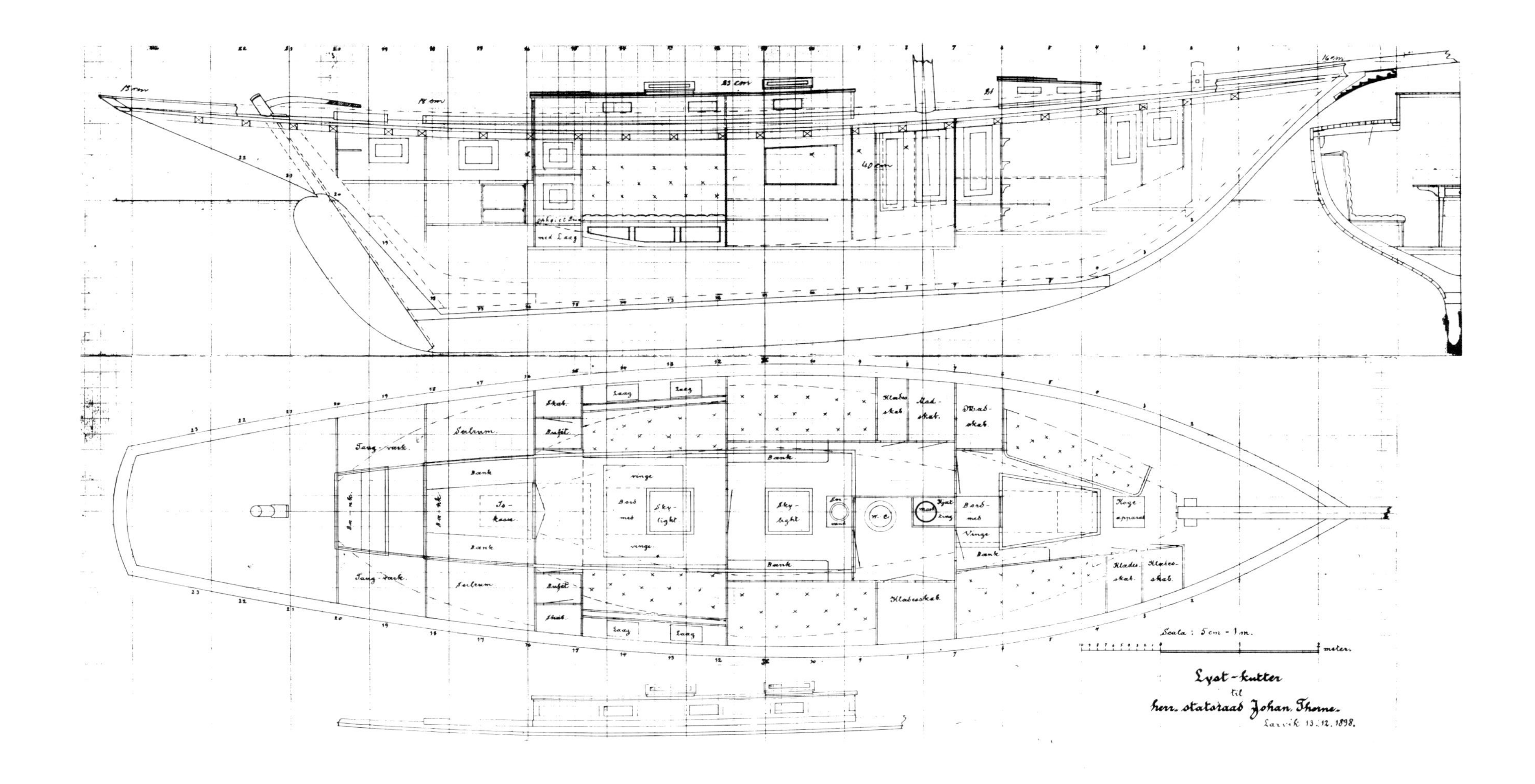
Lyst-kutter
til
herr. statsraad Johan Thorne.
Larvik 13. 12. 1898.
Scala: 5 cm - 1 m.
meter.
Salrum
Tang-vask
Tang-dæk
Skab
Buffet
Sky-light
Bord med Vinge
Bank
Laag
Kladeskab
W. C.
Køge apparat

The cutter *Pipi,* designed in December, 1899, for Herr Rosenberg of Kristiansand, was typical of Colin Archer's cruising/racing yachts of the pointed-stern, Spissgatter type. The Spissgatters were popular craft of lighter displacement and greater speed than the skoite-type yachts. The *Pipi* was 35 feet, 4 inches long on deck; 9 feet, 2 inches beam; and 4 feet, 9 inches draft. Her lines show a narrow, refined, and potentially fast boat, well rigged and practically laid out below. On deck, the pump was located on the bridge deck, in front of the helmsman. Iron floors tied the heels of the sawn frames across the broad, wood keel, instead of the massive wooden floors fitted in working boats. The mast was, surprisingly, sprung forward by the headstays, and the shrouds were set up with deadeyes and lanyards, while most contemporary new yachts used turnbuckles. The mainsail was laced to the boom.

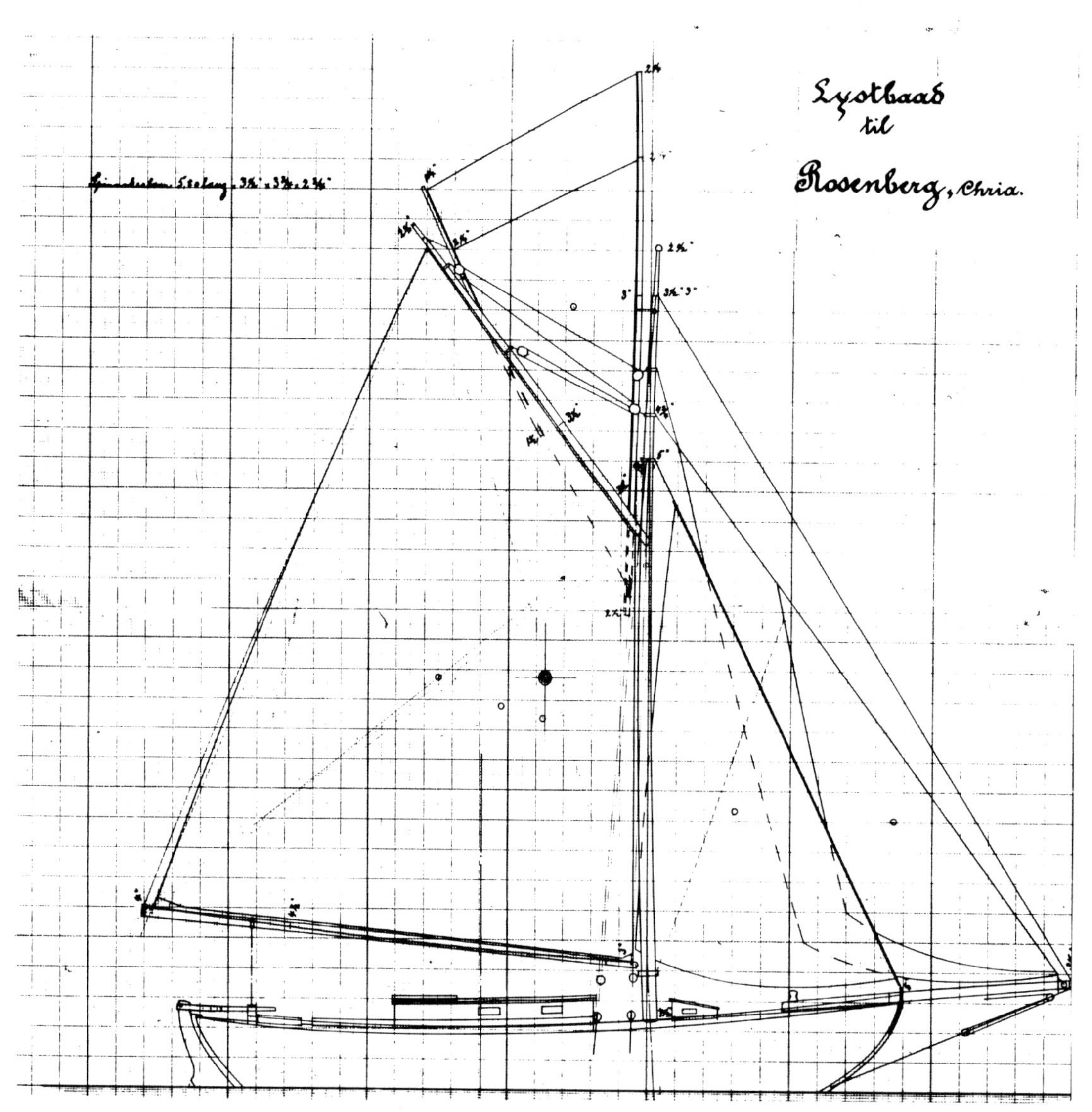

Above and opposite: *Plans of the Spissgatter-type yacht* Pipi *designed by Colin Archer in 1899. (Courtesy of Norsk Sjofartsmuseum)*

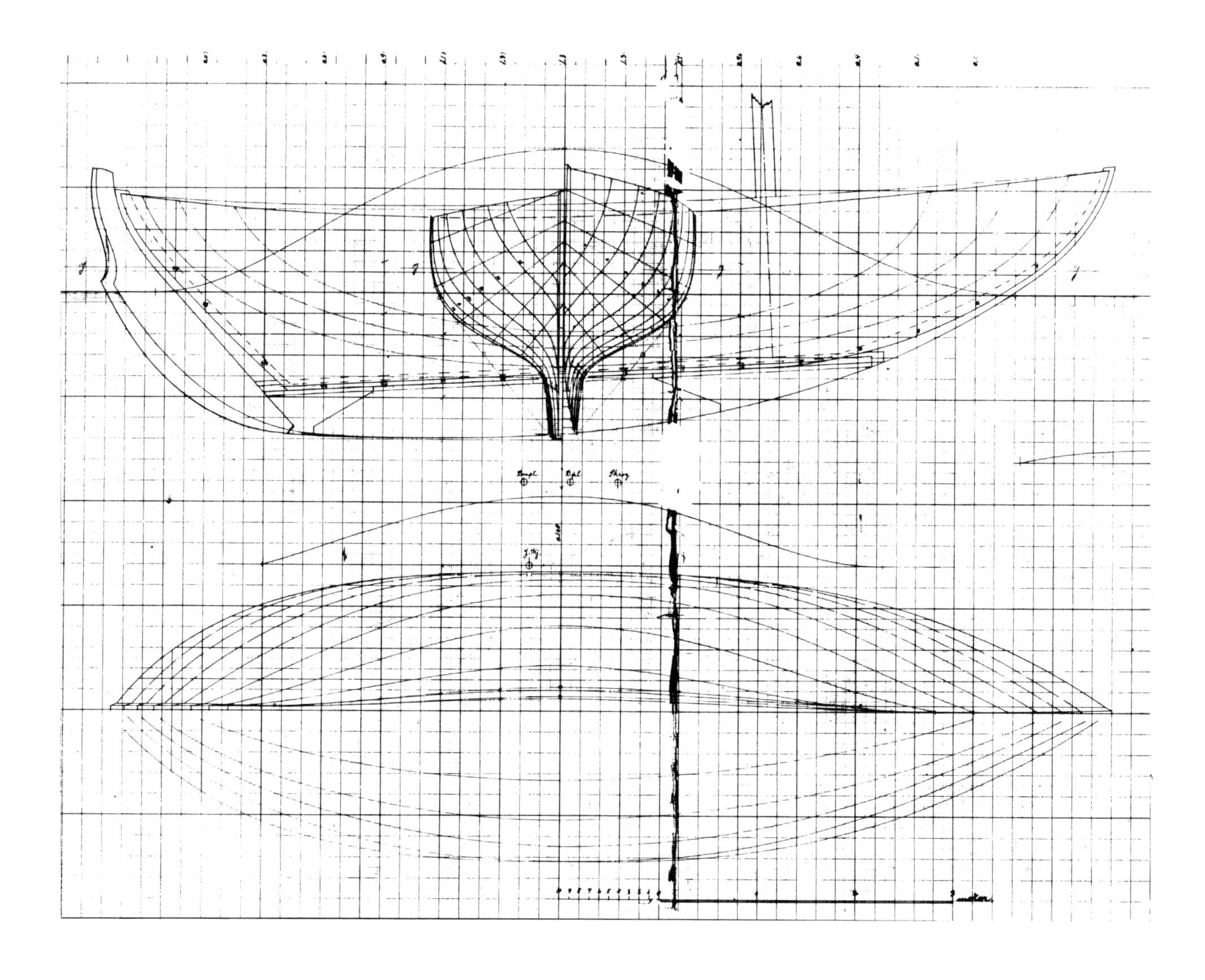

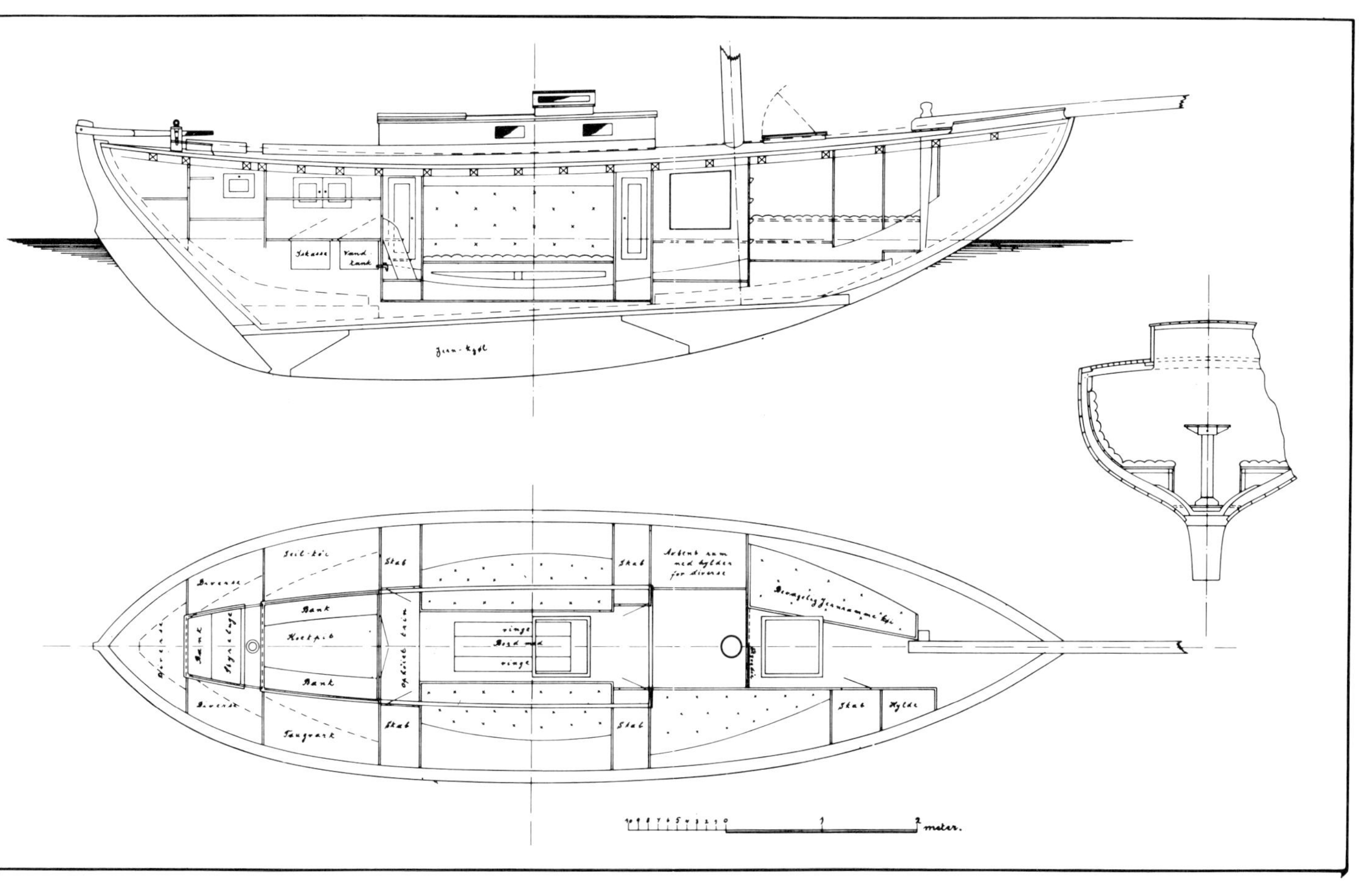

Iskasse
Vand tank
Jern-Kjøl
Seil-Køie
Skab
Aabent rum med hylder for diverse
Diverse
Bank
Kockpit
Bord med vinger
Skab
Hylde
Tougvark
meter.

At the end of 1904, Wilhelm Kloed commissioned Colin Archer to design a cruising and racing cutter named *Utowana.* Her hull was similar to the cutter yacht designed for Johan Thorne but had Archer's interpretation of the rounded yacht stem, which became fashionable in English yachts about 1893 after a change in the rating rule. However, he retained a hollow flare in her bow sections. Dimensions were 58 feet, 4 inches overall length; 42 feet, 8 inches waterline length; 13 feet, 9½ inches beam; and 7 feet, 10 inches draft. She was rigged as a pole-masted cutter, with a loose-footed mainsail, comparatively large staysail, three sizes of jib, and a large "bowsprit spinnaker," which doubled as a reaching jib in light weather. Three sizes of topsail were shown, all set on a topsail yard; the largest had a jackyard to extend the clew beyond the gaff end. By the time Archer designed this boat, he appreciated the use of wire spans to spread the load from the peak halyards on the gaff. The spreaders were fitted below the hounds cheeks on the mast and were supported by two lifts, but he still used deadeyes and lanyards to set up the shrouds. The mainsheet worked on a traveller between two mooring bitts in the afterdeck.

Accommodations in Kloed's cutter consisted of one large four-berth cabin amidships and a forecastle bulkheaded off from it with two berths for the professional crew. The cook did all his work on a coal range by the bowsprit bitt—an uncomfortable place for cooking when at sea.

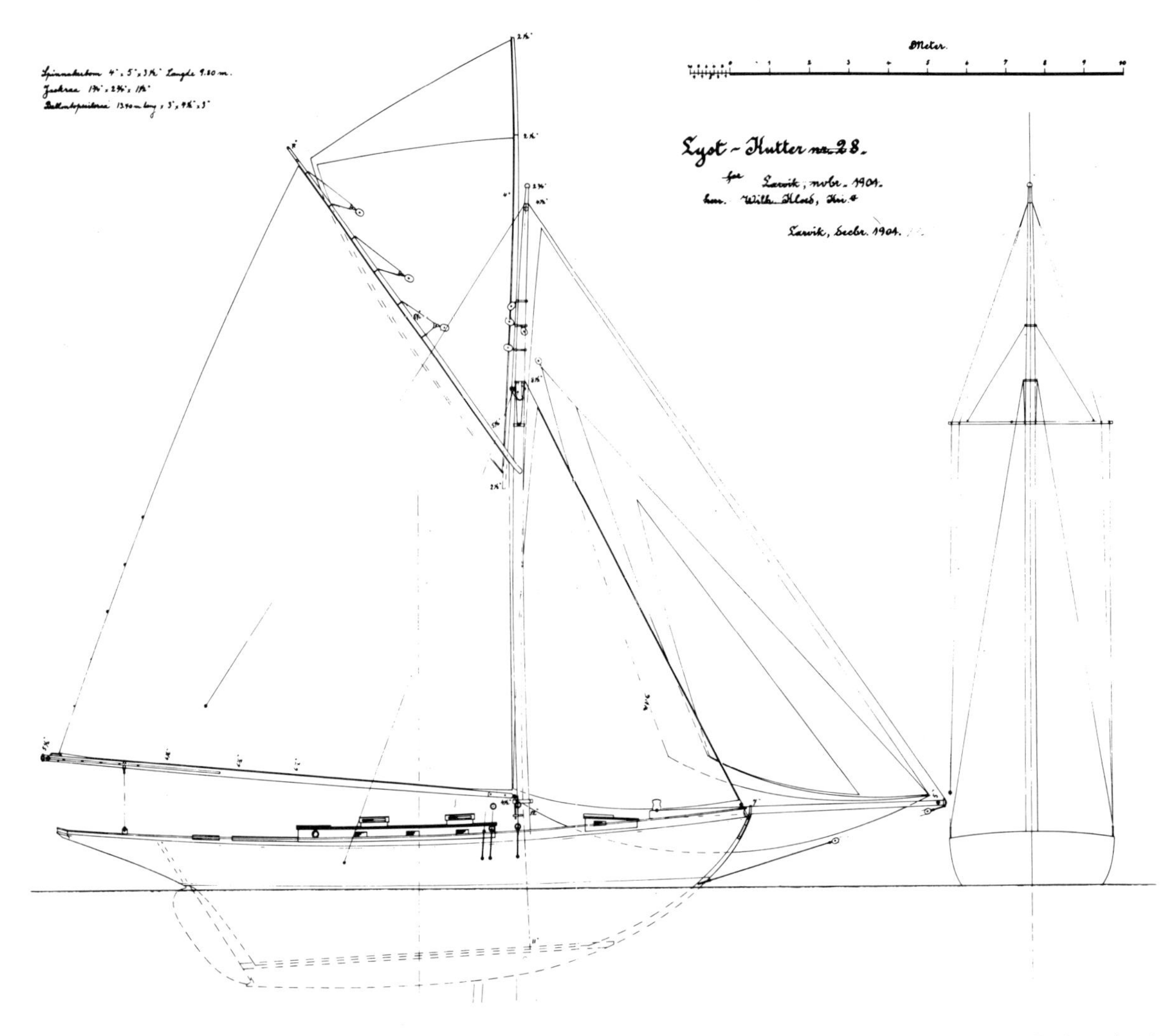

Above and next two pages: *Plans of a cruising cutter designed by Colin Archer in 1902 for Wilhelm Kloed. (Courtesy of Norsk Sjofartsmuseum)*

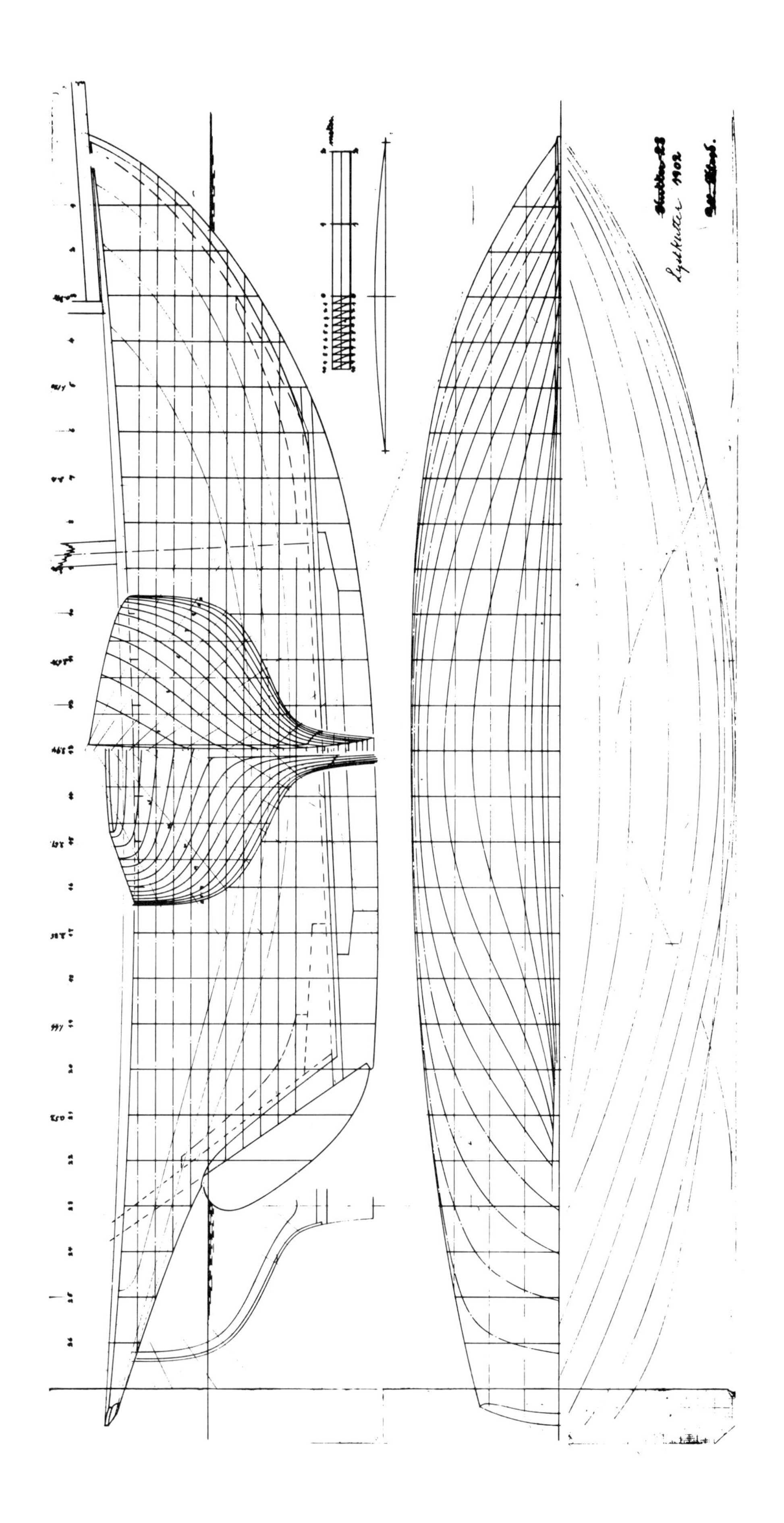

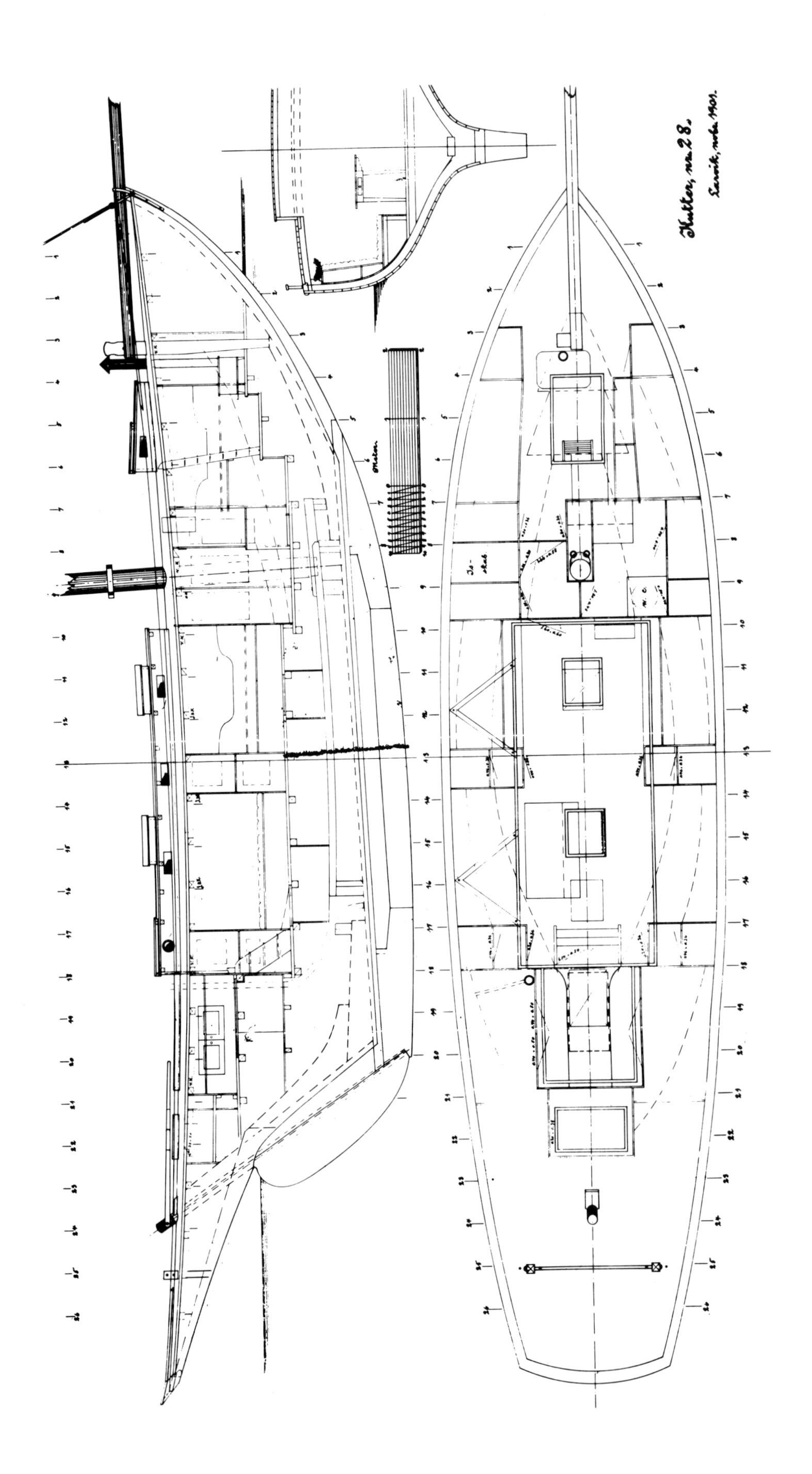
Kutter, nr. 28,

One of Colin Archer's yacht designs that went on to gain notoriety was the *Asgard,* a gaff-ketch-rigged cruising yacht for R. Erskine Childers. Childers was an Irish patriot who was well-known for both his activities in the Irish independence movement and his book, *The Riddle of the Sands*. The latter is at once a charming small-boat cruising story and a chilling detective novel, and is still considered to be the finest book of its type ever written.

The *Asgard* was built in 1905 and measured 50 feet, 9 inches on deck; 38 feet waterline; 13 feet beam; and 5 feet, 10 inches draft. Childers used her for cruising and then running small arms into Ireland. After Childers was captured and shot by an Irish Free State firing squad in 1922, the *Asgard* passed to another owner. After many years she was returned to Ireland and is now maintained as a National Monument, and until recently as a sail training craft.

The Asgard *as she appeared in 1932.*

The cutter *Tatjana,* designed by Colin Archer in 1897 as the *Wyvern,* built by Porsgrund's Baadbyggeri and later owned by a German, C. Stahl, represented the ultimate expression of Archer's work in fast cruising yachts. Her dimensions were 59 feet, 6 inches length on deck; 53 feet, 5 inches load waterline length; 18 feet beam, and 10 feet draft. One-third of her ballast was carried in an external keel; the remainder was stowed in the bilge. The hull sections were beautiful, each blending with the next in probably the most artistic body plan Colin Archer produced.

A cutter of the size of *Tatjana* demanded a housing topmast rig, and her sails included mainsail, staysail, large, working and storm jibs, jib topsail, a jib-headed topsail, a jackyard topsail, and a spinnaker. The mast was sprung forward. This yacht, perhaps more than any other, fills us with admiration for Colin Archer's work. Archer had earlier designed and built the 10-tonner *Fram* for Stahl, who appreciated the type's dryness in a seaway and sail-carrying power in a breeze. He came back for this larger yacht, and installed a Daimler Petrol motor in her during 1909.

The *Tatjana* can be compared with the yacht *Oeger* (the "Dream Ship") whose voyagings are described in Chapter 7. Both of these boats were comfortable and weatherly deep-water cruisers, and the generous beam and powerful sections afforded space on deck and room below. They were very stiff, and the long keel and deep forefoot allowed them to lie-to or run before a heavy gale in severe wind and sea conditions with safety. The boom end was kept plumb over the sternpost, which aided reefing.

Other yachts were designed and built by Colin Archer for owners in Sweden, Russia, and Denmark, and others were built abroad to Archer's designs, such as the 45-foot *Urania* built at Copenhagen by C. Neilsen in 1893.

The search for extreme speed and the changes in the rating rules that encouraged the long-ended, fin-keel style of racing yacht since the early 1890s outclassed Archer's yachts in competition, except among themselves. Yet Archer and other Scandinavian designers continued to refine and produce the pointed-stern yacht, principally for cruising. His yacht design work was a major part of his business—of 180 craft Colin Archer recorded in his journal that he either built, or designed and built, 59 of them were yachts.

Colin Archer's yacht designs made little impression on the yachting world beyond Scandinavia during his lifetime, but the ideals of seaworthiness and usefulness embodied in his designs continue to make these craft appealing to many. Colin Archer summed it up when he wrote of his yachts: "Those I have built for pleasure sailing only are nearly all modifications of the same [rescue and pilot] boats, being designed more for good sea-going yachts than for speed."

4

RESCUE BOATS

Colin Archer is now primarily associated with his designs for sailing rescue boats for the Norwegian coast. His involvement in this work came about in a unique way—by invitation of a stranger.

On a stormy morning in the early 1880s, Dr. Oscar Tybring, a general practitioner in the Tonsberg district, near the entrance to Christiania Fjord, walked the shore after a previous night's gale to make sure his boat was still riding at her moorings. He was astonished to find a ship which, unnoticed, had been wrecked on the outlying rocks during the night. She was deserted and evidently the crew were drowned. The doctor was deeply shocked and commenced a campaign for the formation of a Norwegian lifeboat organization to assist and to save seafarers in distress. Although Norway had always been a nation closely tied to the sea, the doctor's proposals found little support. Probably to many non-seafarers, the large fjords and indented coastline appeared to offer adequate shelter to craft seeking refuge, but that was hardly the truth—the rocky coast could be fatal when approached in bad weather. Dr. Tybring did find some people who were interested, and many of them suggested courses of action. Some favored rowing lifeboats of the type then used in Britain, others thought that rescue steamers should be provided by the government, to be stationed along the coast, while some considered that sailing lifeboats would be the most effective.

Doctor Tybring persevered with his rescue organization proposal. Early in 1887, he wrote to Colin Archer on another matter. He was interested in the design for a seaworthy craft he could use to visit his patients on the islands, in any weather. The correspondence led to an appeal from the doctor for Archer's aid in his lifeboat project, and thus commenced a change in the lifeboat movement's expectations. On September 20, 1887, Dr. Tybring wrote to Colin Archer:

Herr Archer:

I am venturing to apply to you in regard to a proposal in which, I think I have reason to believe, you are likely to take an interest, and be willing to cooperate in setting it on foot, in so far as this may prove to be practicable. The proposal is to establish a Norwegian Society for the rescue of the Shipwrecked, similar to the societies existing for the purpose in England and other countries. If you were prepared to interest yourself in this project, and to help us in launching it, your exceptional technical knowledge, particularly in regard to boats (in this case Rescue-boats) would be of very great assistance to us.

As to procedure, the idea is to get a number of men with special knowledge of the subject to co-operate in working out a plan and estimates of costs—for example the cost of establishing a station, of building a rescue-boat, etc.—and with this in view we intend to get hold of the English Society's Statutes, Annual reports, Accounts, etc., so as to have something to work on. In our plan these, of course, would have to be modified and adapted to the special conditions obtaining here.

Norway is, I believe, almost the only country at all civilized on whose coast a ship can go to the bottom with all hands and no human eye can see the disaster and no hand be raised stretched out to help. To do all it can to remedy this state of things should therefore be the aim and object of the society. No part of the coast unguarded. . . .

Will you then join us, Herr Archer, and give us your help? . . .

Oscar Tybring

Colin Archer replied on the 24th of September:

Herr Dr. Oscar Tybring,

I am in receipt of your much valued letter of the 20th September, and, in the first instance, will merely say in reply that the proposal dealt with in your remarks appears to me to be exceedingly opportune, and that I will gladly do all in my power to further its accomplishment.

While it is probably the case that, owing to the peculiar natural formation of our coasts, with its numerous landing places and secure harbors, a completely continuous system of rescue stations is not so urgently necessary here as in many other countries—as, for example, in Great Britain or on the west coast of Jutland, where a vessel that cannot work clear of the coast must often of necessity be driven ashore—it by no means follows that a rescue organization would not be of great service here and would not result in the saving of many lives. It is reasonable to suppose that the peculiar features of our coast mentioned above will tend to render the work of rescue much less difficult here than on lower-lying coasts, less indented by the sea; and the arrangements prevalent abroad would accordingly, as you remark, no doubt have to be adapted to suit our conditions. . . .

Colin Archer

Several years of preparatory work followed before an association was established in 1891 under the title, Norsk Selskad til Skibrudnes Redning (The Norwegian Society for the Rescue of the Shipwrecked, often abbreviated NSSR). The society voted Kr. 18,000 for the construction, as an experiment, of two sailing rescue boats to be tried at places along the coast where the most loss of life had occurred. A committee was formed in 1892 to report on the most suitable type of rescue craft, and Colin Archer was a member, along with Christian Gunnestad, a leading businessman of Christiania, pilot-master Pettersen of Fredrikstad, and pilots W. Josephsen and K. Johanesen.

The basic problem facing the committee was that the fishing grounds and most of the coast of Norway are subject to west or northwest storms that sweep unhindered from the north Atlantic. The big seas pound the outlying rocks and islands—the skerries—and, meeting the shoaler waters and currents of the coast, create vicious sea conditions. If vessels were wrecked on the skerries during such storms, rescue was usually impossible from land, through the surf, and could only be attempted from seaward by a craft seaworthy and staunch enough to live through the seas. The rescue boat would also need excellent windward ability to effect the rescue and claw off the lee shore. These conditions made the cruising sailing lifeboat the best choice for Norwegian coastal use. The committee proposed an open competition for designs for a Norwegian life-saving vessel, and five designs were submitted.

The design of Christian Stephansen of Oslo was judged best. The design of "Boatbuilder" Arnold of Arendal was second and that of "Shipbuilder" Berandi of Risor, third. However, the committee did not find any of the designs completely satisfactory; rather they commissioned Colin Archer to design a rescue boat developed from his seaworthy pilot boats. (Stephansen's boat, which he had

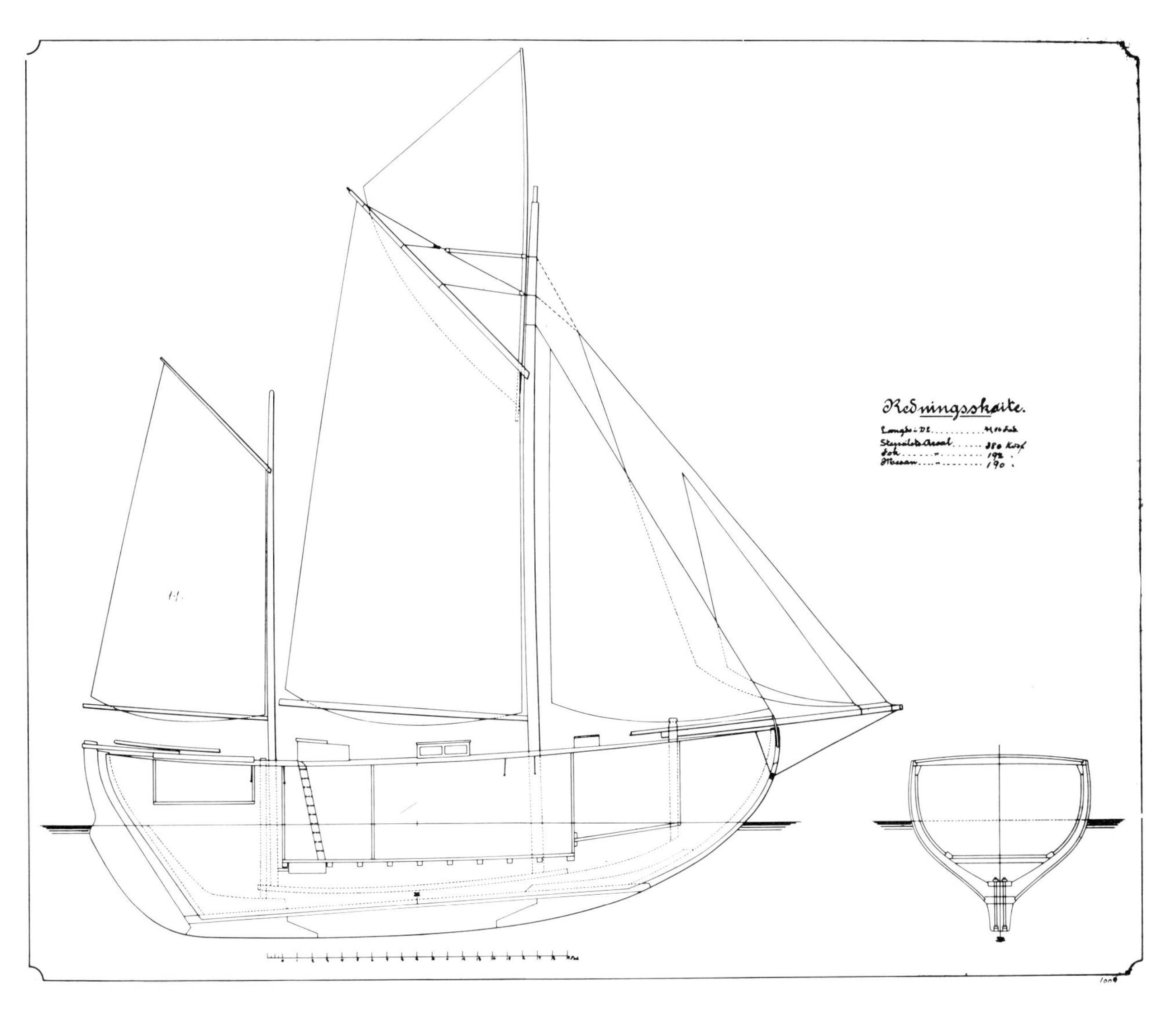

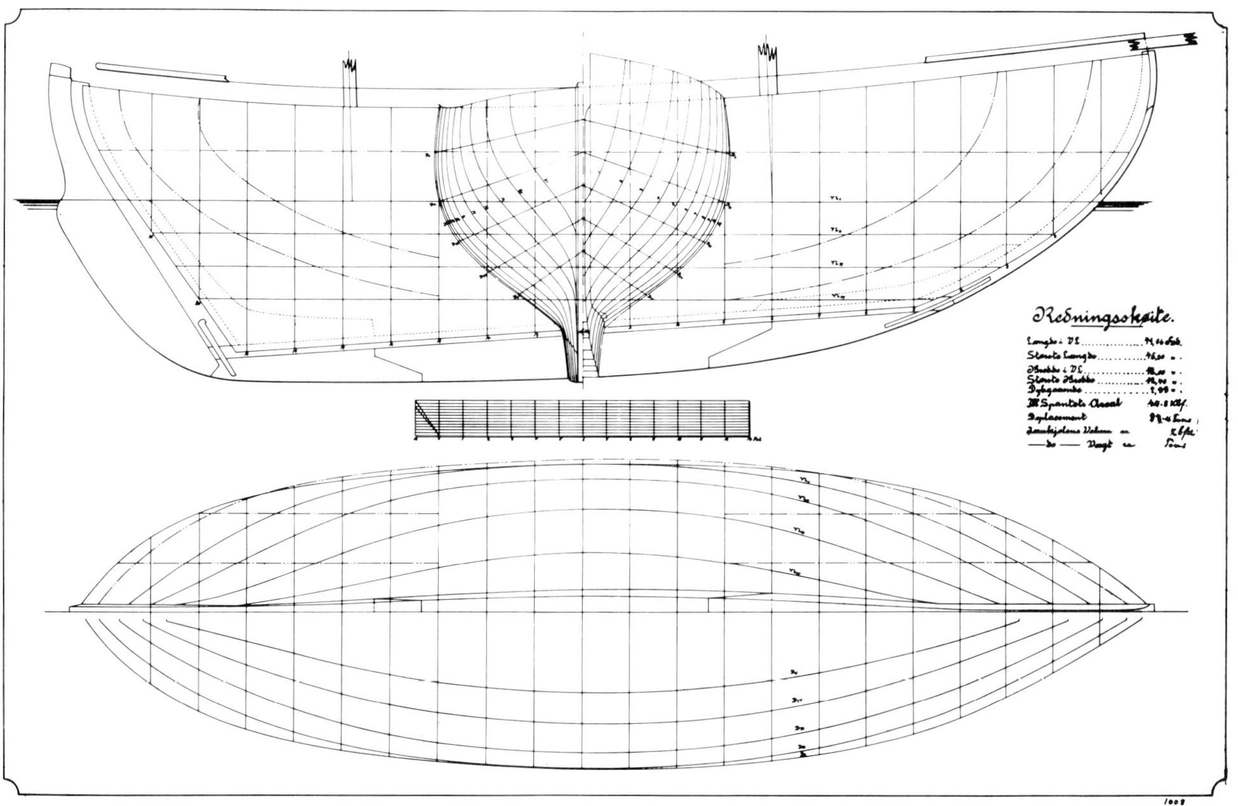

Plans for the rescue ship Liv *(RS 5), designed by Christian Stephansen and chosen by the NSSR selection committee. This draft contains the modifications by Colin Archer. (Courtesy of Norsk Sjofartsmuseum)*

named *Stjernen* (*Star*), was built eventually in 1894 as rescue boat Number 5, *Liv*. Slight modifications were made in the design by Colin Archer.)

Archer drafted a ketch-rigged craft with a pointed stern and hull form, larger but generally similar to the successful pilot boats. Principal dimensions were 45 feet length on deck; 15 feet, 3 inches beam; and 7 feet, 3 inches draft. The boat displaced 27 tons. Half of the ballast was in a cast-iron keel; the other half was in the form of iron pigs, stowed in the bilge and securely ceiled over. She was fully decked and had a watertight cockpit, which could be drained. Hull construction was heavy, with oak planking on sawn frames of pine and intermediate bent-oak frames. Norwegian pine was usually used for framing in vessels built in Norway and could be compared in durability to Baltic oak. The hull ceiling, inside the frames, was caulked watertight, giving her a double skin in case of damage to the outer planking. The four main transverse bulkheads were made as watertight as is possible in a wooden vessel.

The ketch rig of Archer's rescue boat set a loose-footed gaff mainsail, a large staysail, a jib on a running bowsprit supported by a bobstay, and a loose-footed gaff mizzen, sheeted to an iron horse over the tiller. A topsail could be set on a yard above the mainsail in light weather. A storm jib was provided for strong winds, though in storm conditions the boats usually sailed under the mainsail and staysail. The accommodations included berths for 10, but in service the rescue boats carried a crew of four.

Archer's design was accepted, and construction commenced in the yard at Tolderodden. She was launched in 1893 as the *Colin Archer* and was the first of many similar rescue craft or "redningskoites."

Captain N.W. Anthonisen was appointed master of the *Colin Archer.* During December, 1893, she sailed north to accompany the fishing fleet off Lofoten as a rescue ship. Her attendance and support was welcomed by the fishermen, and when the fleet moved farther north, to Finnmark, the *Colin Archer* went also. While lying at Vardo in May, 1894, she was called to a severe test of her abilities that was to establish the rescue ship, particularly Colin Archer's design, as the right choice for Norway's conditions.

The fishing villages of Havningberg and Vardo lie on the northeast coast of Norway, facing the Barents Sea. They are 150 miles east of the North Cape, opposite Spitsbergen, Novaya Zemlya, and the Russian coast. They lie 250 miles north of the Arctic circle in 71 degrees north latitude. Here is what happened there, as reported by Captain N.W. Anthonisen of the *Colin Archer*:

Sunday 20th May (1894).

Wind N.E. Snowstorm and thick weather with extraordinary heavy sea. All boats and vessels of the Vardo fishing station in harbor. At about 5½ p.m. the harbor-master came alongside with a telegram from Havningberg, stating that one ship and several boats had suffered total wreck, that the sea was so high it was impossible to land, and that 20 persons on vessels in the bay were in great danger; and asking that a steamer be sent to the rescue.

We made sail on the Rescue-boat and set out as quickly as possible under a press of sail, steering for Havningberg. The snowstorm was so thick that we had great difficulty in keeping our course, the distance at which the land was visible being never more than one-eighth of a mile, and sometimes only a few ships lengths. About half-past eight we sighted Havningberg. The sea was extraordinarily heavy, we stood down towards the breakers, going as near as was possible. At the entrance to the inlet the whole sea was practically one great breaker. We then went about and put her on the port tack, with two reefs in the foresail. From here we could make out the boats and vessels lying in the harbor.

The conditions were peculiarly difficult, as there was very little sea-room, and the waves were breaking at depths of 10 to 12 fathoms. We sailed round the vessels, poured oil on the sea and maneuvered in such a way as to get the boats into the stream of oil, which moderated the sea considerably.

We carried on in this way, backing, filling, tacking, gybing, as seemed best from time to time; and with good results, as in the course of three quarters of an hour we took on board twenty-two souls, one of them a lady. The persons rescued were ordered below, and we thereupon sailed out past the worst of

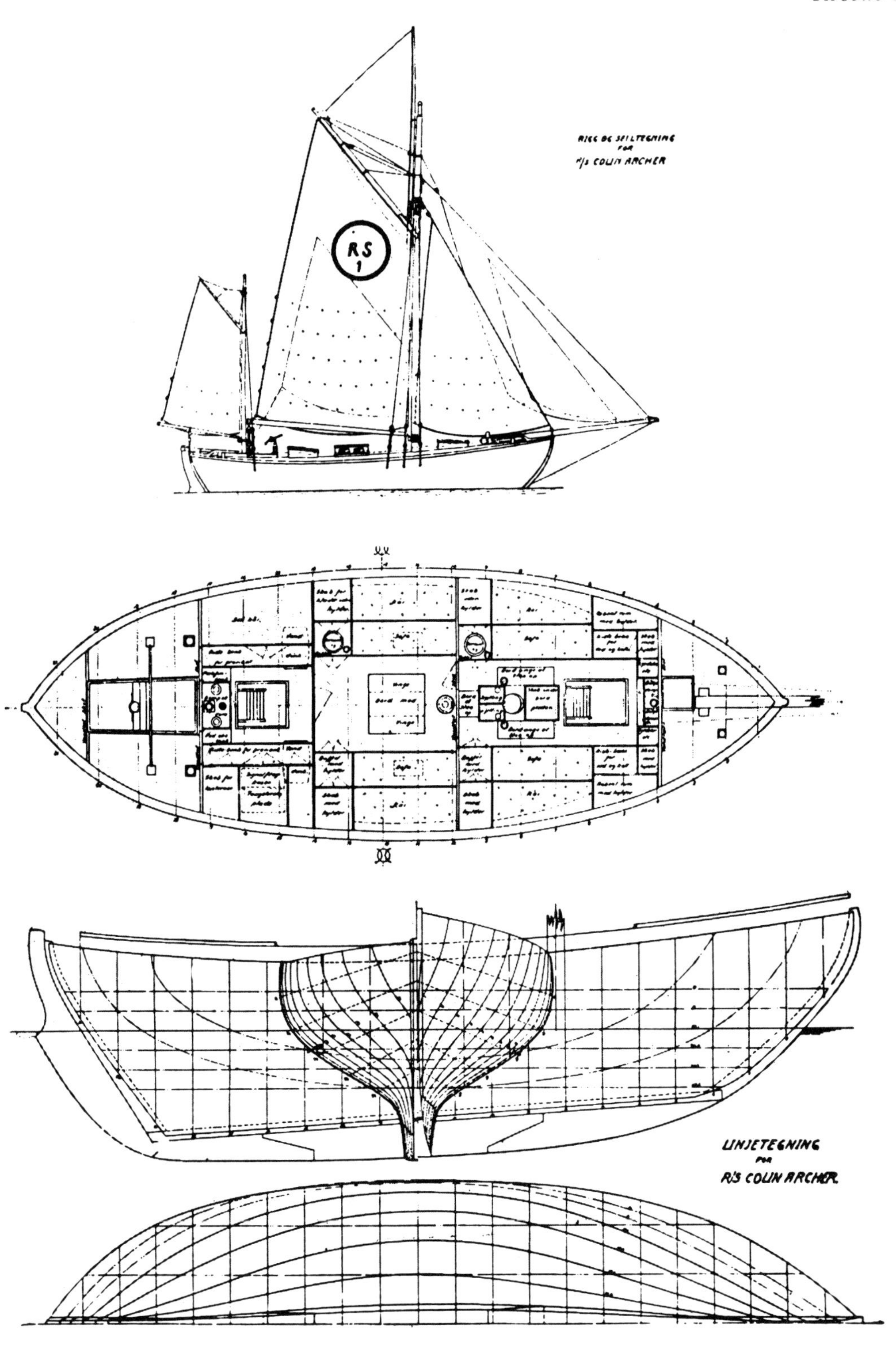

Plans of Colin Archer's first rescue ship, the Colin Archer *(RS 1), built in 1893.*

the breakers, and hove-to, waiting for signals of distress from other vessels in the harbor. I may be allowed to remark here that I did not venture to lie further in among the ships and the breakers, as we had the vessel full of people, and there was a raging sea as already described. When we had lain there about a quarter of an hour looking out for signals without seeing any, we set our course back to Vardo. The snow drove thicker and the storm increased. We learnt after that the other vessels too had distress signals hoisted, but we could not see them. At the mouth of Porsfjord a sea broke over us that would undoubtedly have buried us all if the vessel had not been as solid and seaworthy as she is. The whole of her after part was completely under water, and the pram we carried was smashed, but otherwise there was no damage. We were, I may remark, under suitably reefed-down canvas. At midnight we reached Vardo and landed all our passengers safely.

On our arrival we found telegraphic orders from the scene of the disaster directing us to return as quickly as possible. We went out again at once. The storm was then abating, but the sea was still exceedingly heavy. We reached Havningberg again at 3:20 a.m. and by maneuvering in the same way as before, succeeded in picking up fourteen more people. We then once more laid our course for Vardo. At about 10 a.m. we arrived at Vardo and put the people ashore. Thereafter we moored the vessel and turned in, as there were no more boats at sea.

There is much enthusiasm here over our work. Numbers of people are visiting and inspecting the vessel. . . .

Captain Anthonisen's work was validated a few hours after the *Colin Archer* left Havningberg, when several of the craft lying there were blown ashore and broke up amongst rocks where rescue would have been impossible.

The lifeboat committee, and particularly Colin Archer, were greatly encouraged by the Havningberg rescue, which was quickly followed by similar ones during the winter of 1894-95. The first boat's performance confirmed that the sailing rescue boat was the best type for Norwegian coastal conditions and reinforced the view that the society's main efforts should be concentrated on this type of craft. By 1901, sixteen similar rescue boats had been built and were stationed along the Norwegian coast. The Norwegian name for these rescue sailing roats was Redningskoites, which was abbreviated to the initials RS preceding their names.

Rescue ship captains and crews, a complement of four men, were volunteers but were regularly employed by the NSSR, as these were cruising vessels, usually commissioned for the autumn, winter, and spring months and only laid up during the summer, when many were refitted at one of the society's depots. Thus, the manning of Norwegian rescue ships was quite different from the system in Britain, where local fishermen and other seafarers manned the shore- or harbor-based pulling and sailing lifeboats. In contemporary British practice, only the coxswain received retaining pay, which supplemented his usual income as a fisherman. The Norwegian system was also different from that in the United States, where government agencies employed enlisted personnel using both shore-based lifeboats, or surfboats, and cruising steam cutters. The NSSR system of cruising needed far fewer craft than both the British and U.S. methods, but must have been almost as expensive to maintain from voluntary donations as was that of the British Royal National Lifeboat Institution.

After a British lifeboat disaster at Kingstown, Ireland, during 1896, Colin Archer was in correspondence with Charles Dibdin, secretary of the Royal National Lifeboat Institution. Archer's letter of February 10, 1896, expressed his views of the Norwegian rescue ships:

. . . What we have aimed at is to produce a boat sufficiently powerful to contend with wind and sea in any weather, and under the most trying circumstances not only to be able to carry out safely any maneuver necessary for doing the work for which she is intended, viz: rendering assistance to those in distress. As far as our experience goes we have succeeded in attaining these ends beyond expectation. These boats have never as yet been prevented from going to sea by the severity of the weather during the 3 or 4 years they have been in commission. They have frequently kept at sea all night in the middle of winter in heavy gales and have when properly canvassed and handled shown themselves capable of beating off a lee shore in the strongest blow, while as for handiness they leave nothing to be desired. The crew consists of four hands and the boats are kept in commission the greater part of the year. They have been particularly useful at the great cod and herring fisheries on the west and north coast where sudden gales off the land frequently carry the fishing boats out to sea.

Yet, the conditions around most of the British coasts were unsuitable for the Norwegian sailing type, and so no experiments were then made with them. It was not until the 1960s that the RNLI tried the Norwegian system of employing cruising lifeboats, when it ordered its first two cruising motor lifeboats.

What were the basic features of Colin Archer's sailing rescue ships? The ability to ride seas buoyantly and lie-to without attention in the worst conditions were amongst the principal requirements, but speed to windward was unimportant, though ability to make to windward in very bad sea conditions was naturally necessary. Generally, Colin Archer's designs for the rescue ships were notable for considerable beam at the deck, often with an overall hull length 2½ times the beam. They had pronounced flare in the bows and quarters, and some flare carried through amidships, which provided reserve buoyancy. A long, straight keel and a raking sternpost that curved forward at its head were other distinctive features. The rudder was narrow and ran the full depth of the sternpost. The staysail was large and the mizzen smaller than is usual with a ketch rig. The mainsail and mizzen were loose-footed, and double reef cringles were fitted in the leech of the mainsail. The staysail foot was cut high to relieve its pressing effect, and so it did not hold water going to windward in bad weather. There were three shrouds on each side, set up with deadeyes and lanyards, but no runners or backstays were fitted—an advantage of the pole-masted rig. The mizzen was supported by a single shroud on each side, led down usually forward of the mast. The outer planking was all oak to withstand the scour of floating ice in winter at sea and in harbor. A stout rail (the strict English term is "rough tree rail") ran from forward to aft on the heads of stanchions side-bolted to the heads of the frames. The resulting open "bulwark" allowed water on deck to flow overboard quickly when seas were shipped. Stout bitts aft were intended for towing small fishing boats caught out in bad weather. A wooden davit was fitted on each side of the bowsprit to lead the anchor chain clear of the bow.

The redningskoites carried a lapstrake-planked Norwegian pram of the original long-bowed type. This boat measured about 12 feet by 5 feet and was able to carry four or five men in fine conditions. The pram was stowed upside-down on the deck amidships and was used for general boatwork in fine weather and occasionally in rescue work. A small line-throwing gun could be mounted on a deck pedestal amidships to fire a strong, light line to a distressed vessel, by which a tow line could be sent across.

In bad weather, the rescue ships were very lively but comparatively dry, were never fast to windward or on other points of sailing, but were craft that inspired and deserved the full confidence of their crews in the worst gales. One of their remarkable features was the ability to tow four or five smaller fishing boats off a lee shore under sail in bad weather. Such towing survived well into the twentieth century, as the auxiliary motors with which many became fitted were not thought sufficiently reliable for the task.

The first ten rescue ships were built from Colin Archer's design, with the exception of the *Liv,* whose plans Archer modified as mentioned previously. Four of the first ten were built in Archer's own yard at Larvik and the remainder by other builders. The second of those built by Archer, in 1894, had finer bows than the others and was rigged as a cutter, but the third, and all subsequent boats, reverted to the ketch rig. The next ten

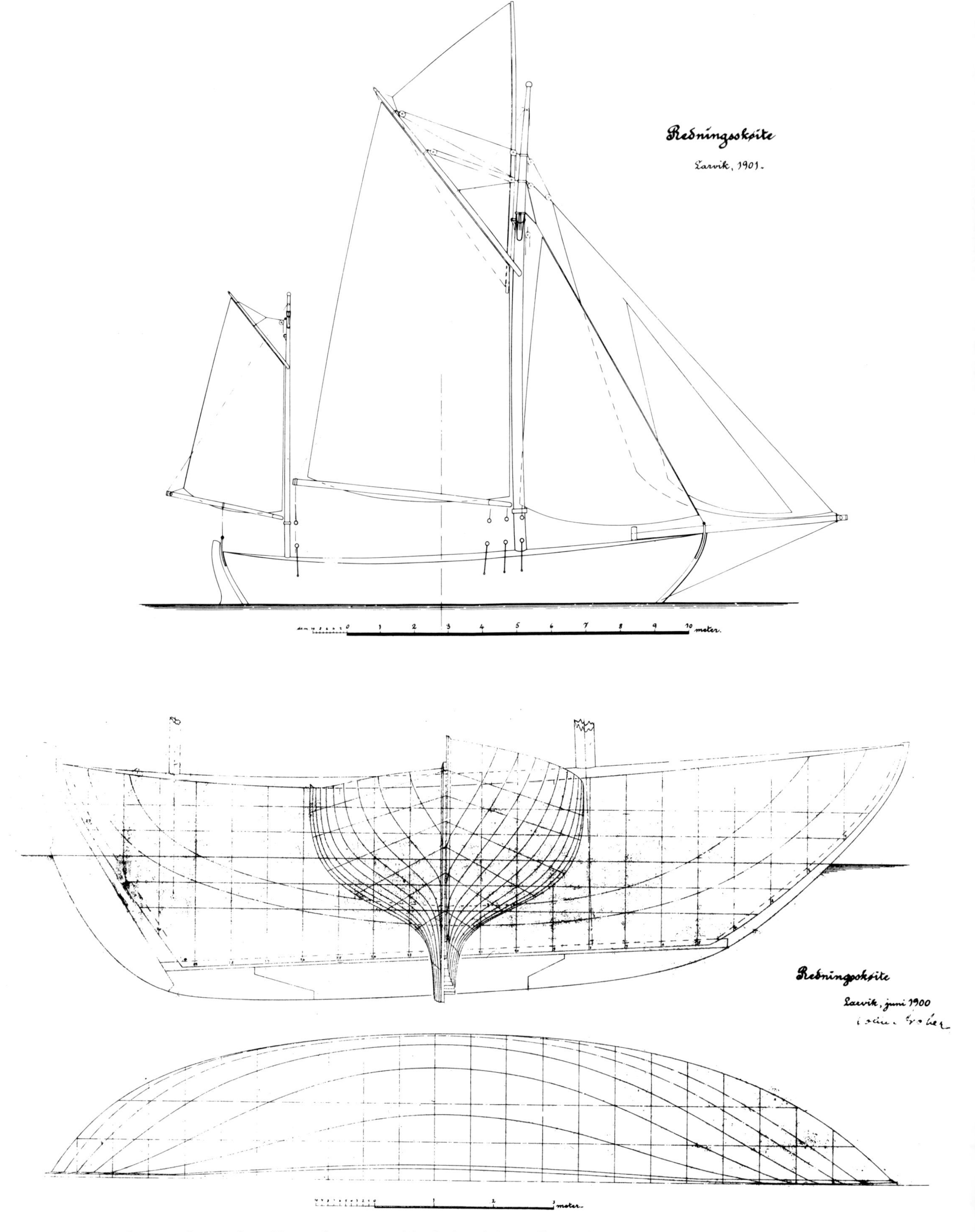

Above and opposite: *Plans of a rescue ship designed by Colin Archer in 1901. (Courtesy of Norsk Sjofarts-museum)*

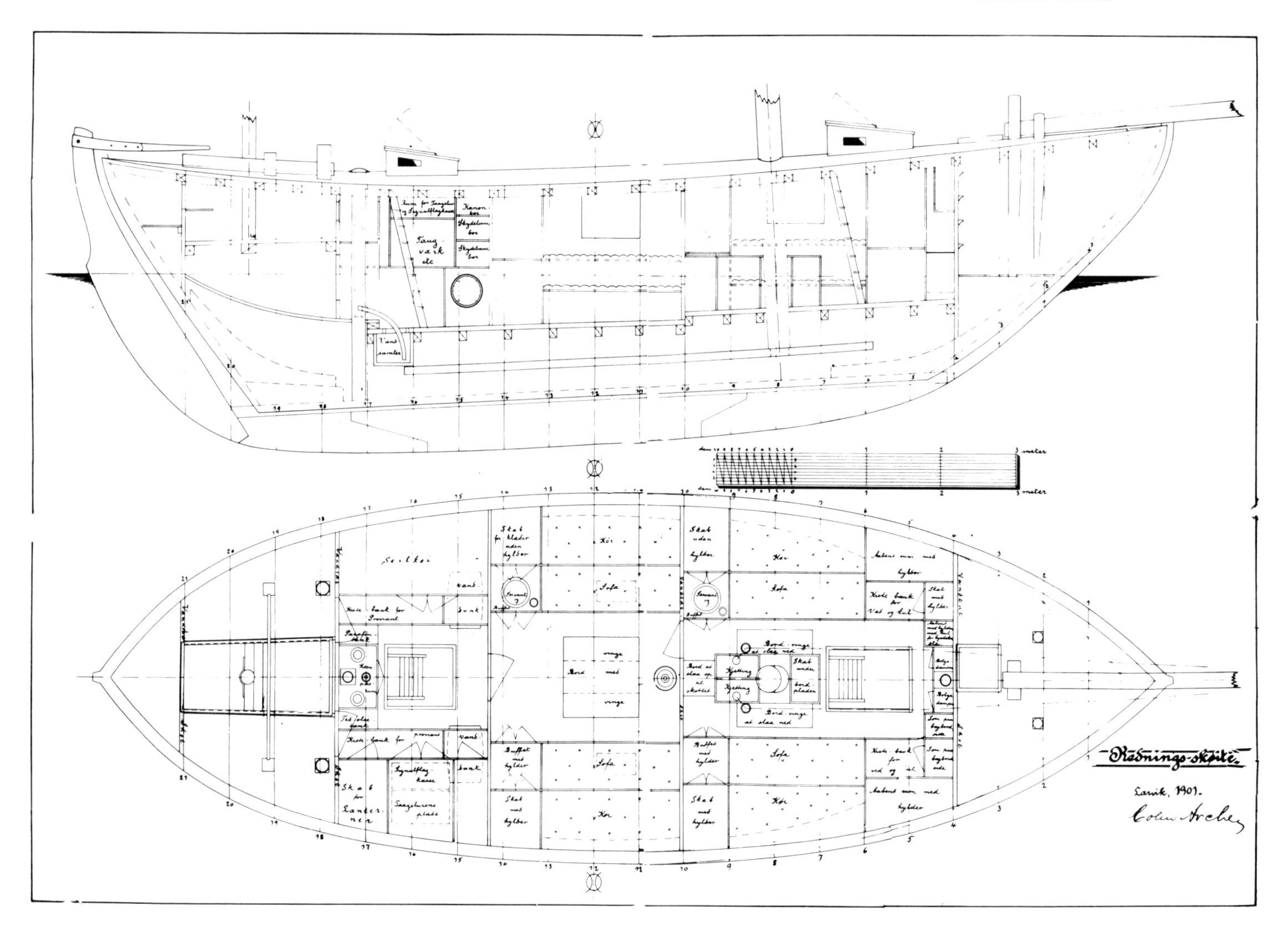

rescue ships, built between 1897 and 1907, were all to the same design, which differed from that of the first ten boats in minor ways. Seven of these were built by Colin Archer. The following ten rescue ships were built alike, and the original Colin Archer design was amended—the boats were increased in length by one foot and in beam by 6 inches. Appendix C to this book shows the scantlings and rigging details of this amended design.

The last purely sailing rescue ship built for the NSSR was the *Johan Bruusgaard.* (For a complete tabular record of the rescue ships, both sail and power, see Appendix B.)

Only three sailing rescue ships were recorded as being lost. The *Risor* disappeared in 1913 without trace (a second *Risor* was built and is still sailing as a yacht in British ownership). The *Nordland I* went ashore and was lost during 1900, and the *Bergen I* suffered the same fate in 1907. This small number of losses is a fine tribute to craft doing dangerous work on that exposed coast.

The reputation of the redningskoites spread beyond Scandinavia. As a result, Colin Archer received commissions to design and build craft for several Baltic countries, and rescue boats for Russia, a design later used as the basis for the first Norwegian rescue ships built with auxiliary power. The Russian vessels

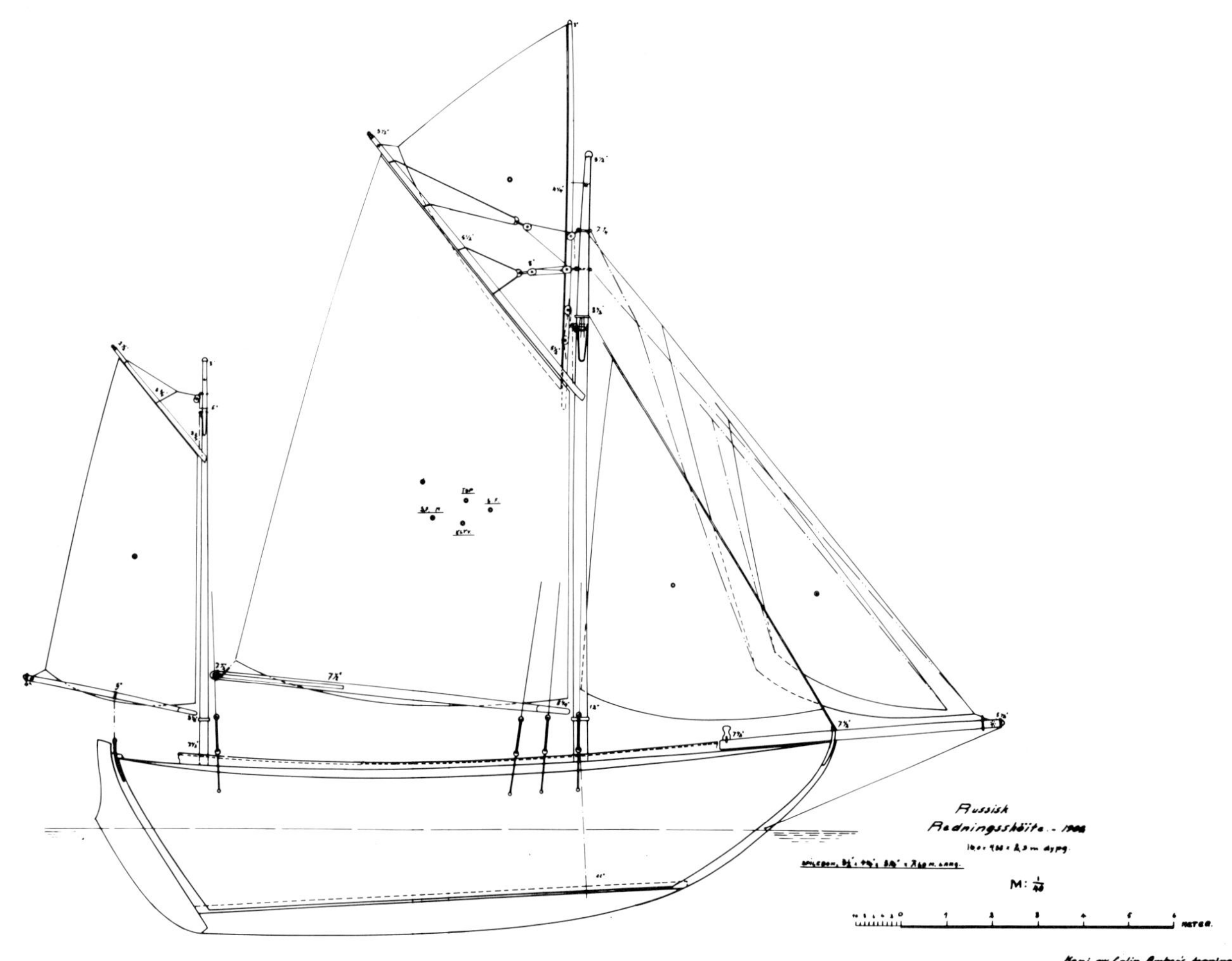
Russisk
Redningsskôite
M: 1/40
METER.

Kopi av Colin Archer's tegninger.
Oslo januar

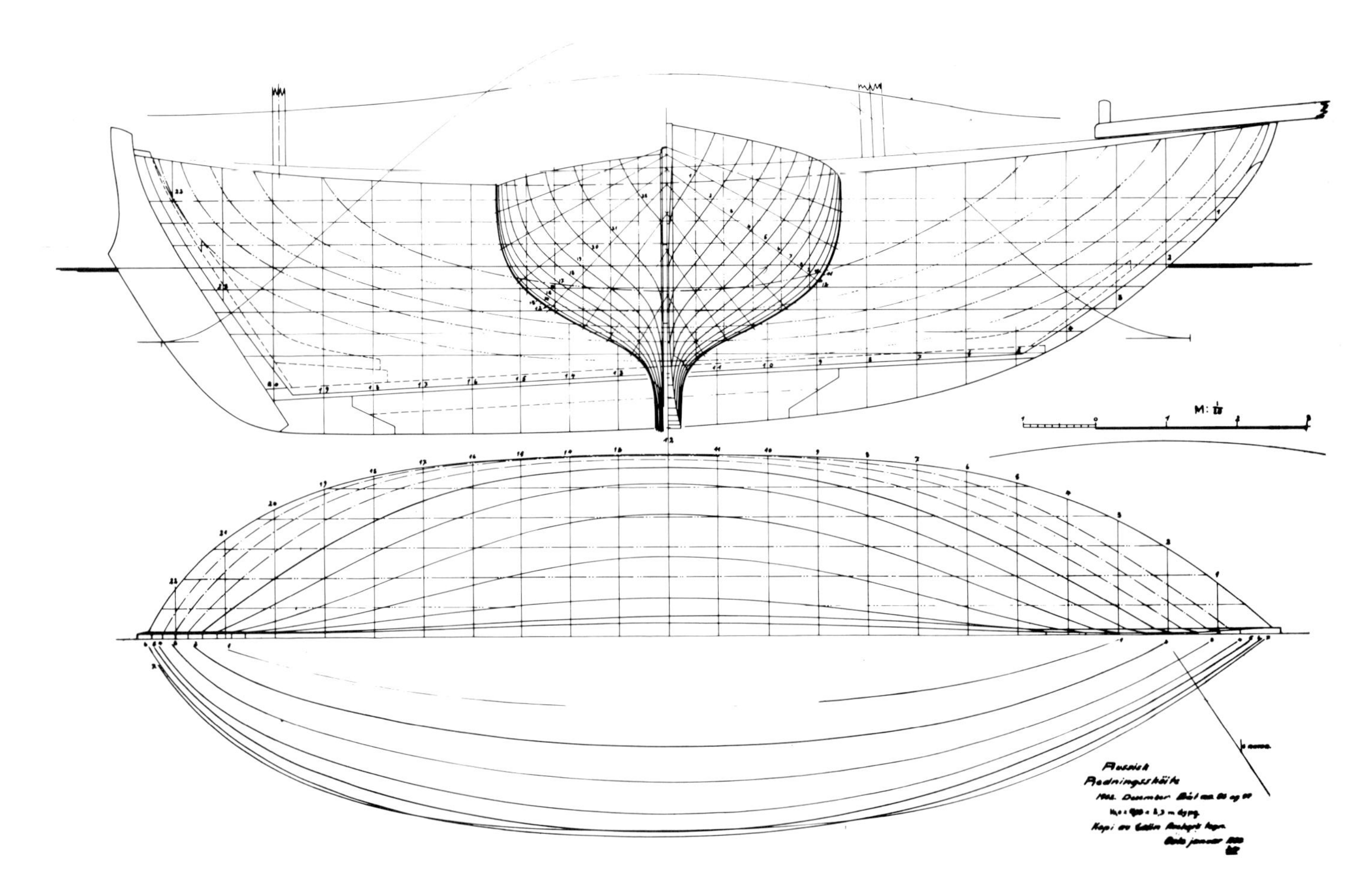
Russisk
Redningsskôite
Kopi av Colin Archer's tegn.
Oslo januar

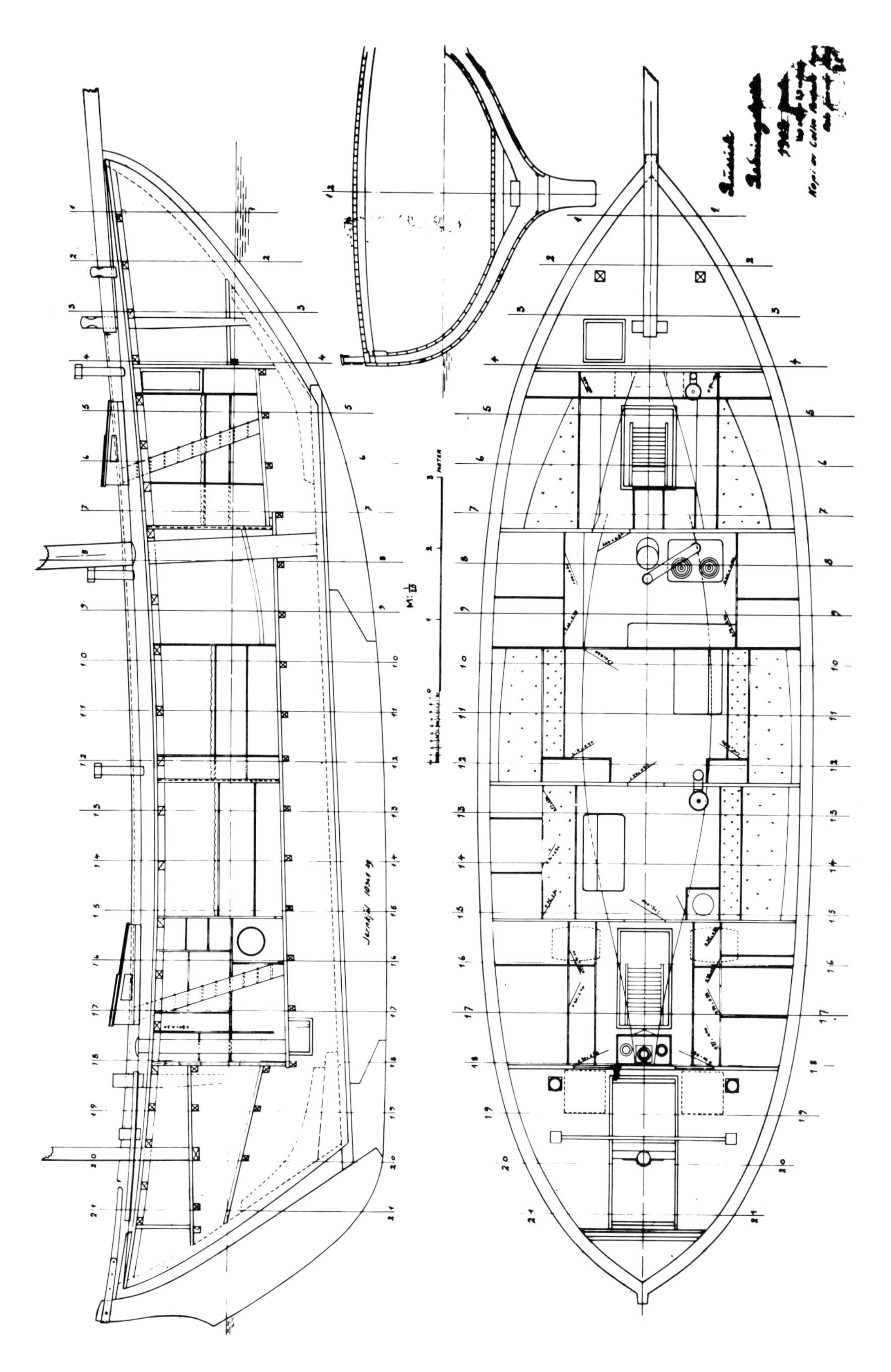

Above and opposite: *Plans of the rescue ships designed by Colin Archer in 1902 for Russia. (Courtesy of Norsk Sjofartsmuseum)*

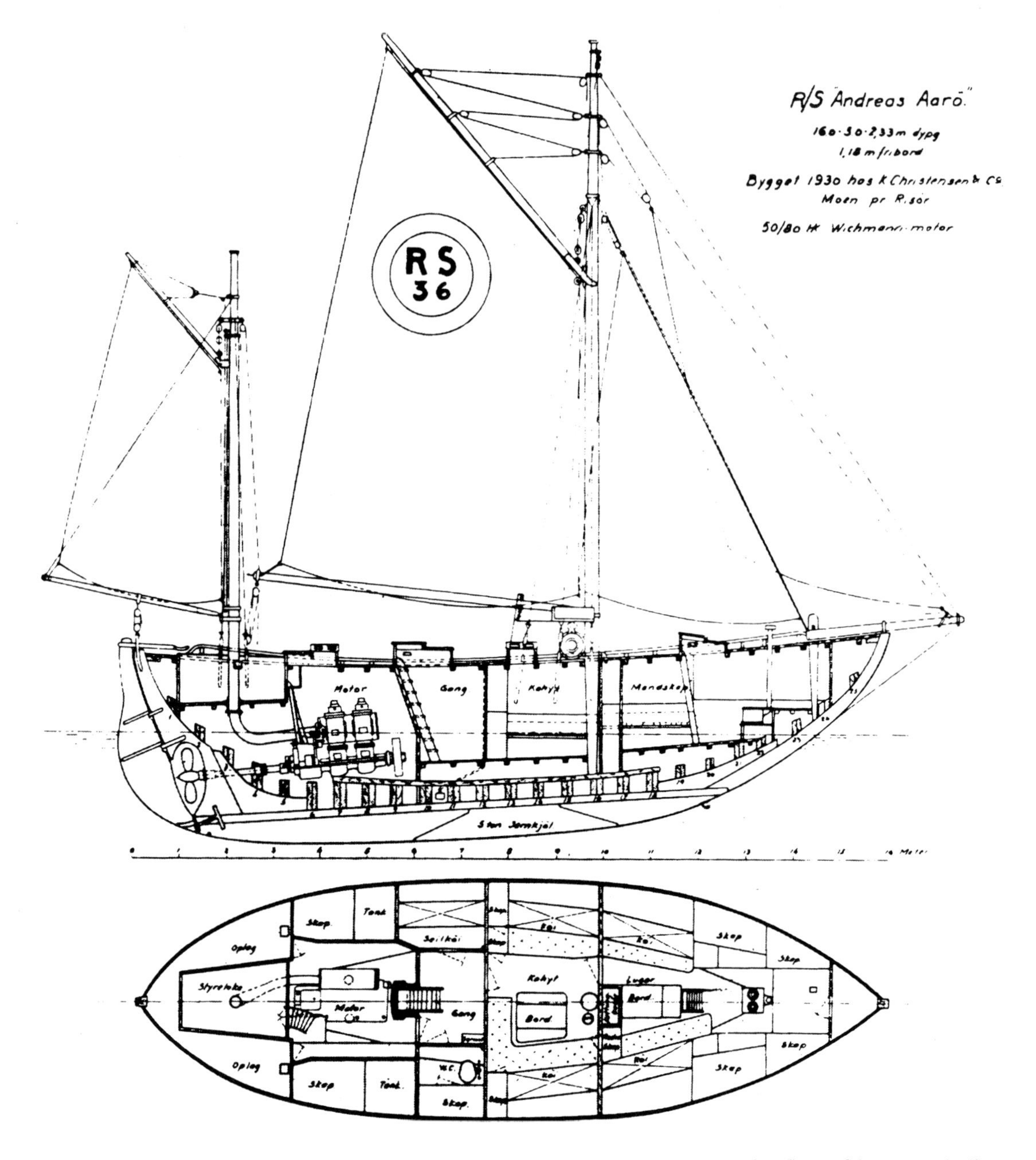

The rescue ship Andreas Aaro, *built in 1930 by K. Christensen. She was the first of her type built with an auxiliary engine. Note that the mizzen mast serves as the engine exhaust stack.*

were a fine example of Archer's rescue ship designs. They had powerful, shapely hulls with dimensions of 53 feet, 2 inches length on deck; 45 feet, 11 inches waterline length; 16 feet, 3 inches beam; and 7 feet, 6 inches draft. Most of the ballast was in an iron keel. The sections indicate good windward ability and the buttocks potential speed. The ketch rig had the usual areas and proportions for the type, but the mizzen was stepped in the steering cockpit and clamped to a strong beam across it, abaft the mainsheet horse. The accommodation was more elaborate than in many rescue ships; a vessel of this type would make an exceptionally fine cruising yacht.

By 1930, motors had become relatively reliable and compact. Other countries had been using motor lifeboats for some time, though sail was retained as auxiliary propulsion. The NSSR considered a "motorskoite" type desirable for future rescue ships, and plans were drawn by designer Ottar Vogt for the first Norwegian motor lifeboat, with auxiliary sails. She was the *Andreas Aaro,* built in 1930 by Knut Christensen and Company of Moen, near Risor. She was 52 feet, 10½

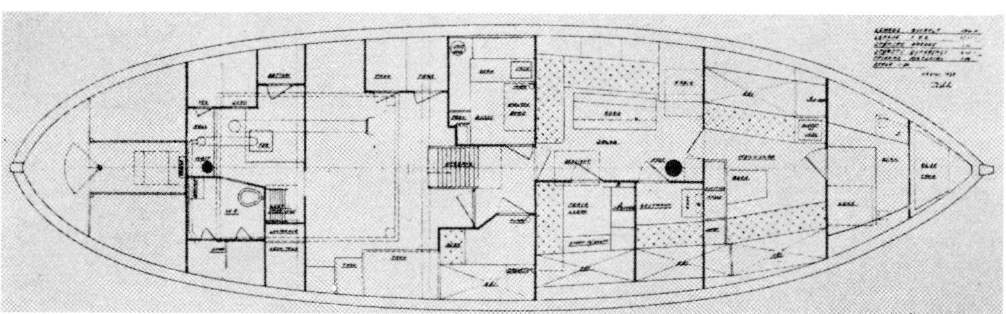

Above and next page: *Plans of the rescue ship* Gustav B. Bull, *built in 1939. She represents the final development of the sail-carrying rescue ship.*

inches long; 16 feet, 4¾ inches beam; and 7 feet, 7¾ inches draft. Her hull form and construction remained close to the original Colin Archer type, but a 50/80 horsepower Winchmann diesel was the prime propulsion, and the ketch rig was of modest area, with a short bowsprit and the staysail tacked down well inside the stemhead.

Despite the commitment to power craft, during 1931 the NSSR purchased the ketch *Catherine Booth,* which had been designed and built by Colin Archer in 1901 for the Salvation Army, an English charitable institution, for a mission to deep-sea fishermen. But the *Catherine Booth* was only a temporary measure. Between 1930 and 1940 the new rescue ships had powerful motors, carried wheelhouses, and only set a steadying and emergency rig. Some of the older rescue ships were given powerful auxiliary engines, but many were sold, usually to become cruising yachts.

The motorskoite *Biskop Hvoslef* followed the *Andreas Aaro* type in 1932. She was designed by Bjarne Aas, a Norwegian yacht designer noted for his racing yachts. Aas refined the older sailing rescue ship form to suit a motor-sailing use but retained the basic, practical, seaworthy appearance set by Colin Archer in his sailing craft. The motorskoites built until 1940 were the last rescue ships to follow the basic form and proportions of Colin Archer's concept. After 1945, new craft were designed as twin-screw motor vessels, though the wooden motorsailers of the 1930s remained in use for another twenty years, their steadying rigs, buoyant bows, and bold sheers a reminder of the days of sail.

The careers of the Norwegian rescue ships varied, with the earlier boats generally ef-

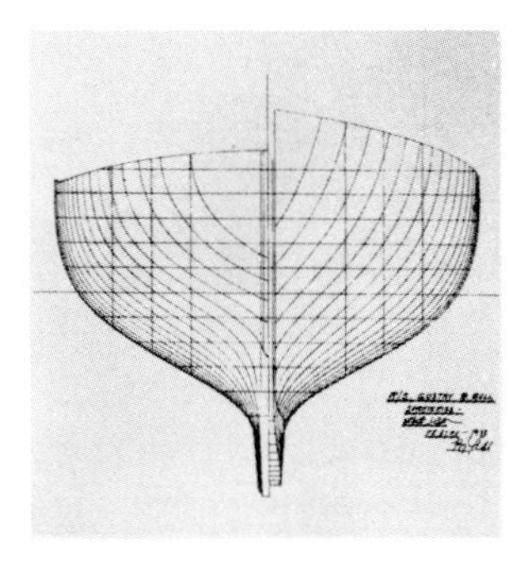

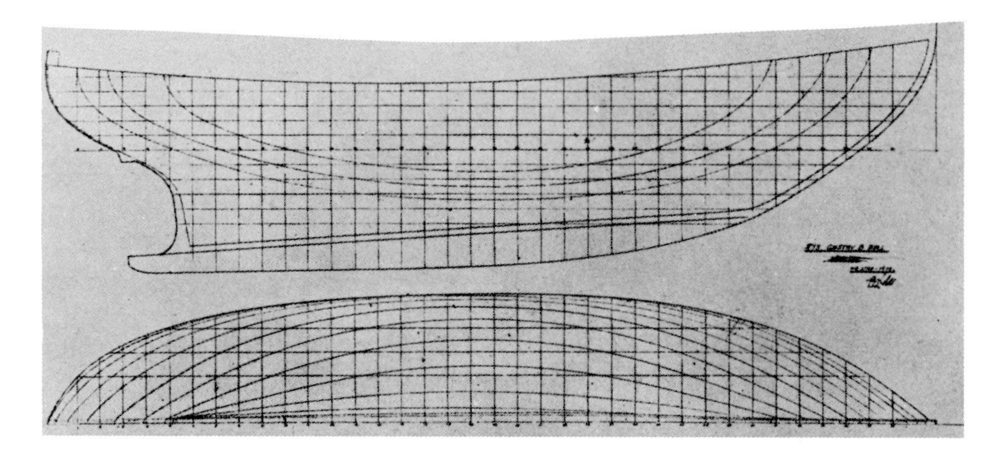

fecting the most rescues in the days of sail and oar, and with later craft, though braving the same seas and storms, finding less work in an increasingly mechanized age afloat. For instance, the *Oscar Tybring,* designed and built in 1895 by Colin Archer, was credited with assisting 102 craft and saving 329 men's lives, while the equally seaworthy *Christian Bugge* of 1935 saved 57 lives before being sold in 1967.

Some of the redningskoites have survived varied careers and are still sailing. The *Christiania* (1896) ended her working life carrying steel scrap on the west coast of Norway for twenty years. The battered and bruised hull was then bought by Erling Brunborg, who restored and then sold her as a yacht. She now sails from the Oslofjord.

In 1961 the *Halten* (1907) sailed with an expedition under Helge Ingstad to the Labrador coast, seeking the sites of early Greenlander settlements. Afterwards she was left at Halifax, Nova Scotia, for two years before being sold as a yacht. The *Risor II* (1914) is an English yacht sailing from Plymouth Sound. The *Stavanger* (1901) is owned by the Neilsen family of Snaroya, Norway. *Fele* (1894) and *Oscar Tybring* (1895) are yachts in America and retain much of their original appearance.

The *Colin Archer* was retired from service during 1933, having assisted about 1,500 craft and 4,500 seafarers and having saved 237 lives. She became a yacht and in 1938 was sailed to America, where she remained until 1961, when she returned to Norwegian ownership. She was refitted and in 1972 was presented to the Norwegian Museum of Navigation for preservation as a relic. She was subsequently loaned to the Sea Scouts for training before becoming flagship of the Colin Archer Sailing Club, whose members maintain and occasionally sail her. The old lifeboat carries her age well, probably due to her extremely robust construction and well-seasoned materials.

The Colin Archer *when new. In the inset is her skipper, N.W. Anthonisen.*

Left: *The* Colin Archer *about 1893. (Courtesy of Redningsselskapet, Oslo)*

Below: *The* Colin Archer *at sea about 1914. (Courtesy of Norsk Sjofartsmuseum)*

Opposite, top: *Ten rescue ships dressed for inspection at Bergen in 1910. The* Halten *and* Stavanger *are nearest the camera. (Courtesy of J. Neilsen)*

Opposite, bottom: *The rescue ship* Svolvaer *on patrol about 1900. (Courtesy of Redningsselskapet, Oslo)*

HALTEN

RS
12

The Johan Bruusgaard, *the last sailing rescue ship to be built, launched in 1924. (Courtesy of J. Neilsen)*

The Risor *(right) and the then-new* Sandefjord *(left) becalmed off the small port of Risor in 1913. The* Risor *was lost shortly afterward. (Courtesy of J. Neilsen)*

The Christian Bors, *built in 1904, represented Norway at an international gathering of lifeboats on the River Thames, London, in 1924. The forward-raking masthead can be clearly seen. Her bowsprit is housed. (Courtesy of the Royal National Lifeboat Institution)*

A rescue ship on winter patrol off the coast of Norway. (Courtesy of Norsk Folkemuseum)

The William Eger, *built in 1904, forms part of the background for her skipper and a friend. (Courtesy of J. Neilsen)*

The Svolvaer *closes with another rescue ship on patrol about 1934.*

The Svolvaer *under sail about 1934. (Courtesy of Norsk Folkemuseum)*

The Larvik *jumps to windward under her motor-sailing rig some time after 1934. She was built in 1920 and a motor was installed in 1934. (Courtesy of J. Neilsen)*

The Nordland II, *built in 1910. The crosses prominently painted on the side of the ship indicate this photograph was probably taken in wartime. (Courtesy of J. Neilsen)*

The Vadso, *later renamed the* Oscar Tybring, *built in 1913.*

The motor-sailing rescue ship Christian Bugge, *built in 1935, underway under reefed mainsail and staysail. She has a canoe stern and an inboard rudder post. (Courtesy of Redningsselskapet, Oslo)*

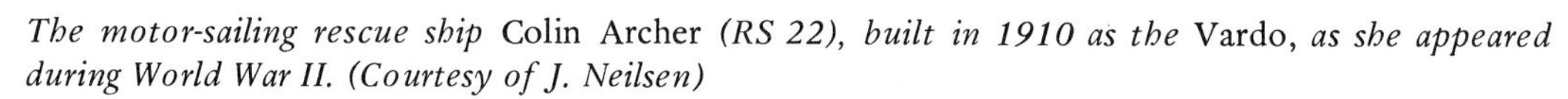

The motor-sailing rescue ship Colin Archer *(RS 22), built in 1910 as the* Vardo, *as she appeared during World War II. (Courtesy of J. Neilsen)*

The motor-sailing rescue ships Idun *(1937),* Christian Bugge *(1935), and* Osloskoyta *(1940) in harbor about 1940. (Courtesy of J. Neilsen)*

The restored rescue ship Colin Archer *(RS 1) sailing again as a Sea Scout training ship in 1973. (Courtesy of J. Neilsen)*

5

POLAR SHIPS

During 1891, Colin Archer was approached to undertake an unusual design for a polar exploration ship to be built for Professor Fridtjof Nansen, a noted Norwegian explorer and biologist. For centuries men had attempted to reach the North Pole for both scientific reasons and simply to be the first to get there. The attempts failed for many reasons, but the primary deterrent to success was the zone of surrounding ice that repelled and sometimes crushed the explorers' ships far short of the mystical pole at distances and in conditions that rendered impossible final journeys by sledge and foot over the ice.

In 1879, the ship *Jeanette*, carrying an American expedition commanded by Captain G.W. De Long, was caught in the ice soon after passing the Bering Strait to enter the Arctic Ocean. She drifted to the northwest for a year and ten months until her hull was crushed by the pressure of ice six feet thick. The *Jeanette* sank in June, 1881, north of the New Siberia Islands. Captain De Long and most of his men died attempting to reach the Siberian coast. In 1884, an account of this voyage stirred the imagination of Professor Nansen, who conceived the novel plan of drifting over the Pole. He would sail and steam a ship into polar waters and allow the ship to become frozen in the moving ice, which would then drift over the North Pole with the prevailing currents, taking the ship and Nansen with it.

Nansen attempted to raise interest in his proposal and during 1890 sought the design and construction of a ship capable of withstanding the pressure of any ice she might encounter. He had faith in the projected voyage, but few designers and builders shared his hope of constructing such a vessel. Nansen discussed it with a Norwegian yard building sealing ships, and they referred him to Colin Archer as a man fond of developing small craft and improving existing types. At first Archer refused to undertake even a design study, pleading inexperience in ships for polar use, but Nansen and Captain Otto Sverdrup (to be the captain of the new ship) persuaded him in April, 1891, to commence a design.

Nansen's ship was a complex design problem. Many preliminary plans were drafted and half-models made, only to be discarded for various reasons. Archer attempted to design a ship that would be of rounded transverse section so that, as ice closed on the hull, it would at first resist the pressure, then slowly rise partially above the crushing ice, like an orange seed squeezed between finger and thumb. It was expected that most of the ship's hull would emerge above the ice surface with, perhaps, just the lower bottom and the keel embedded in it. In this way, Archer hoped the ship would remain intact so she could stay with the ice as it drifted north. Archer's theory was developed from the experiences of many Norwegian small craft that fished and sealed from Spitsbergen and Novaya Zemlya at various seasons. When caught in ice, these craft, which had considerable rise of floor (bottom sections that are sharply rising), were squeezed up from the water, above the ice, usually without damage. In contrast to contemporary sealing and whaling ships, which were strongly reinforced internally at the bow and stern with wooden packing to enable them to ram ice floes under their powerful engines, Nansen's ship was likely to suffer the most damage amidships from ice pressure, probably around the waterline and sides.

Colin Archer's final design was for a wooden, three-masted, auxiliary steam schooner, 128 feet long, 36 feet beam, 15 feet, 6 inches depth, and 800 tons displacement. Her hull necessarily departed from Archer's usual

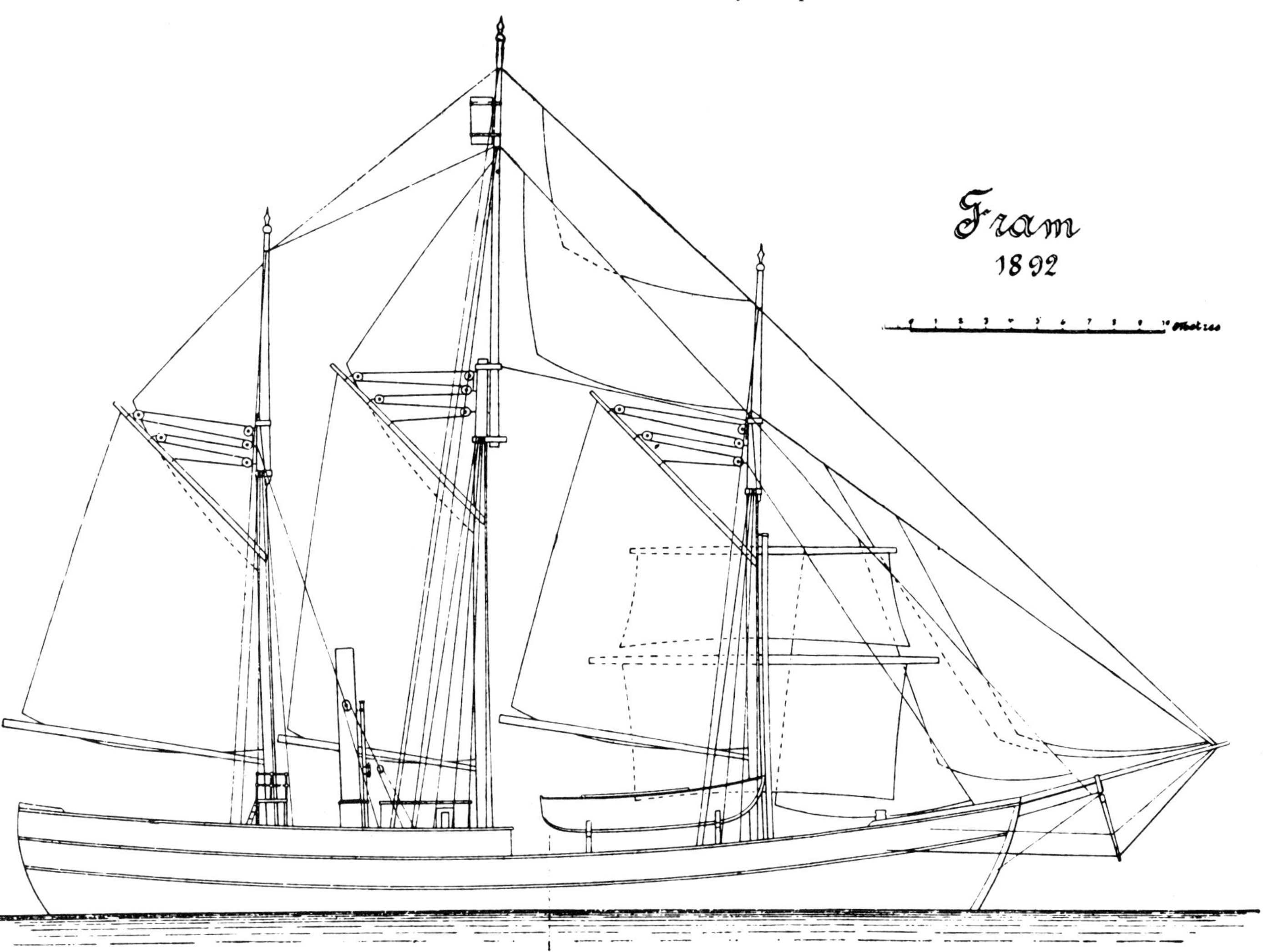

Above and next page: *Plans of the polar ship* Fram.

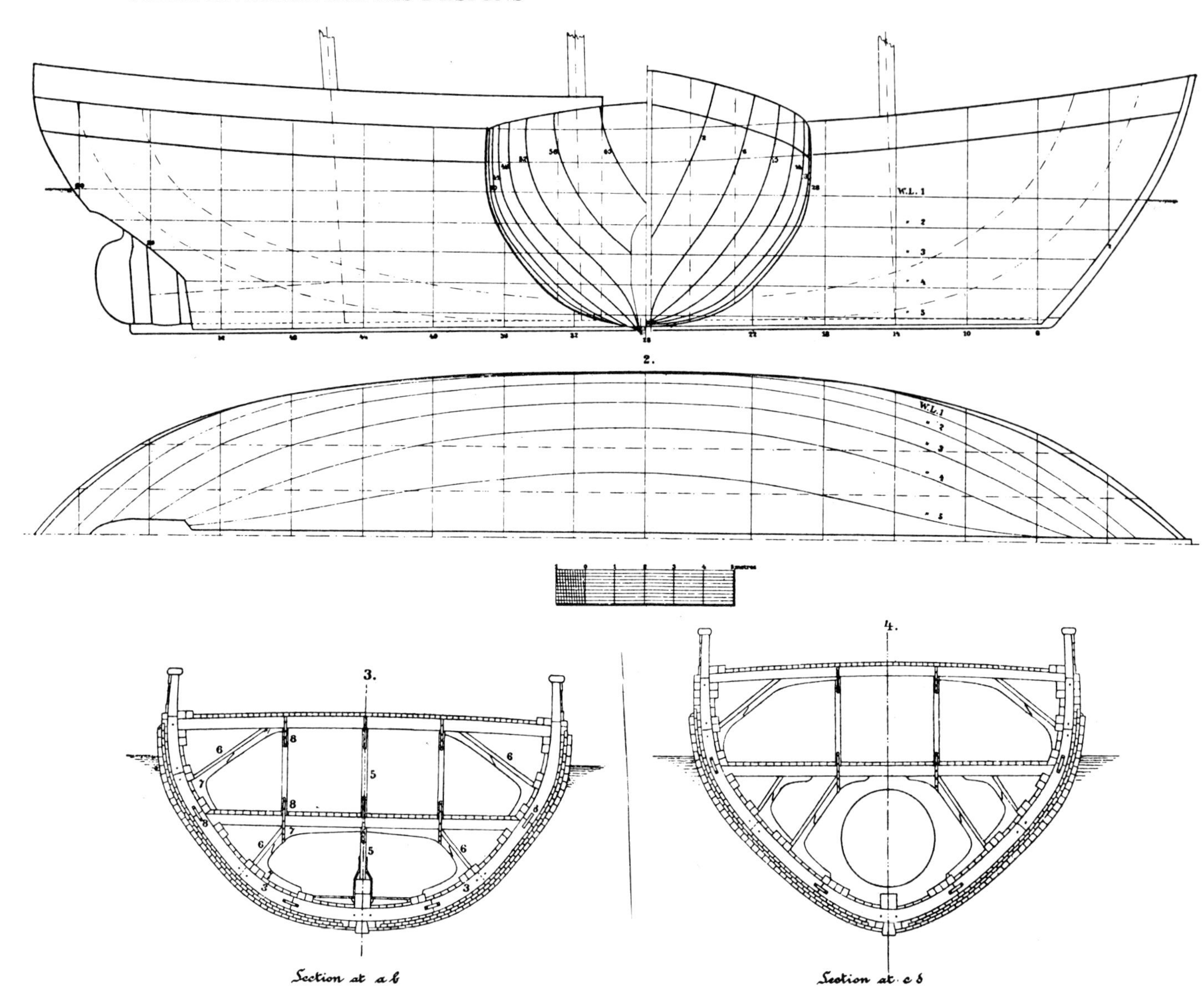

form: the lines showed no flat or concave surfaces but were full and rounded. Besides resisting ice pressure, this shape allowed large pieces of ice to pass around and under the ship more easily. Her beam was considerable by sailing ship standards, but only sailing considerations restricted Archer from increasing it further, better to withstand the crushing force of ice.

The hull construction for Nansen's ship was the stoutest Colin Archer had ever considered. Three skins of hull planking were fitted—the inner of 3-inch-thick oak, the middle of 4-inch-thick oak, and the outer of greenheart, 6 inches thick at the waterline to 3 inches thick at the garboard strake, next to the keel. The bottom of the keel projected only 3 inches below the garboard to give little for the ice to grip. The sawn frames were massive: 10 or 12 inches by 21 inches. The space between the frames was only 1¼ inches, and to resist rot this was filled with a compound of tar and sawdust, with pitch added, boiled in coppers and trowelled in hot. The ceiling was 4- to 8-inch-thick pine, making the total thickness of the side structure from 28 to 32 inches. The hull was further braced internally by struts and knees, scarphed together at right angles to the frames and bracing the underside of the deck beams, which were further braced by vertical wooden pillars. The hull seemed likely to resist ice, but the rudder and propeller posed a serious possibility of damage, so Archer designed them to be unshipped, if necessary, to protect them from damage.

Although the ship was not expected to sail well because of her shape, she had to carry sail to extend her radius and conserve bunker coal. Experienced whalers advocated that she be square-rigged for maneuvering under sail in the ice, as that rig enabled a vessel to "back and fill" in a confined space. Archer had limited experience with square rig, however, so he drew a three-masted gaff-schooner sail plan that carried a square fore course and topsail. Captain Sverdrup agreed with this combination. The ship could be worked under sail by a deck watch of two men—an important consideration for a small crew.

The *Fram,* as Nansen's ship was to be named, was too large to be built at Tolderodden, so the keel was laid at Colin Archer's yard in Raekevik Bay. The best available materials and workmanship went into the ship, which was launched during October, 1892, before crowds of guests and spectators.

The design of the *Fram* and the nature of Nansen's forthcoming expedition had many critics predicting she would be crushed in the ice. She sailed from Christiania in June, 1893, and Colin Archer steered her to sea and was then taken off in a small boat. Inevitably, the *Fram* rolled heavily in the open sea; this rolling was accentuated by her heavily laden condition. However, when she first entered pack ice off Novaya Zemlya, the strangely shaped hull proved itself, twisting and turning through the floes. Nansen praised her strength, ". . . even when she goes full speed at a floe, not a sound is to be heard in her; if she gives a little shake it is all she does." In September, 1894, northwest of the New Siberia Islands and approximately 200 miles west of the position where the *Jeanette* had been lost 13 years previously, the *Fram* became frozen in and commenced the long drift, hopefully toward the pole. In January, 1895, she began to experience great pressure from the ice as it packed together. The crushing and grinding of the nearby floes brought a

The polar ship Fram.

hummock of ice nearer to the ship, until it collided with her hull. The explorers prepared to abandon the *Fram*, which groaned and creaked from the strain, but she eventually broke free. In spite of the strain, the ship did not leak. Archer's design was proved, and the *Fram* continued on what would prove to be a 22-month drift, reaching farther north than any previous ship.

In February, 1895, the slow rate of drift and the probability that the ship would miss the Pole convinced Nansen that he should attempt to reach the Pole with a party traveling by dog sleds and kayaks. The explorers set out, but increasing irregularity of the ice surface slowed and finally beat them short of their goal. They did reach a latitude higher than man had then reached. The party turned back and, after many hazards, finally made Franz Josef Land by kayak. By chance they found there the American Jackson-Harmsworth expedition and were given passage to Vardo.

By June, 1896, the *Fram* had drifted to the north of Spitsbergen and was freed from the ice with blasting charges. The ice closed in again, however, and it was August before she drifted into open water. She sailed for Tromso, where Nansen rejoined her. Captain Otto Sverdrup telegraphed her arrival at Skjervo to Colin Archer: "The *Fram* anchored here today in as good condition as when she left Norway after having drifted over the Polar Sea as planned. All well on board. Greetings."

The *Fram*'s return, with Colin Archer sharing in the Nansen expedition's partial success, led to Archer being raised to Commander of the Order of St. Olaf, "for services rendered in ship construction and for the furtherance of scientific voyages of discovery." Appropriately, Anders Olsen, the foreman-shipwright during the *Fram*'s construction, received a gold medal from the Norwegian government.

The enthusiasm and national pride engendered by Nansen's return led to proposals for a second Arctic expedition to be led by Otto Sverdrup, again using the *Fram*, which would be loaned by the Norwegian government (the government of Norway was an original principal owner). The *Fram* was taken to Larvik in the spring of 1897 and was thoroughly surveyed. With the exception of some strained bolts in one place, she was in every way sound and tight. A new spar deck was fitted from the bow to the forward engineroom bulkhead to provide more accommodation. A false keel 10 inches deep was added beneath the structural keel, hopefully to reduce her rolling and to improve her poor windward ability.

The *Fram* sailed from Larvik during June, 1898, on her second Arctic expedition, which discovered the islands named the Sverdrup Group, to the northeast of the Parry Archipelago. The large isles off the northeast of Greenland were explored and the western shores of Greenland were mapped. The *Fram* returned to Norway during 1902, after four years in the north. She was laid up at the Horten dockyard of the Royal Norwegian Navy.

Meanwhile, Colin Archer's fame as the designer and builder of polar ships spread, and more business came his way. For instance, in 1898, the Italian exploration ship *Stella Polaris*, owned by the Duke of Abruzzi, a wealthy mountaineer and yacht owner, arrived at Archer's Raekevik yard to be adapted and strengthened for Arctic voyaging. Soon after that the Russian ship *Zaria* was similarly converted.

During 1907, the *Fram* was surveyed and some rot was removed from her structure. A year later the Norwegian explorer Roald Amundsen proposed an Arctic expedition using the *Fram*. He wanted to voyage round Cape Horn to enter the Arctic Ocean by the Bering Strait, hoping to be the first to reach the North Pole. Roald Amundsen had earlier become noted for his transit of the Northwest Passage. The *Fram*'s steam engine and boiler were removed, and an oil engine of 180 horsepower was installed. This engine gave a speed of only four knots, about half what she achieved on a broad reach under sail.

The *Fram* was not ready for the voyage until late in 1910. Shortly before sailing, Amundsen's plans were advanced because of the return of the explorers Cook and Peary, each of whom claimed to have reached the North Pole. When ready to go, Amundsen secretly resolved to voyage to the South Pole instead, but it was not until the *Fram* reached Madeira on her way south that her crew were told his intentions. Amundsen had Antarctic experience, having been mate of the ship *Belgica,* the first vessel to winter there, during 1898-9.

In southern latitudes the *Fram* met severe gales and huge seas, but proved herself as good a sea boat as Archer's small craft, though she was a great roller. In January, 1911, she arrived at the Bay of Whales, an inlet in the Ross Barrier, where she remained anchored for five weeks while winter quarters were built for Amundsen's exploratory party, which would attempt to reach the Pole in the following Antarctic spring. The *Fram* then sailed under command of Lieutenant T. Nielsen to Buenos Aires, via Cape Horn, to refit. Afterwards she carried out oceanic work in the South Atlantic before returning to the Bay of Whales to recover Amundsen's party, which had reached the Pole on December 14, 1911.

On the way back for Amundsen, the *Fram* met fog, snowstorms, and floating ice packs, and survived a hurricane that gave her the final test of seakeeping. Her captain wrote:

> . . . a furious hurricane was blowing. The clouds were brown, the color of chocolate; I cannot remember ever having seen such an ugly sky. Little by little the wind went to the north and we sailed largely under two storm trysails. At last the sea positively raged and we had it abeam. And now the *Fram* showed herself in all her glory as the best sea boat in the world. It was extraordinary to watch how she behaved. Enormous seas came surging high to windward and we, who were standing on the bridge, turned our backs to receive them with some such remark as: "Ugh, that's a nasty one coming!" But the sea never came. A few yards from the ship it looked over the bulwarks and got ready to hurl itself upon her. But at the last moment the *Fram* gave a wriggle of her body and was instantly at the top of the wave which slipped under the vessel. Can anyone be surprised if one gets fond of such a ship? Then she went down with lightning speed from the top of the wave into the trough, a fall of fourteen or fifteen yards . . . it was so quick that we seemed to be lifted off the deck. . . ."

A week later the *Fram* met a cyclone equally well, then she went on to meet Amundsen's victorious party. Her work was done, but her voyaging was not. During the next two years she sailed from Antarctica to Tasmania, then to Buenos Aires, and on to Colon, Panama. By then, 1914, her structure was feeling the effects of warm climates, and it was decided to bring her back to Norway for examination at Horten. There it was found that she was rotting from lack of ventilation of the heavily built hull. Most of her gear was transferred to a new polar ship designed under Amundsen's direction. The *Fram* lay forlorn and stripped-out in Horten, constantly under threat of being broken up. But in 1925, her old captain, Otto Sverdrup, began efforts to preserve her for posterity—after all, she had ventured from 85° 55′ North to 78° 41′ South, latitudes not previously reached by any other vessel. The *Fram* was then one of the most famous ships in the world.

Sverdrup died before the *Fram* was finally towed to Oslo in 1934, to be brought out of the water for preservation at Bygdoy. A glazed building, the Fram Huset, was built over the rerigged ship. The *Fram* can still be seen there—a monument to the gallant men who sailed her and ventured from her, and to her designer, Colin Archer, and the men who built her.

6

FISHING VESSELS

Colin Archer's success with his designs for rescue ships brought a challenge to his skill from the fisheries. The Norwegian coastal fisheries were, and still are, an important part of the national economy. In 1895, when Archer became involved, they were still largely worked with open rowing and sailing boats. During the early nineteenth century, open boats were abandoned in southern Norway in favor of decked, sailing fishing craft, but rowing and sailing boats continued in use on the north and northwest coasts, which were remote regions noted for the conservatism and traditional attitudes of the inhabitants. Some fishermen along those coasts did change to decked fishing craft, and some builders constructed boats principally intended to sail, with oars retained as a secondary means of propulsion. These craft varied in type and were not always suited to the needs of the fisheries. The Society for the Advancement of Norwegian Fisheries, at Bergen, sought to improve the fishing boats and commissioned Colin Archer to design and build a sailing fishing craft especially for the Nordland and Finnmark fisheries. If found suitable, such a craft would serve as a prototype for evolution and improvement.

During the spring of 1895, Colin Archer traveled to the Lofoten Islands and then to the adjacent mainland fishing ports. For two months, he examined craft, discussed boats, gear, and conditions with the fishermen, and assessed the needs of a new design in consultation with them. He found several types of Nordland fishing boat in use. The largest was the Femboring, a 10-oared boat about 40 feet long by 9 feet beam, and of shallow draft. She usually had a crew of six and could carry seven to eight tons of fish. Farther south, the fishermen favored the smaller, eight-oared Ottring of less extreme hull form and possibly a superior sea boat to the Femboring. As ever, the fishermen differed in their opinions as to the best form of boat for their work, but among the various types, the old, established Nordland boat was still the favorite, particularly in the smaller sizes.

The rowing and sailing Nordland boat had evolved during many centuries and was capable of efficient fishing in fine conditions, but could not fish in bad weather. If caught at sea by a sudden storm, the Nordland boat could not sail against the storm to reach the beach or shelter, nor was it physically possible to pull the boat against very strong winds and a big sea. The Nordland fishermen were good small-boat seamen and often lived through very wild weather, but the odds were against their reaching safety in open boats, and many were drowned each year. Meeting sudden storms off the land and rowing open boats in temperatures of perhaps 15 degrees took a vicious toll. It has been said that one man in four from northern Norway was lost at sea during the fifty years before 1900.

Although frequently rowed, the Nordland boats were also sailed. During the nineteenth century, they gradually developed improved sailing ability. The long, low-freeboard hull swept up at each end in a high stem and stern, and was reminiscent of the longships of the Viking sagas. Almost all of them were undecked, and spray swept them in rough water, when constant bailing was needed. Their light displacement enabled them to ride over seas like gulls, but, if the helmsman was inattentive in a seaway and the boat was caught by a breaking crest, she could be capsized quickly. The small amount of ballast was stowed in the bilges, and not too securely. If the boat did capsize, the crew hoped the ballast would fall out and allow some hope of righting her, helped by the high ends.

The single mast was stepped almost amidships and on it was set a squaresail of powerful cut. The sail was suited to the hull's characteristics but was not as efficient as a fore-and-aft sail and was a poor thing when attempting to beat to windward, though the fishermen were skilled in its handling. The boats frequently would not tack and had to be worn around before the wind.

Many fishermen preferred the open boats for their work and did not wish to replace them. They contended that their boats could be rowed, while decked craft could not—an important consideration in the days before motors. When he was standing in an open boat, the fisherman's hands were at a working level with the gunwale, while his legs were securely braced against the boat's side. In that position, he was closer to the water for working lines or hauling nets than he would be in a decked craft and he would have more security in a seaway. Also, a fisherman's small, lapstrake-planked craft could be hauled up on a shore by its crew in bad weather, while a

Replica of a Nordland boat of the type used in the Norwegian fisheries until the end of the nineteenth century, when decked, gaff-rigged fishing vessels were introduced. This replica of a six-oared boat was making a 500-mile voyage when photographed by Robert S. Carter in 1973.

deeper, decked craft could not. However, the few fishermen who were ordering craft of differing types and those others who were considering improvement and change were the hope of the Society.

After assessing the fisheries, Colin Archer knew that he could design a more seaworthy type of fishing craft, completely different from the shallow, open boats then in use. He had in mind a boat that would be a powerful sail carrier, based on his rescue and pilot craft. However, his improvements had to be reconciled with the practical requirements of the fisheries, and, most difficult, the fishermen had to be won over to the use of what would be to them radically different and more expensive craft.

Colin Archer proposed a sailing fishing vessel, 44 feet long overall; 39 feet, 4½ inches waterline; 13 feet, 11 inches beam; and 6 feet, 1½ inches draft. She had an iron ballast keel of 2.95 tons and almost as much internal ballast. The easy sections, pronounced flare at the ends, light displacement, and great beam were comparable to his rescue and pilot boats. As a consequence, motion in a seaway was lively. The freeboard was low for handling fishing gear. Construction was of pine throughout—keel, keelson, frames, planking, floors, ceiling, bulkheads, deck beams, deck planking, and even knees were pine. All scantlings were very strong. He specified carvel planking instead of the traditional lapstrake then favored for Norwegian fishing vessels.

Unlike most English and European sailing fishing craft of similar size, which were usually rigged as cutters, Colin Archer gave his fishing boat a ketch rig. The mizzen was of yawl proportions, with the rig so balanced that the boat would sail to windward under mainsail and foresail only. The mizzen was stepped as far aft as possible and sheeted to a short bumkin, which was angled and offset from the port quarter. A working jib and a smaller one were provided, set on a bowsprit 14 feet outboard and supported by a bobstay. The mainmast was made to lower in a wooden tabernacle below deck, at the forward end of the long main hatch. The intention was that, when drift-netting or lying-to for other fishing, the mast could be lowered, presumably by a stay-fall tackle at the stemhead. In this way, the boat would ride more easily. This seems a most impractical arrangement, as the main hatch would have to be open while the mast was down, and the masthead would protrude some 4 feet abaft the stern. It is possible Archer's thinking was swayed by the lug-rigged British drift-net vessels, whose masts were lowered. But the masts on British luggers were generally proportionately shorter than those on Archer's boat, and lowering the masts did not usually involve leaving a large hatch open.

Colin Archer attempted to overcome the fishermen's major dislike for decked boats by providing three hatches on each side of the deck amidships, for use as "standing rooms" when hand lining. One man could stand in each of these small cockpits to work his gear much as he did in the open boats. Another point of persuasion was the large main hatch, which provided access for the preparation of fishing gear and the stowage of the catch. Accommodation was provided in wooden bunks in the forecastle and under a small cabin top aft, entered by double doors from the tiny steering cockpit.

The Society ordered the first boat of the new type in 1896, and she was sold at less than cost to Jakob Andersen of Berlevaag, East Finnmark. Andersen, although he did alter some details, was pleased with his new ketch, in which he kept at sea for a month to prove her ability. That he could stay out for so long meant he wouldn't have to lose scores of fishing days each year, as in the old type of boat. Unfortunately, most other fishermen did not share his confidence and enthusiasm, and for a time Andersen had difficulty in finding a crew. Gradually, prejudice was overcome, and numbers of these and similar decked fishing craft were subsequently ordered by northern fishermen. They proved to be excellent sailing

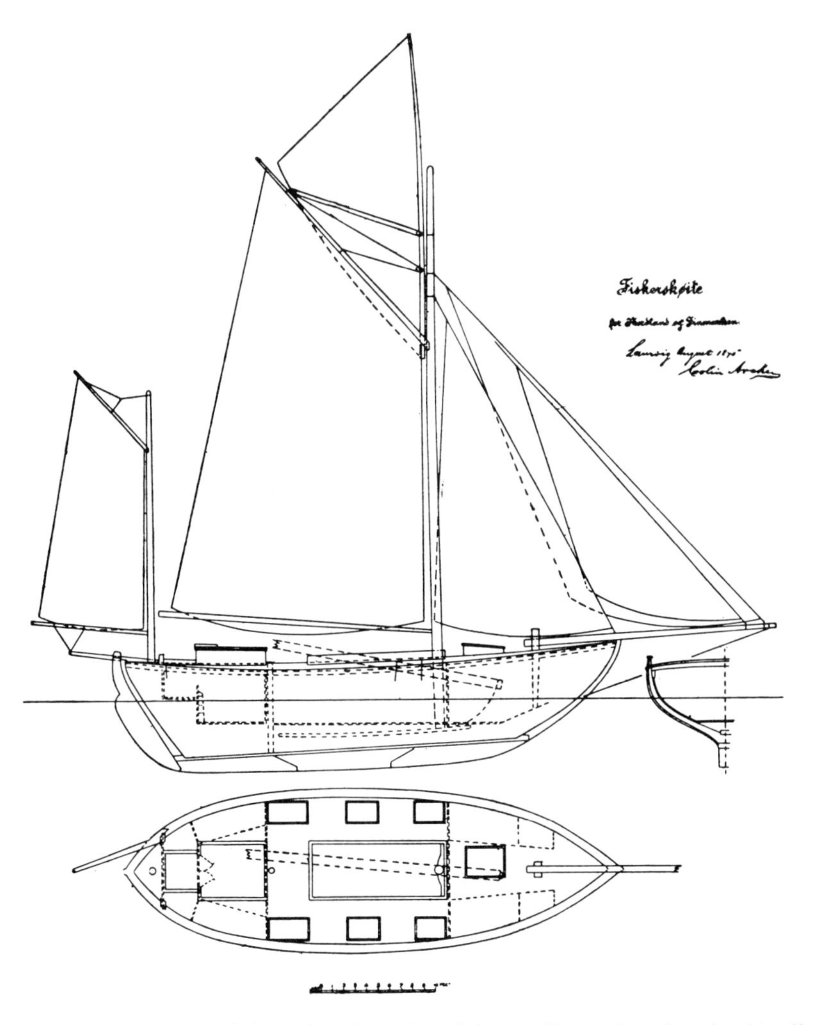

Above and next page: *Plans of a fishing ketch designed by Colin Archer for the Nordland and Finnmark fisheries, 1895.*

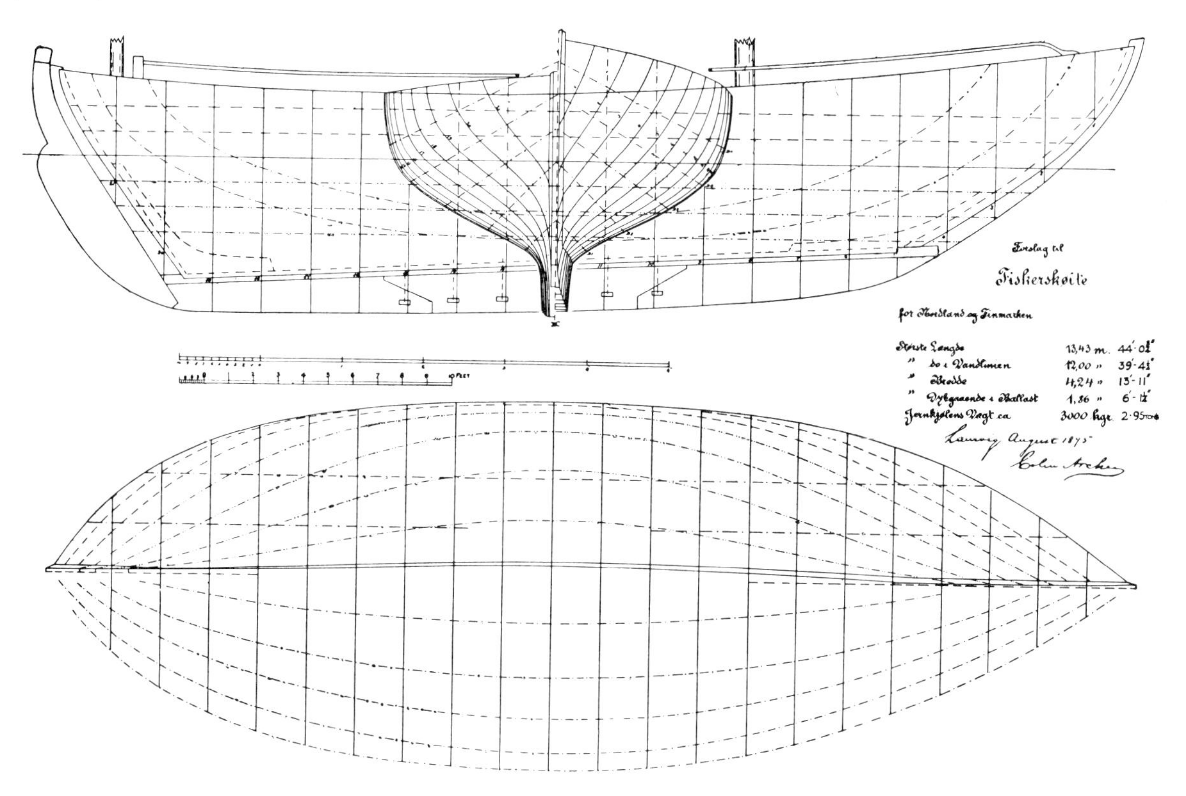

craft, profitable and practical in the fisheries, not only along the coast but also in the open sea as far north as Spitsbergen.

Other fishing ketches and cutters were designed by Colin Archer. In 1905 he was commissioned to design a fishing skoite with moderate draft, all inside ballast, and a simply constructed centerline structure to keep building costs low. The hull dimensions were 39 feet, 6 inches length on deck; 34 feet, 9 inches waterline length; 14 feet, 8 inches beam; and 5 feet, 10 inches draft. The sections show a slack-bilged form having considerable flare and moderate freeboard for handling fishing gear. The rig was surprisingly lofty considering the shoal draft. The boomless mainsail indicated she was probably intended for the drift-net fishery for herring or mackerel. The spritsail mizzen with a horizontal head was then common in Scandinavian craft.

Colin Archer's fishing-boat design work was not confined to pure sailing craft. Motors were being installed in Scandinavian fishing vessels early in the twentieth century, and in September, 1905, Archer was commissioned to design an auxiliary fishing cutter for Jens Jensen. She was developed from the pilot boat types and was a potentially fast and powerful craft under sail. She is one of the most shapely designs in this book. The hull had fine sections and sweeping buttocks. Her dimensions were 33 feet, 9 inches length on deck; 30 feet waterline length; 12 feet, 6 inches beam; and 5 feet draft. A small iron keel of 2,100 pounds was fitted, with the remainder of the ballast in the bilge. The auxiliary motor was installed in the after compartment, and the two-bladed propeller worked in an aperture between the sternpost proper and an extension of an upper sternpost on which the usual-shaped rudder was hung. The hull form and the immersion of the propeller probably allowed her to make efficient speed under power. The low bulwarks and cutter rig give her a pilot-boat appearance, and her arrangement suggests she was used for line fishing, with the amidship compartment used as a cabin and the forecastle as a storeroom. The heel of the heavy bowsprit was set against a single bitt.

Colin Archer's designs for fishing vessels—ketches, cutters, and motor craft—performed hard but less spectacular work and received much less publicity than his rescue boats. However, their superior design and construction, which led fishermen to adopt them, probably saved many lives in the rough and tumble of the extensive Norwegian fisheries, and their yacht-like lines and seaworthiness endeared them to their owners and crews.

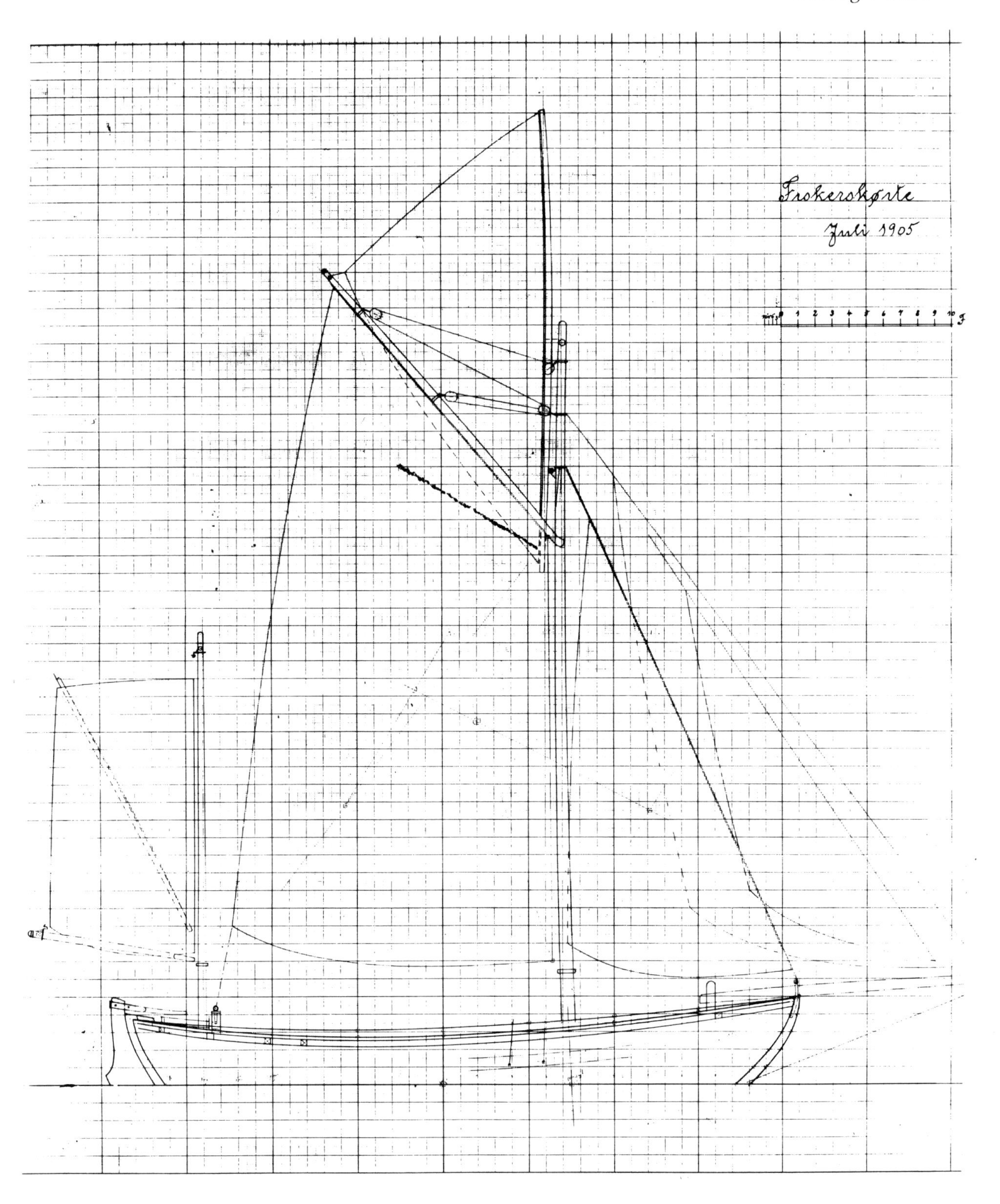

Above and next page: *Plans of a dandy-rigged fishing vessel designed by Colin Archer in 1905. The square-headed spritsail mizzen was unusual in his designs. (Courtesy of Norsk Sjofartsmuseum)*

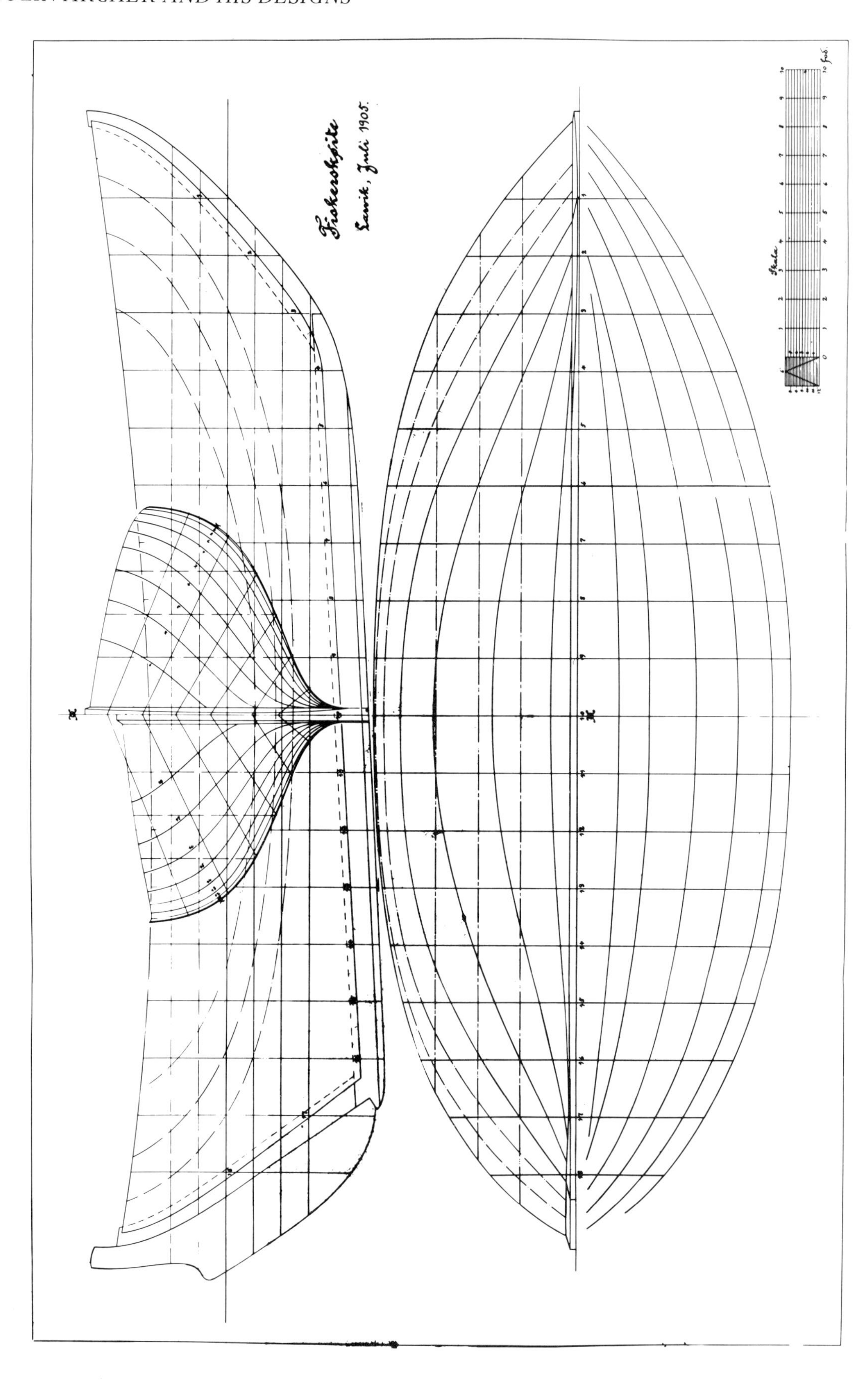
Larvik, Juli 1905.
Skala

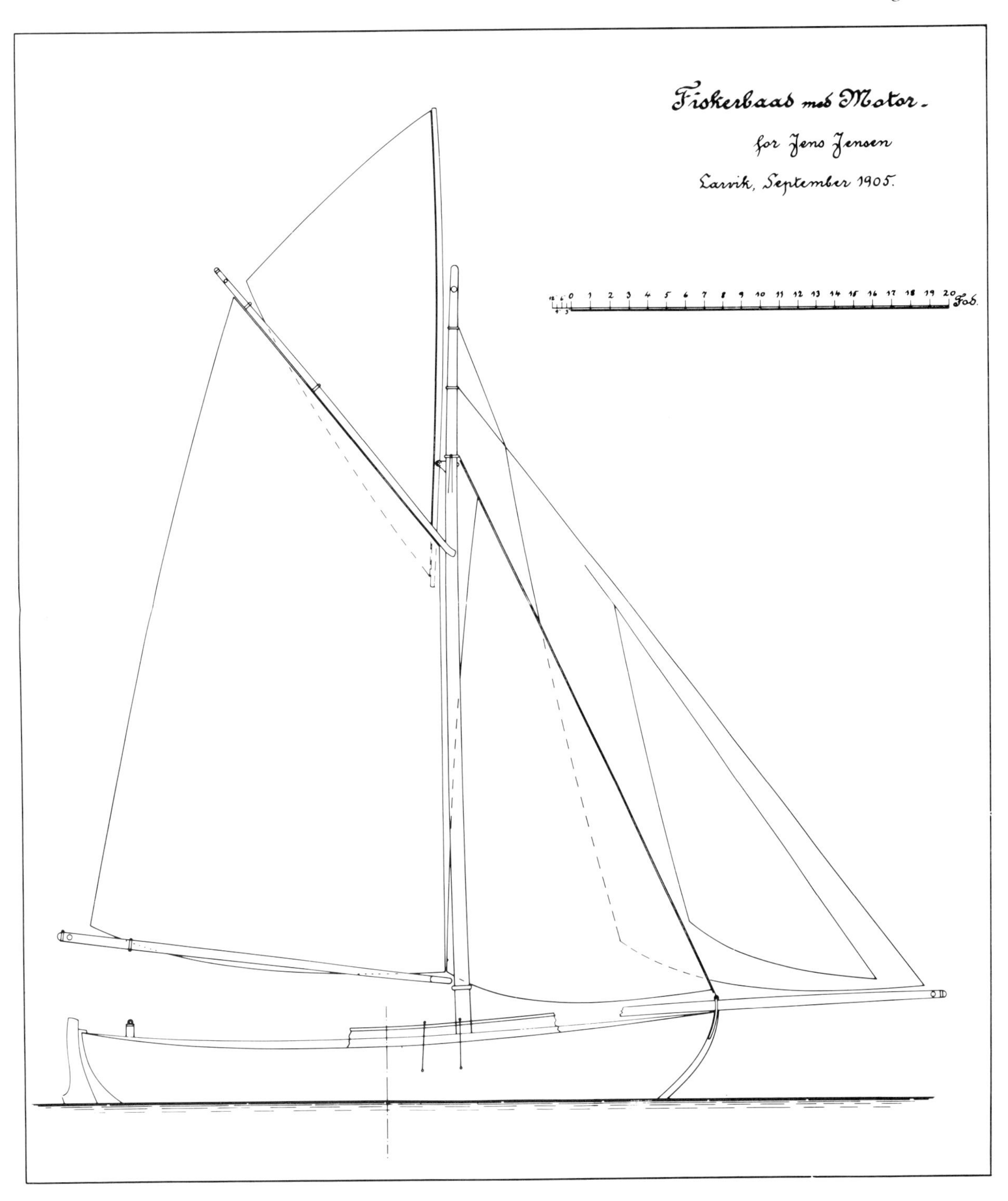

Above and next two pages: *Plans of an auxiliary fishing cutter designed by Colin Archer in 1905. (Courtesy of Norsk Sjofartsmuseum)*

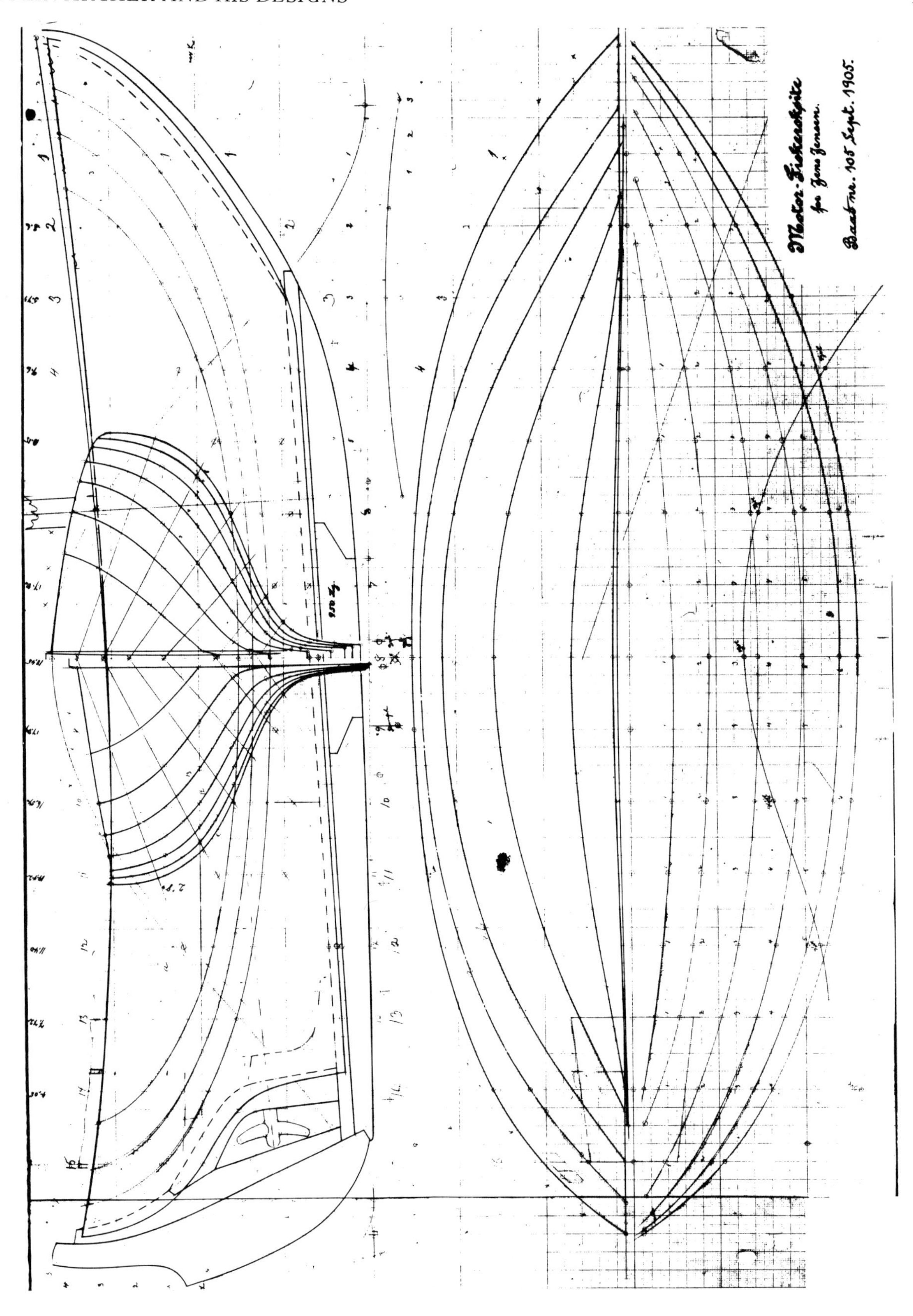
Motor-Fiskerskøite
for Jens Jensen.
Baat nr. 105 Sept. 1905.

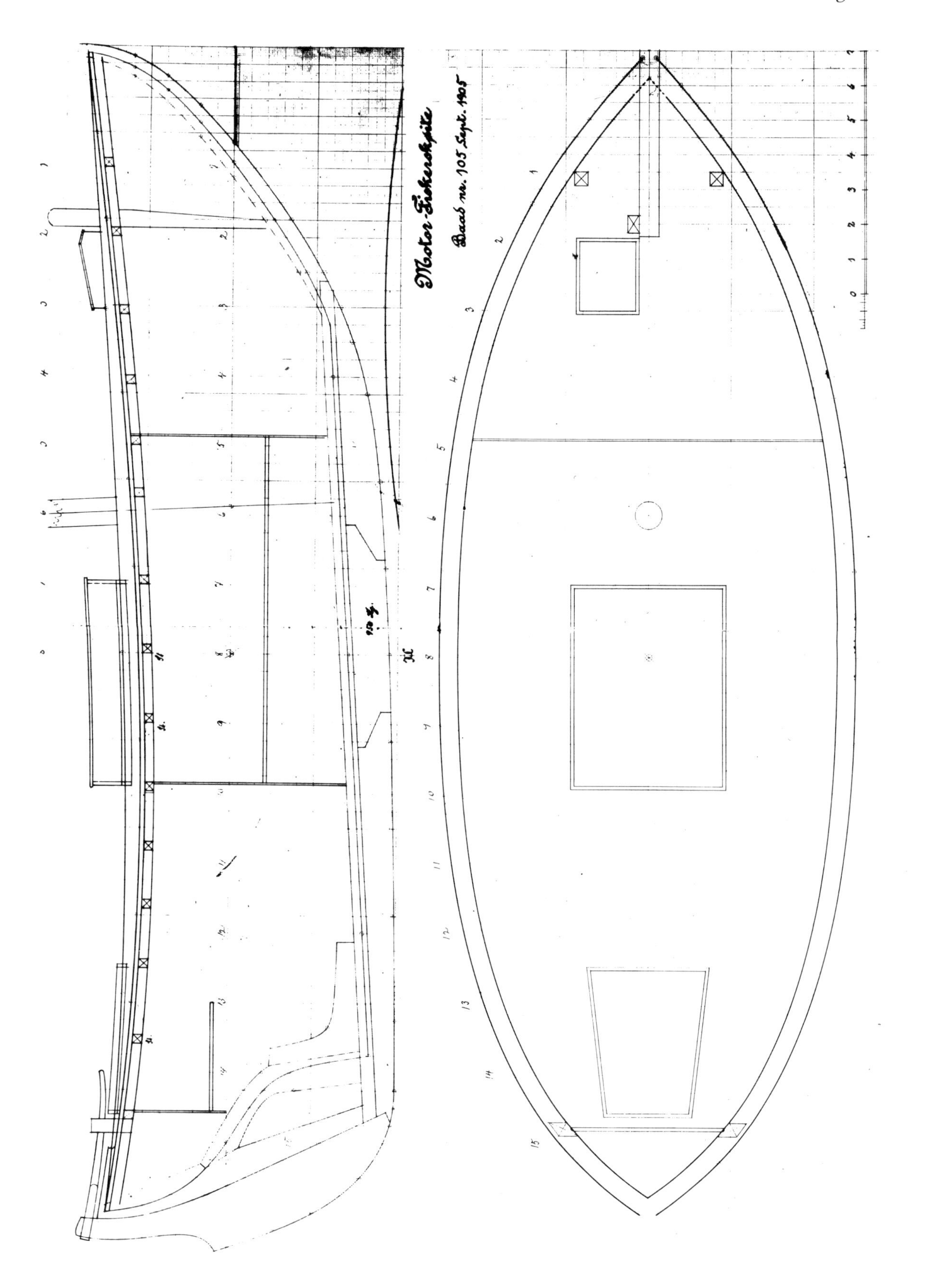
Motor-Fiskerskøite
Baab nr. 105 Sept. 1905

The 32-footer Dragon, *shown proceeding under power, is a cutter designed in 1925 by William Atkin.*

PART II

BOATS IN THE ARCHER TRADITION

7

DREAM SHIPS

As is obvious from Part I of this book, Colin Archer's influence on boat design lay primarily in the field of working craft—pilot boats, rescue ships, polar ships, and fishing craft. He designed yachts, many of them successful, but they were a minor part of his work. Yet his fame after the first decade of the twentieth century was kept alive by yachts, not working craft. Today one cannot mention the name Colin Archer without evoking images of yachtsmen sailing the oceans of the world in boats either modified from existing Archer craft, such as pilot boats and redningskoites, or new boats strongly influenced by Archer's designs.

RALPH STOCK AND THE DREAM SHIP

During the early years of the twentieth century, the bold, seaworthy Norwegian rescue ships and pilot and fishing boats from designs by Colin Archer and others following his style caught the attention of cruising yachtsmen in Britain and elsewhere. They brought commissions for designs and orders to yards in southern Norway for yachts based on these types. The 47-foot cutter *Oeger* was typical of these, designed by Colin Archer and built by T. Jensen at Porsgrunn, Norway, in 1908 for E.W. Haig, an English yachtsman.

Although the lines of the *Oeger* appear heavy, study will reveal the ease of her underwater body. She averaged 7 knots close-hauled crossing the North Sea on her delivery passage. The sections contrast with the snubbed ends, the freeboard, and the beam. The *Oeger* had a 15-foot beam and a 6½-foot draft, and was built with Italian oak planking on Norwegian pine sawn frames, copper fastened. She would have remained an inconspicuous cruising yacht if she had not been bought during the First World War by Ralph Stock, an Englishman who wanted a craft suitable for ocean voyaging. The *Oeger* became the heroine of Stock's book, *The Cruise of the Dream Ship,* aptly subtitled "On Dreams and the Means to Realise Them." The book became a minor classic and, in the post-war reaction of the early 1920s, set many enthusiasts scouring yards and creeks for vessels fit, and unfit, for long-distance cruising.

Ralph Stock served in the army during the First World War, and the vision of a cruise

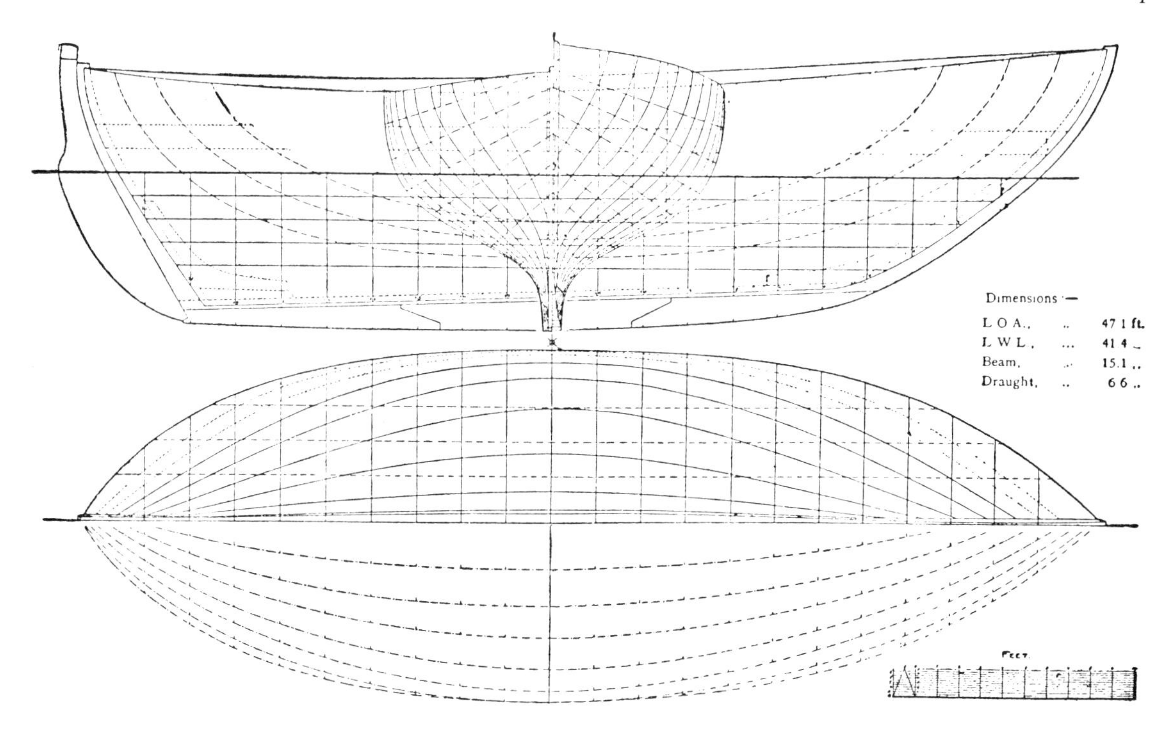

The lines of the Oeger. (The Cruise of the Dream Ship *by Ralph Stock)*

through the islands of the South Pacific in a yacht stayed with him through the trenches of France and in a hospital as he recovered from wounds. As soon as he was released from service, with the war still raging, he began looking for a suitable boat. He found the *Oeger* laid up and for sale, and bought her for £300.

To earn money to pay for his voyage, Stock and the crew who were to sail with him worked at many jobs. The most profitable venture turned out to be trawling for fish out of Brixham. The *Oeger* might not have been designed for such an occupation, but she was successful at it. According to Stock, she sailed ". . . at a seven knot clip for precisely 10 miles. We could beat the ketch-rigged smacks of the fleet to windward, without topsail or staysail."

Having made sufficient money to fit out the *Oeger*, Stock withdrew from fishing and, along with his crew, commenced refitting the boat. He corresponded with Colin Archer during the *Oeger*'s refit. For ocean voyaging he reduced her sail area to suit crew strength, which made her slow to windward, but he was well satisfied with her deep sea sailing. The cutter rig suited Stock as well as any other, and such a rig gave the *Oeger* reasonable windward ability, even in its reduced state. In subsequent bad weather he recorded, "She would heave-to in a gale under single reef like a duck and with the wind abeam would go for hours on end with the tiller pegged."

In April, 1919, the *Oeger* cleared for Brisbane, Australia, with a crew of three augmented by a retired schooner master who had taught Stock navigation. The old skipper accompanied them as far as Spain.

The cruise of the dream ship took Stock and his crew to the Canary Islands, across the Atlantic to the Caribbean, through the Panama Canal to the Galapagos Islands, across the Pacific to the Marquesas Islands, on to Tahiti, and then to the Society Islands. At Tonga Tabu, Stock sold the *Oeger* and eventu-

The Oeger *using a big foresail in the Doldrums.* (The Cruise of the Dream Ship *by Ralph Stock)*

ally made his way back to England by steamship.

Ralph Stock had a lot to say about the dream ship in his book. Here is his description of her performance in the hurricane he met on the way to the Society Islands:

> It is an easy thing to run; the difficulty is to know when to stop. There is always the possibility of being pooped . . . . To the uninitiated it would appear that the faster a ship travels the better chance she has of escaping a following sea. But this is not so. No one has yet succeeded in explaining the phenomenon satisfactorily, but it seems that the wake caused by even a small boat passing down the face of a comber induces it to break prematurely, and if the boat and comber chance to be travelling at the same speed, the latter breaks aboard, that is all. It is a chance that all who go down to the sea in ships must take when they run, and the only way of obviating the disaster is to restrain a very natural desire to "get on with it" while the weather is fair, and heave to in time.
>
> In the case of the dream ship there was no need to do this, as we had reduced canvas to such an extent that she was not doing more than ten knots and rose to the summit of each breaking comber like a cork. I have yet to see the weather that she could not face without flinching, and I treasure her design beyond price.

Stock's book, *The Cruise of the Dream Ship*, reached a wide audience of people interested in ocean sailing, and what he had to say about the Colin Archer type of boat had an influence on future deep-water cruisers:

> The dream ship was of life-boat or "double ender" build, which means that she was "all ship," and had no counter. Various stems and sterns are recommended by various people, but I have found nothing better than the life-boat. She was cutter rigged, and, always provided that the boom does not extend too far beyond the counter to be easily accessible, it is as handy an arrangement of sail as any other, and admittedly the best for sailing.

> I can almost hear the noble army of schooner, ketch, and yawl-owners howling their execration at these remarks, but I cannot help it. I have tried most rigs, and come back to the cutter. The howlers will at least admit that she sails as close to the wind as any, and closer than most; and as for facility in handling by the smallest possible crew, we of the dream ship had no trouble on this score, for she would heave-to in a gale under single reef like a duck, and with the wind abeam would go for hours on end with the tiller pegged.
>
> Our main difficulty was that the dream ship was too heavily sparred. The boom was the size of an average mast for a vessel of her tonnage, and the gaff little smaller in proportion. Next time we shall have smaller spars, and a topmast instead of a pole mast. Aboard the dream ship our topsail yard was twenty-three feet long, and many were the anxious moments in lowering it when taking in the topsail during a squall. The topmast does away with any necessity for a yard, and can be lowered to the deck in foul weather, thus also eliminating considerable top-hamper.

As luck would have it, there was no next time for Ralph Stock in a boat designed by Colin Archer. He was in correspondence with Archer about a new design, but it came to naught. He did find another dream ship—a Bristol Channel pilot cutter, which he sailed to the South Pacific. It is believed that she was wrecked in the Society Islands in the 1920s.

THE INFLUENCE OF WILLIAM ATKIN

Ralph Stock wasn't the only person who was intrigued by the Colin Archer designs during the First World War, nor were Englishmen the only sailors aware of their potential. Archer's design work had filtered across to America early in the twentieth century but received little attention from yachtsmen. In 1915, William Nutting, a noted American cruising yachtsman and editor of *Motorboat* magazine, visited Scandinavia and there saw pointed-stern sailing craft, including Colin Archer designs, at first hand. He became fascinated by them and resolved to have built one day a similar cruising yacht.

In 1924, Nutting and his cruising friend, Arthur Hildebrand, were studying the lines of a Norwegian auxiliary lifeboat designed by Colin Archer, which had been reproduced in a book, when the shape of her body plan, with its beamy sections and quick turn of bilge, attracted them. This boat was 47 feet long, and they decided they could afford a copy reduced to 32 feet in length, which would provide headroom under a cabin house of reasonable height, with sitting headroom under the side decks. The plans were photographically reduced, and Nutting made a skeleton hull model that looked satisfying—the original great beam became normal in the projected smaller boat. However, Nutting and Hildebrand felt the boat could be improved by being made finer forward, though the stern could not be altered as, although the buttock lines appeared steep, the waterlines were correspondingly fine and would reduce drag at the speeds she could be driven under sail or power. The diagonals were perfect, and the curve of sectional areas was a versed sine forward and aft, with the center of buoyancy a little aft of amidships, which brought the curve of sectional areas nearer to the "wave form" in character. In its true form, the curve of the wave form is a versed sine forward and a trochoid aft. (For more on the wave-form theory, see Appendix A.)

Nutting and Hildebrand approached William Atkin, then a rising designer of cruising auxiliaries as well as powered craft, and after consultation they had the yacht's lines laid out with the originally shaped sections spaced farther apart from amidships forward. The model was shown to John Alden, another noted American yacht designer, who agreed with the proposed alteration, as did other interested yachtsmen of experience. The fine bow would improve windward performance, and, as Nutting and Hildebrand had decided to have the boat rigged as a cutter instead of the original ketch, this was a logical change.

The mast of the cutter rig was well aft, and William Atkin designed it with considerably greater proportional area than that in the original Archer boats. An auxiliary engine was to be installed, bulkheaded off from the cabin. Accommodation was to be for four, with two berths forward, a main cabin with a pilot berth outboard to port and an L-shaped seat before it, a settee berth to starboard, and a folding leaf table. Aft of this was the galley to port and room for food stowage to starboard. From this area the companionway ladder led on deck through the hatch to the cockpit, with the engine under. The final dimensions of this craft, named the *Eric*, were 32 feet overall; 27 feet, 6 inches waterline length; 11 feet beam; 5 feet draft; 19,000 pounds displacement; and a total sail area of 790 square feet.

Afterwards, Nutting was told that similar craft could be built or bought much more cheaply in Norway, and the projected building of *Eric* was dropped. But publication of her plans and the background to her design in the *Motorboat* aroused immediate interest. William Atkin designed a development of the *Eric,* with the lines amended to his ideas but the same dimensions retained. The bow was fined, reducing displacement and placing the center of buoyancy aft of amidships. The forefoot was slightly cut away and the sheer increased, both of which helped to improve the balance of the ends and the sheerline.

Three boats to Atkin's refined design were laid down at the Long Island yard of Richard B. Chute, all to the order of his partner, Henry D. Bixby of Huntington, New York. These were tentatively named *Faith, Hope,* and *Charity,* but when sold they became the *Freya, Valgerda,* and *Eric.* All three were ketch rigged, which allowed a larger cabin house, as the mainmast was placed a foot farther forward than in the cutter version. The boats were yacht versions of the revised pilot boat, with a two-headsail rig that set 588 square feet. This was a better rig than the cutter, as drawn for the *Eric,* but the *Eric*'s accommodation layout was retained. William Atkin proposed an auxiliary engine of between 7 and 14 hp, as low-power auxiliaries were then normal.

Other yachtsmen were following Ralph Stock's example. For instance, a replica of a Colin Archer design was built in China for four Danes, who sailed her home to Denmark in 1923-24. She was strongly built but plainly finished. This 47-foot-long, ketch-rigged boat, the *Shanghai,* was built from the plans of a redningskoite. Her dimensions were 41 feet, 6 inches waterline; 16 feet, 2 inches beam; 10

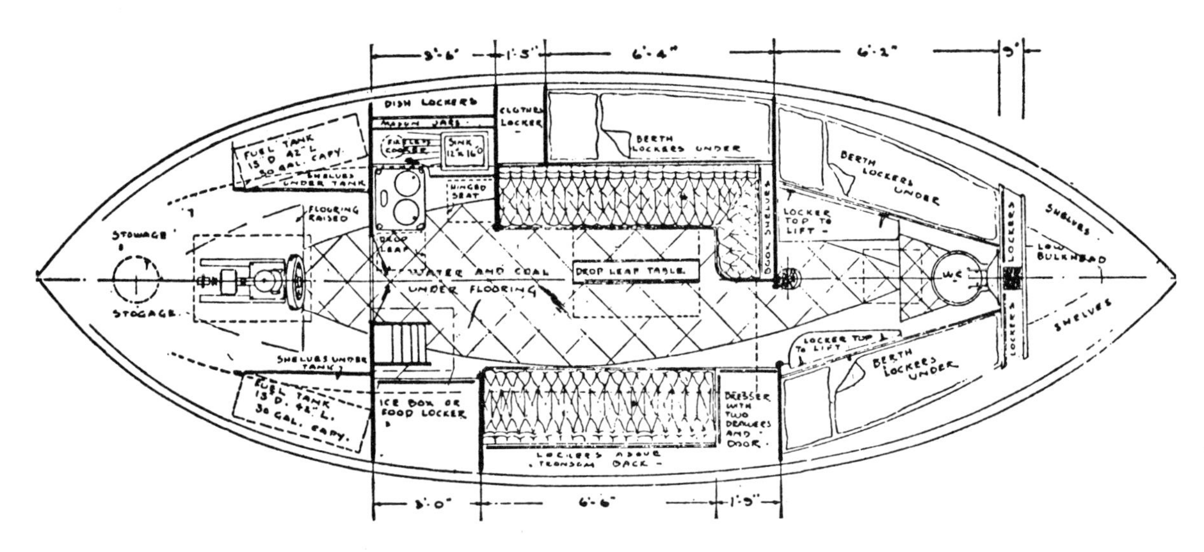

Above and next two pages: *Plans of the* Eric. *(Courtesy of John Atkin)*

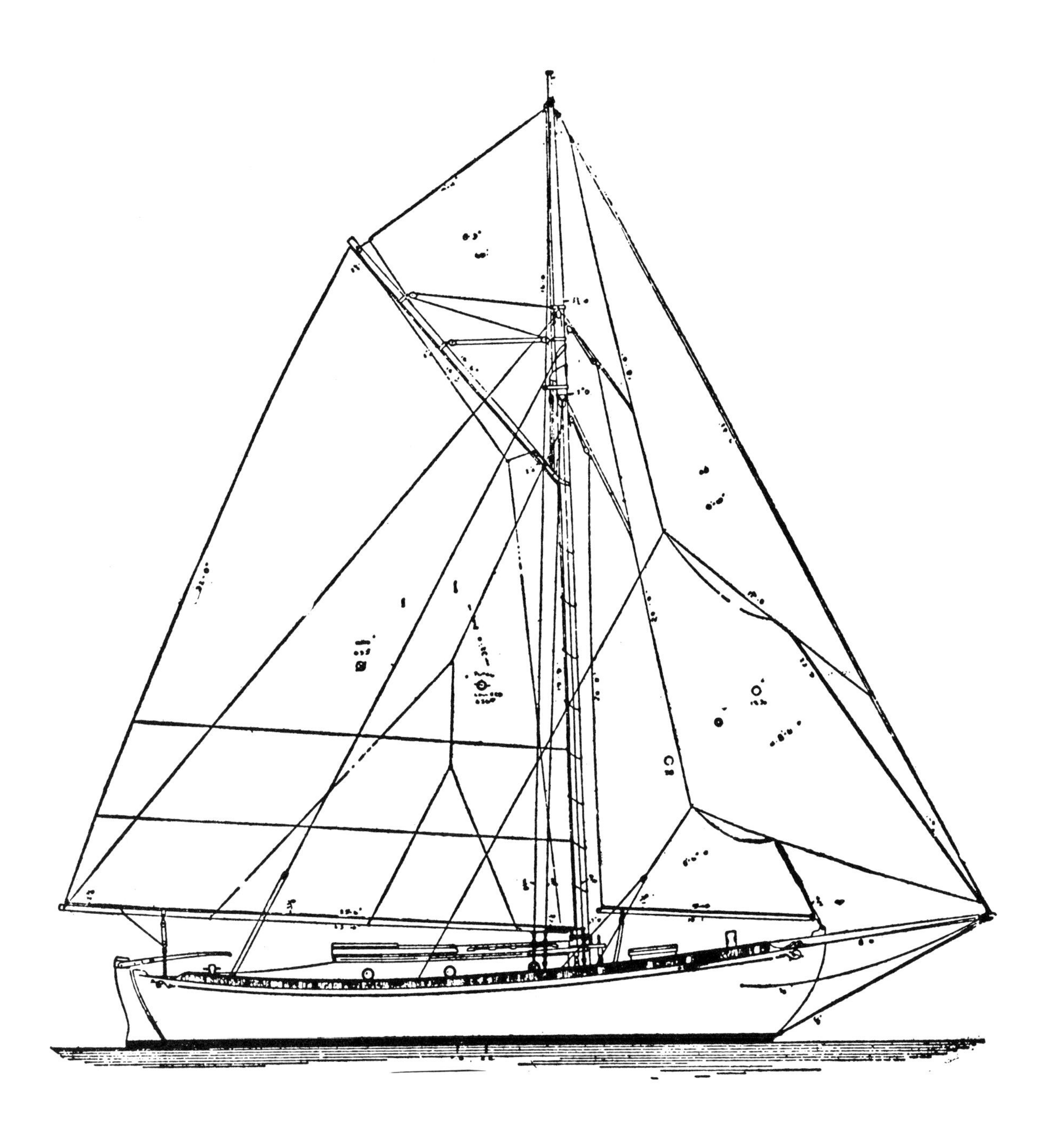

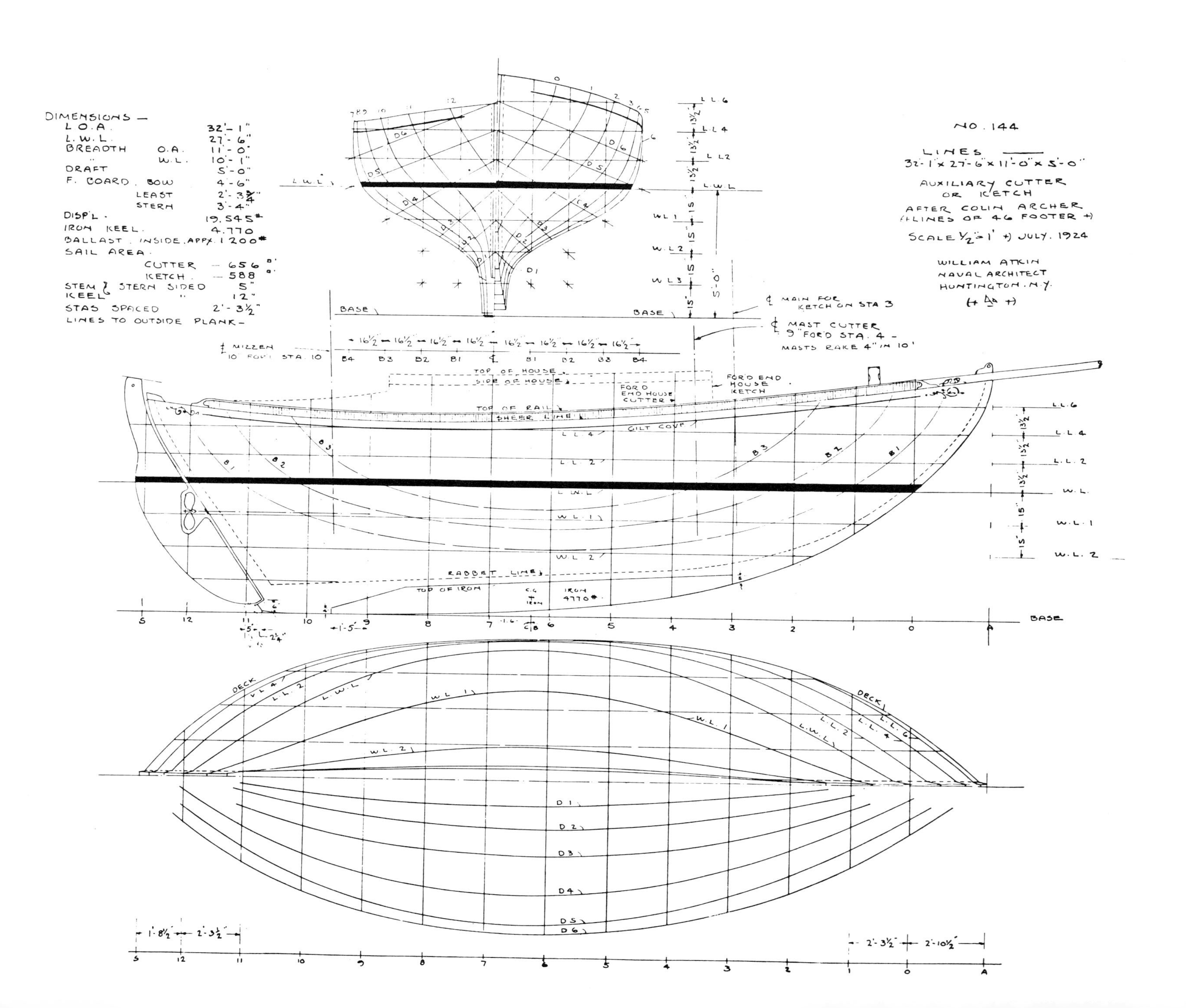
DIMENSIONS —
L.O.A. 32'-1"
L.W.L. 27'-6"
BREADTH O.A. 11'-0"
" W.L. 10'-1"
DRAFT 5'-0"
F. BOARD. BOW 4'-6"
LEAST 2'-3¾"
STERN 3'-4"
DISP'L. 19,545#
IRON KEEL. 4,770
BALLAST. INSIDE. APPX. 1200#
SAIL AREA.
CUTTER — 656 □'
KETCH — 588 □'
STEM & STERN SIDED 5"
KEEL " 12"
STAS SPACED 2'-3½"
LINES TO OUTSIDE PLANK—
NO. 144
LINES
32'-1" x 27'-6" x 11'-0" x 5'-0"
AUXILIARY CUTTER
OR KETCH
AFTER COLIN ARCHER
(LINES OF 46 FOOTER)
SCALE ½" = 1' JULY. 1924
WILLIAM ATKIN
NAVAL ARCHITECT
HUNTINGTON. N.Y.
℄ MAIN FOR KETCH ON STA 3
℄ MAST CUTTER 9" FORD STA. 4 —
MASTS RAKE 4" IN 10'
℄ MIZZEN 10 FORD STA. 10
TOP OF HOUSE
SIDE OF HOUSE
FORD END HOUSE KETCH
FORD END HOUSE CUTTER
TOP OF RAIL
SHEER LINE
GILT COVE
RABBET LINE
TOP OF IRON
IRON 4770#
BASE
DECK

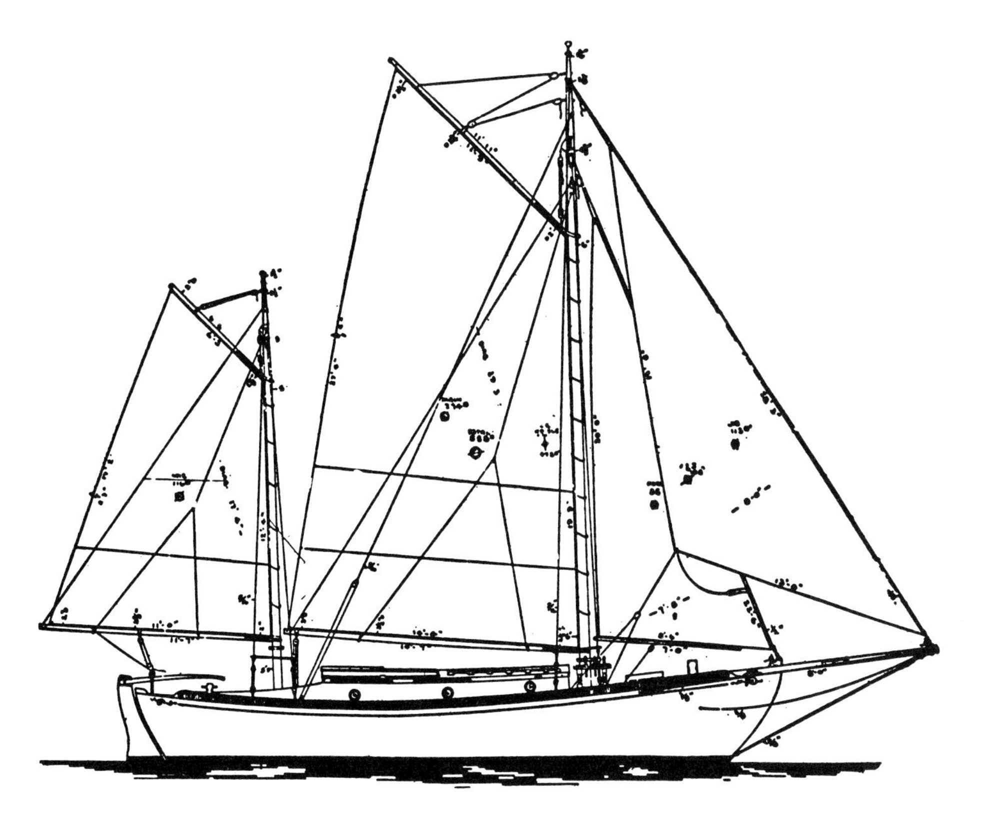

The ketch-rigged version of the Eric. (Of Yachts and Men *by William Atkin)*

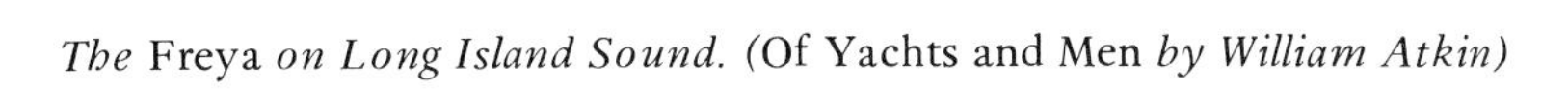

The Freya *on Long Island Sound.* (Of Yachts and Men *by William Atkin)*

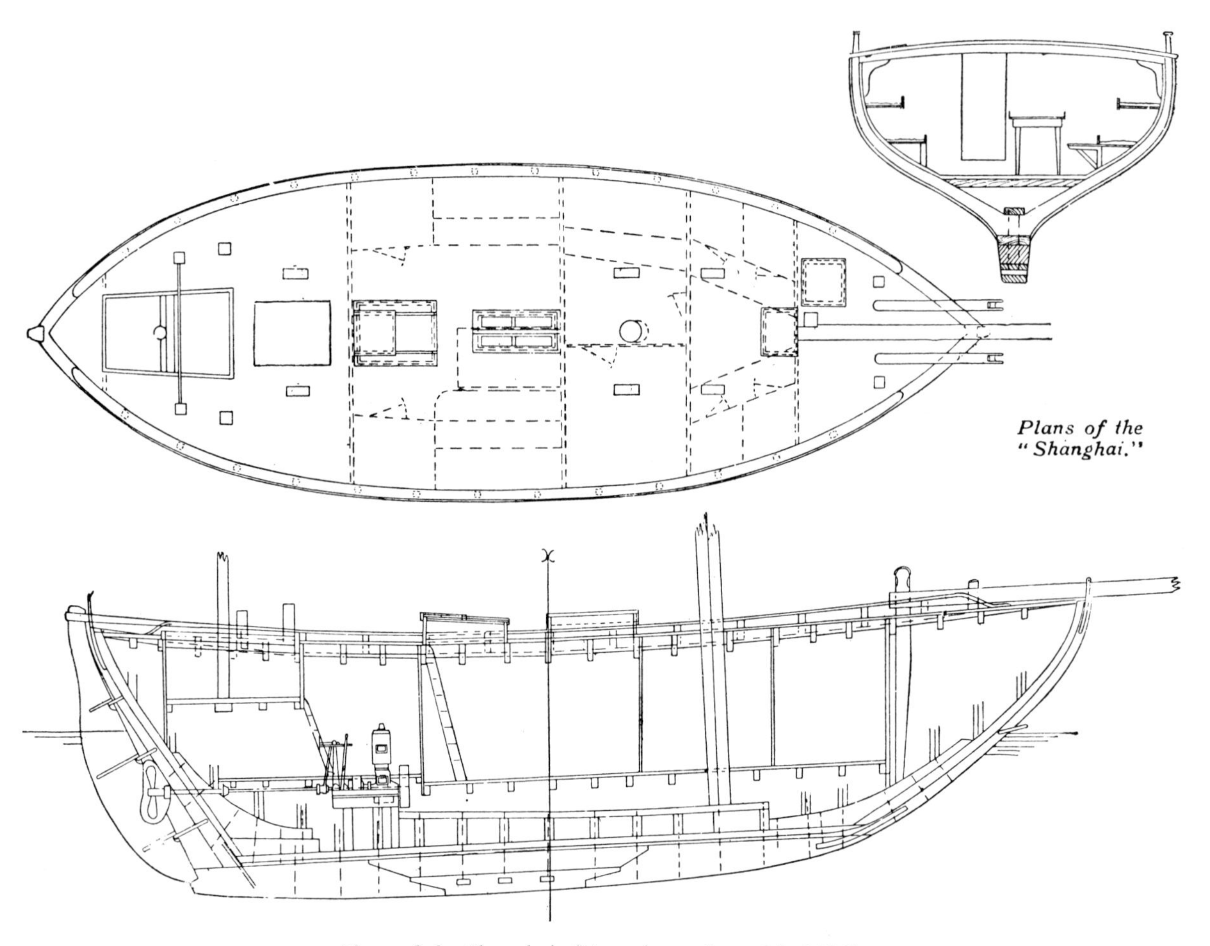

Plans of the Shanghai. *(*Motorboat, *June 29, 1923)*

feet, 6 inches depth; and 7 feet, 6 inches draft. She was planked with 1¼-inch teak on elm sawn frames, 5 inches by 6 inches, spaced 24 inches between centers. The cast-iron keel weighed slightly less than 4 tons, and just over 4 tons of ballast was stowed in the bilge. A 10 hp, single-cylinder, hot-bulb Grei engine was installed; it drove a 28-inch reversible propeller. The *Shanghai* made 6 miles per hour under power in a calm.

After the *Shanghai* arrived in Copenhagen in May, 1924, she was offered for sale. The voyage to Denmark received international publicity and inspired an American judge, F. DeWitt Wells, to buy her as a way to realize his dream of making a transatlantic passage in the wake of the Viking voyages to America. At the same time, William Nutting was in Norway, repairing his recently purchased Norwegian double-ender, *Leiv Eiriksson,* for a similar passage.

Both the *Shanghai* and the *Leiv Eiriksson* left Bergen, Norway, for the passage west in July, 1924. They met again in Reykjavik, Iceland, and then sailed for Greenland a few weeks apart. From Greenland, the *Shanghai* departed for North America. She went ashore at Cape Canso, Nova Scotia, during a tropical hurricane when her engine broke down and her sails blew away. Wells and his crew got safely ashore, but the *Shanghai* was a total loss.

Nutting was not so lucky. He left Julianehaab, Greenland, in September, 1924, which

The Shanghai *at sea, from a painting by Clayton Slawter. (Courtesy of Mrs. J. Wells)*

William F. Nutting's Leiv Eiriksson. *(Courtesy of Carl Vilas)*

was late in the season. He and the *Leiv Eiriksson* were never seen or heard from again.

Nutting's enthusiasm for the Colin Archer type of vessel had taken root in American yachting, however. During 1925, William Atkin designed another version of the type for Henry Bixby. This time he maintained the original Archer lines on the reduced 32-foot length, but he reduced the sheer at the side by 4 inches and increased the draft to 5 feet, 6 inches, with a 6,500-pound iron ballast keel and 1,500 pounds of iron inside. The *Dragon,* as Bixby's boat was named, was cutter rigged with 831 square feet of canvas and the mast about two fifths of the waterline length from forward, following a rather arbitrary rule expounded in Claud Worth's writings. The sail plan seems too "yachty" for these craft. The

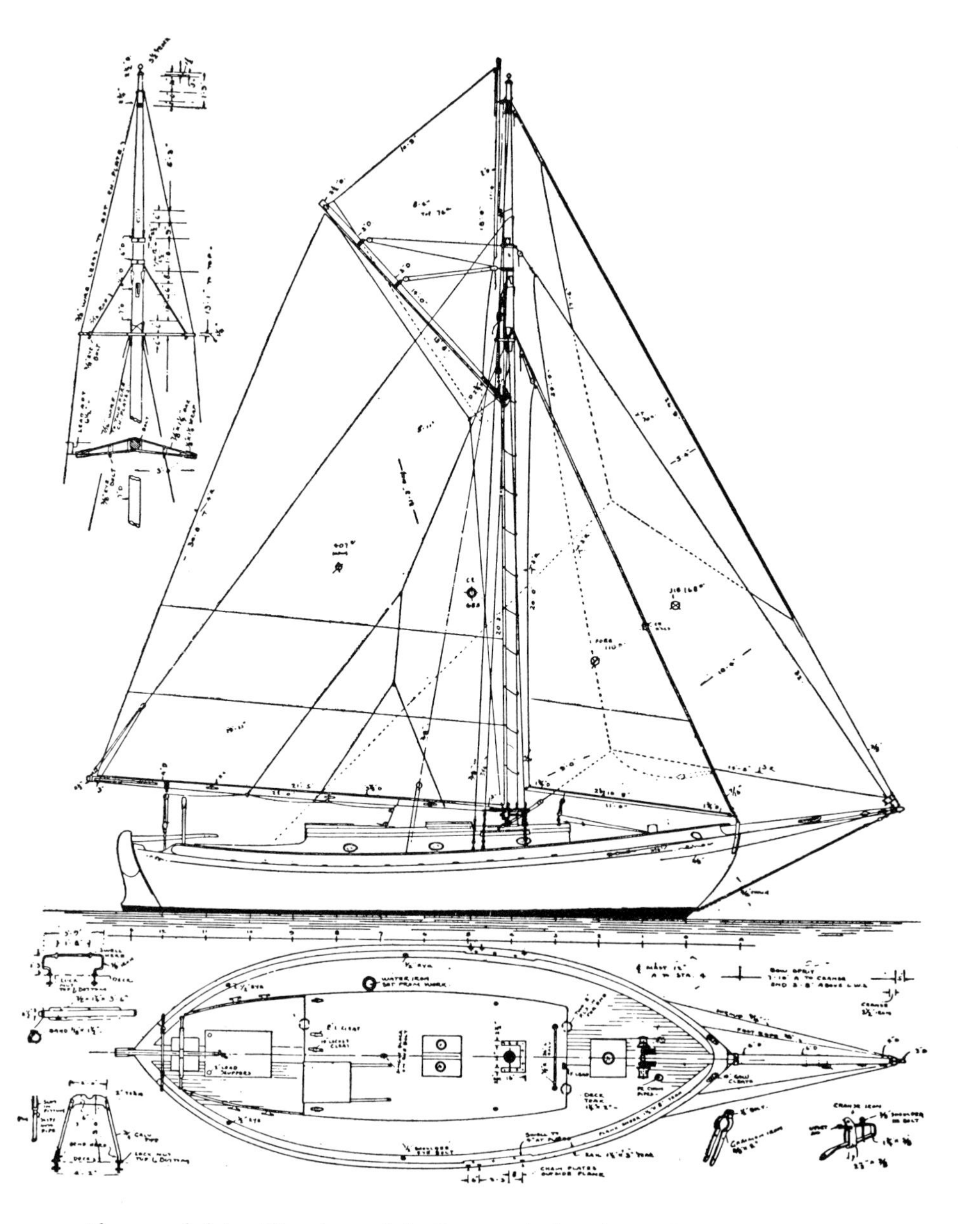

Above and right: *The plans of the* Dragon. (Of Yachts and Men *by William Atkin)*

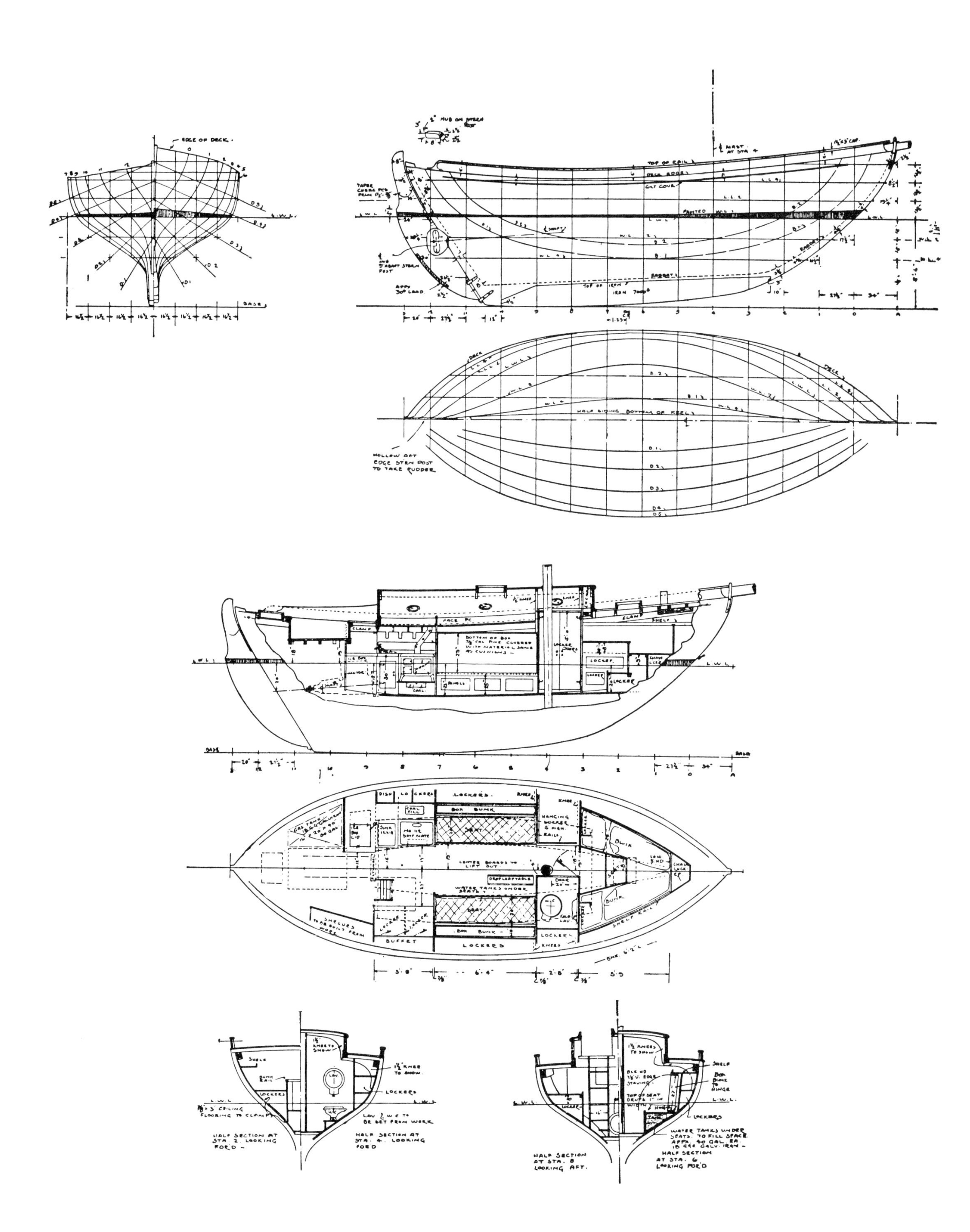

EDGE OF DECK
TOP OF RAIL
DECK EDGE
PAINTED W.L.
L.W.L.
BASE
HOLLOW AFT EDGE STERN POST TO TAKE RUDDER
HALF SIDING BOTTOM OF KEEL
FACE PC.
CLAMP
SHELF
LOCKER
LOCKERS
BOX BUNK
SEAT
HANGING LOCKER & HIGH RAILS
BUFFET
LOWER BOARDS TO LIFT OUT
SHELF RAIL
LOCKERS
LOU & W.C. TO BE SET FROM WORK
HALF SECTION AT STA. 2 LOOKING FOR'D
HALF SECTION AT STA. 4 LOOKING FOR'D
HALF SECTION AT STA. 8 LOOKING AFT
HALF SECTION AT STA. 6 LOOKING FOR'D
WATER TANKS UNDER SEATS. TO FILL SPACE APPX. 40 GAL EA

boom was two feet outboard over the narrow stern, making the sail difficult to reef. The bowsprit was slightly longer than desirable, the small topsail would be inefficient, except well off the wind, and the boom on the staysail would make that sail set badly when sailing to windward. The mainsail was fitted with lazyjacks, which were worthwhile, and the mainsheet led forward along the boom, to belay on the cabin top—a sensible arrangement that allows the sheet to act as a kicking strap and reduce twist in the sail. The accommodation followed Atkin's earlier boats of this type, but allowed 6 feet, 3 inches of headroom.

Soon after designing the *Dragon,* William Atkin designed a 36-foot Bermudian cutter of the same type for H.S. Sayers. She was a good example of Atkin's adaptation of Colin Archer's work. Atkin reduced the proportionate beam and gave the yacht deeper, easier sections. Dimensions were 36 feet length on deck; 30 feet, 6 inches waterline length; 10 feet beam; and 5 feet, 6 inches draft. A 7,100-pound lead keel was fitted. Sail area was 849 square feet. The rig had the long-boomed mainsail and heavily raked mast of cutters of the time. The foredeck was raised to the sheerline, and there was only a raised main hatch and skylight over the main cabin. Accommodations included a two-berth forecastle, a toilet, a two-berth main cabin, a galley, and a chart table. There was an auxiliary engine under the watertight cockpit.

William Atkin, followed by his son John, was one of America's most practical yacht designers, and designed many other pointed-stern sailing yachts evolved from his original adaptation of Colin Archer's work, but most differ considerably from the original for various purposes. However, Atkin set a trend in the Americas that others followed.

One person who was influenced by William Atkin was the Argentinian naval architect German Frers of Buenos Aires. He read of William Atkin's design for the *Faith,* the *Hope,* and the *Charity* in *Motorboat* magazine and was inspired by the lines, despite the criticism of yachtsmen of the racing fraternity to which he belonged. Frers designed a 25-foot pointed-stern yacht developed from Atkin plans and built her for his own use. *Fjord I,* as she was named, was a success. German Frers was so encouraged that he gathered as much information as possible on pointed-stern sailing craft, and Norwegian boats in particular, and designed and built a successor, the *Fjord II.* Let Frers tell the story:

Fjord proved to be exceptionally good for her size and proportions, and I thought that the wonderful balance of her lines, so characteristic in the Colin Archer boats, had something to do with her good behavior and speed. It was only natural that the task of designing a new and improved boat along the same lines was fascinating for me.

I made the new boat narrower in proportion to length, with less flare in the bows, with the fore end of the waterline straighter than her predecessor, and with the weights concentrated amidships. I had a rather vague notion, I must confess, that I was improving the pitching motion on the new boat, when sailing against the short seas of our estuary. The result was very good, even surprising for a beamy, short boat. The relation of the waterline length was a happy one. I designed afterwards the lines of four new cutters, only 3 feet, 6 inches shorter, and the difference is so great that no rating can make up for the difference in speed. The first *Fjord* was 22 feet load waterline, and was so small as nearly to merit the name of "tabloid cruiser;" but she was *not* designed around the accommodation. These tabloids in general look all right on paper, but they are a failure for sailing in short seas. Even in longer seas the motion is very tiring, and it is always better to put money on *length.* The midship section of *Fjord II* is easy, but not so flaring as in some of the old Norwegian pilots. Her garboards are fuller and the bilges a little harder. These excessive flaring boats are very dry but the seas stop them more, as they lift too much out of the water when heeling. On the other hand, this moderate flare amidships lends naturally to easy flare in the ends. The garboards were filled to have a displacement or weight adequate to meet the impact that a boat of this beam and shape receives when punching against a head sea. This decreased her wetted surface a little, which is only important at small speeds and when sailing to windward. After some years of racing we arrived at the correct flotation line for good

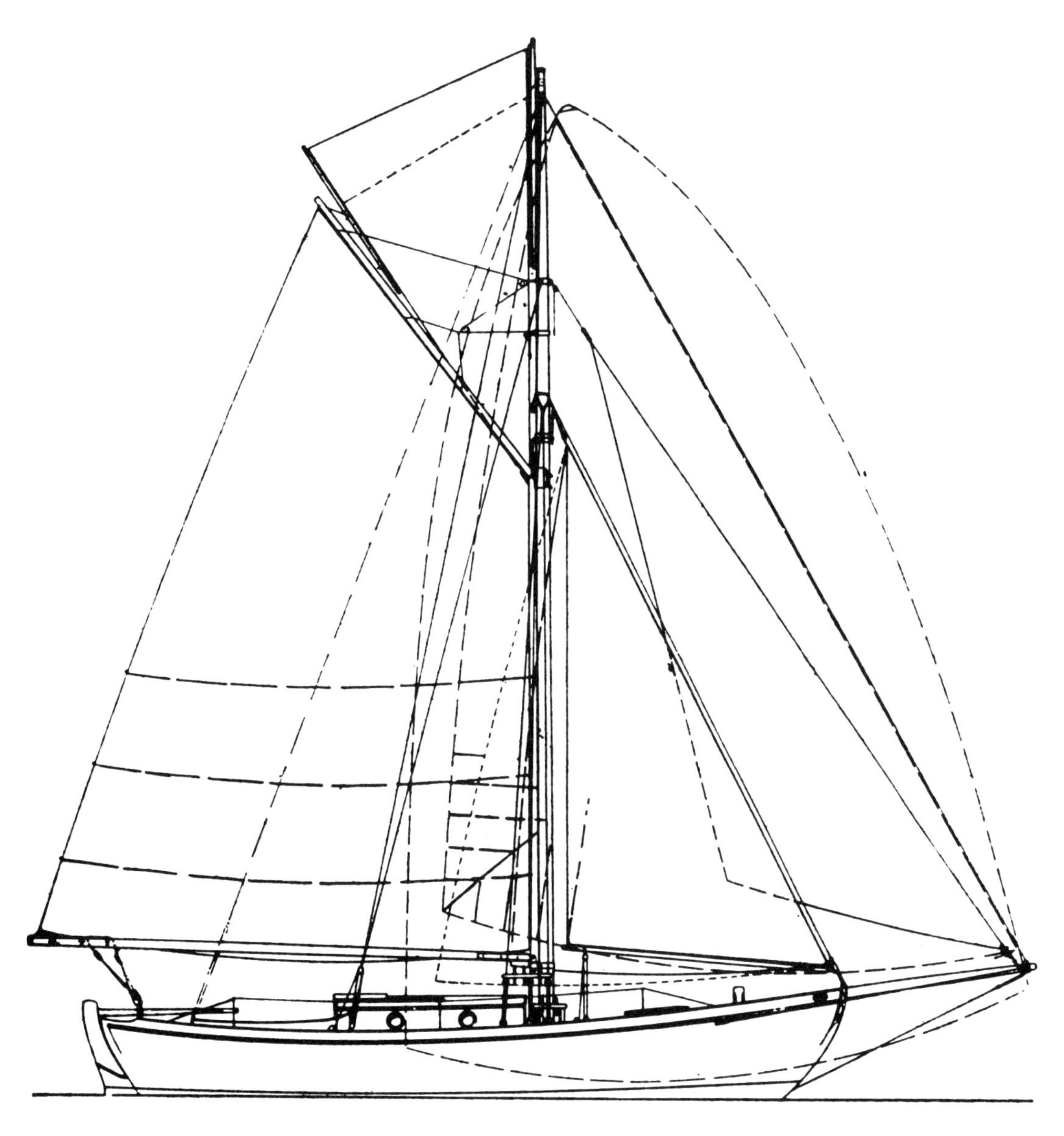

Above and next page: *Plans of the* Fjord II. *Her approximate dimensions are: length on deck, 32 feet; length on the waterline, 28 feet; beam, 10½ feet; and draft, 5 feet.*

average results; that is, two inches *deeper* than shown in the lines plan. More weight slows her down in strong, fair winds, and with less ballast she is not so good to windward, with short seas and light winds.

The sail plan shows *Fjord II* as we use her for racing and ordinary cruising. The position of the mast is farther aft than in her predecessor; in fact it is at 36 percent of the load waterline from the forward end. The classical English cutter position was 40 percent, but they had usually a counter and no overhang forward. The gaff is hollow and only three quarters of the boom length. For cruising and racing in strong head winds we have a rather small forcsail, working on a boom; it is loose footed, and, perhaps for this reason, the handiest sail of the lot. It can be stretched quite flat, and in spite of being the oldest sail it has retained its good shape. For serious cruising we have a smaller mainsail, with a short boom and a jib headed topsail. The cruising mainsail has only two big reefs, and, like the others, is loose footed. The reef tackles are in this case permanently rove, and are of canvas-served wire, being hauled along the boom with a

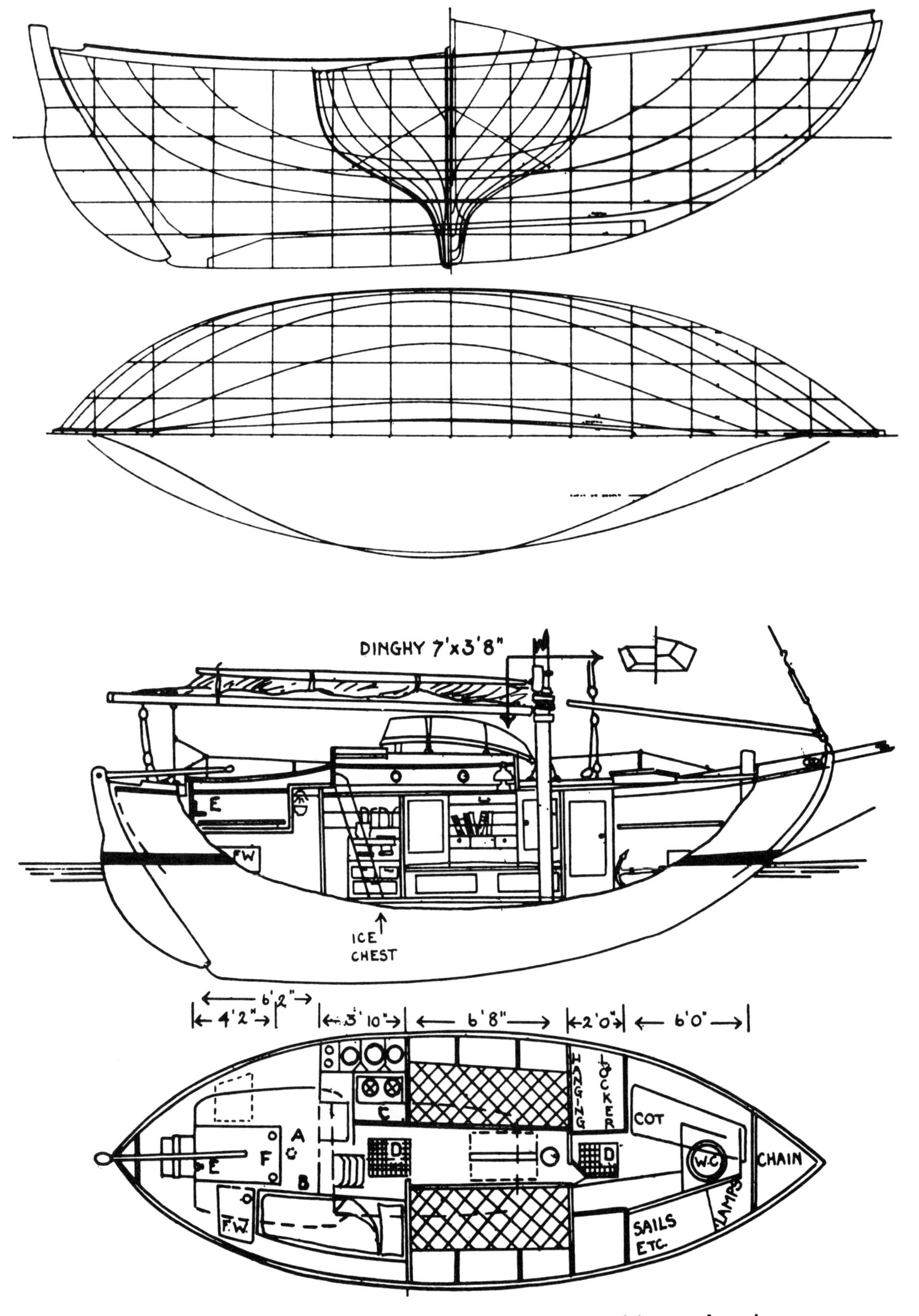

The general lay-out is planned for off-shore cruising and racing.

A Compass.
B Oilskins.
C Galley.
D Gratings.
E Rotary bilge pump.
F Self-draining well.

single block purchase. As we use a permanent boom crutch of galvanized iron, reefing or lowering sail is very easily performed, by one man at most times.

All the light halyards are of wire, and, in general, chafe is avoided by good care in the lay-out of the rigging. The crosstrees are of the swinging type, and we never trouble about chafing or tearing the mainsail at this point.

After building *Fjord II,* I designed and built some double-enders with gaff and Bermuda rig, one of the Bermudians having a sister hull of my boat. Having sailed and raced in many of them, and in the first *Fjord* for eleven years, I think now that for this particular beamy hull I prefer a good topsail for racing and a moderate Bermuda for cruising.

She had to her credit some 5,000 miles of sea cruising, apart from the cruising races. Two years ago, with my friend Bincey, the strongest man in the crew, we sailed from Buenos Aires to Rio de Janeiro and back. We started in winter and ran from the first day in a succession of hurricanes or pamperos. The bad weather lasted 14 days. In those days we had the opportunity to test the seaworthiness of our boat. We were impatient (a very bad condition for a sailor), and lured by visions of warm weather and tropical sunshine, we carried on, running before some of the gales with very little sail but with considerable speed. We knew we were ignoring the more elementary rules of seamanship, but the behavior of the boat was grand and we were in the mood of experimenting. In one of these runs we were handsomely pooped and knocked down on our beam ends. We lost only one bucket from the cockpit and a toothbrush from the cabin, but we both were badly hurt. After that, the boat being free from the hands of the speed maniacs, she hove-to with sea anchor, in company with a big cargo steamer, 100 miles off South Catalina, to the end of this particular blow that lasted 80 hours. She would heave-to very quietly under close reefed mainsail and small "spitfire" jib hoisted on the bowsprit and sheeted abeam [to weather?].

For handicap racing the old lady looks so stumpy and slow against the slim moderns, yet each year she manages, despite all, to gather a goodly collection of prizes in the long distance races. She can indeed gather up her skirts and move.

The *Fjord II* would be an ideal cruising boat for three, since the forecastle is a doubtful berth for more than sheltered sailing. Her sail area will appear large to modern tastes, but she was built to be sailed fast. Her lines are probably among the most interesting in this book and are worth close study, as they reflect the thoughts of a distinguished designer and sailor who successfully developed Colin Archer's theme.

ERLING TAMBS AND THE TEDDY

Paralleling the development of new designs based on Colin Archer's work during the 1920s was the modification of original Colin Archer pilot boats and rescue ships for cruising purposes. Take the exploits of Erling Tambs in the pilot boat *Teddy* as an example.

Changes in shipping operations after the First World War (such as the greater speed of ships, fluctuations of trade, and a depression in shipping) caused the sale of many sailing pilot boats in favor of powered craft. By the late 1920s, many Norwegian pilot boats were offered for sale, among them the *Teddy,* the 40-footer designed and built by Colin Archer in 1890 for a Larvik pilot. The *Teddy* was purchased by Erling Tambs, a native of Larvik who had served eight years as a seaman in sailing ships and had enjoyed some success as a novelist. As a small boy, Tambs had admired the *Teddy*'s staunchness and seaworthiness. He refitted her but left her interior and rig almost unchanged from her pilot boat days. The *Teddy* was to become home for Tambs and his bride, and a cruise to the South Seas was to be their honeymoon.

The voyage of the Tambses in the *Teddy* was like a blueprint of those that had gone before and those that were to follow: From the North Sea down to Spain, across the Atlantic with stops in Madeira and the Canary Islands, through the Panama Canal, and into the Pacific Ocean, stopping at such classic places as the Marquesas and Tahiti. They had the usual amount of foul weather and placid seas—including a desperate race for Moorea after leaving Tahiti when the *Teddy*'s topside seams opened badly from the heat. The pump broke, and with water streaming through the seams, Tambs pressed the cutter hard, even setting the trysail as a spinnaker. He appreciated the virtues of the pilot boat as never before: "How that sail pulled. Onward *Teddy* flew like a bolting racehorse. I had not the time to log her speed but I am convinced she did eleven knots or more. Oh, she was grand."

The *Teddy* pulled through that difficulty, but eventually was wrecked on a ledge off

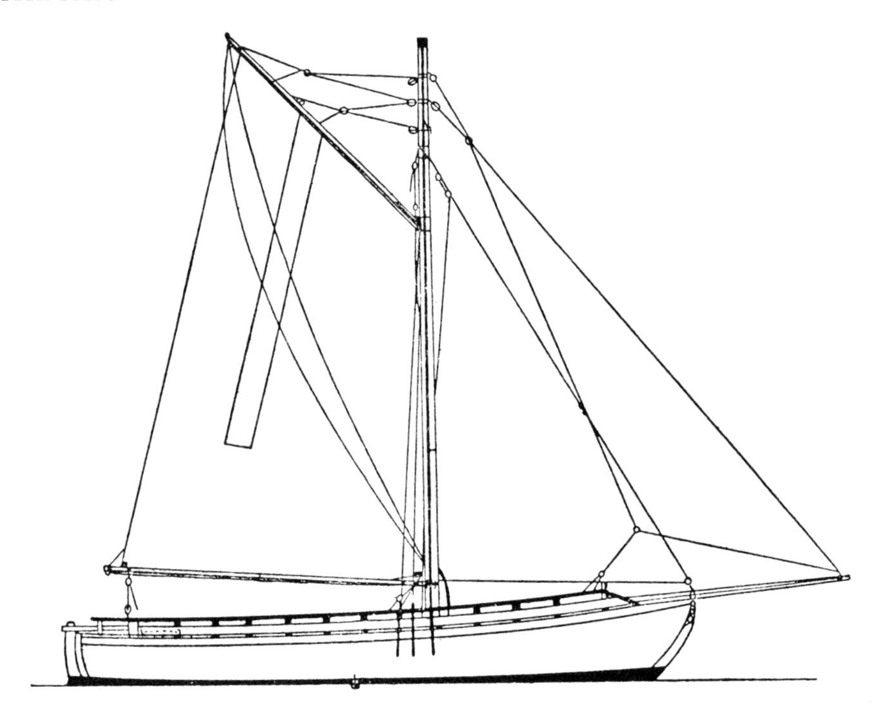

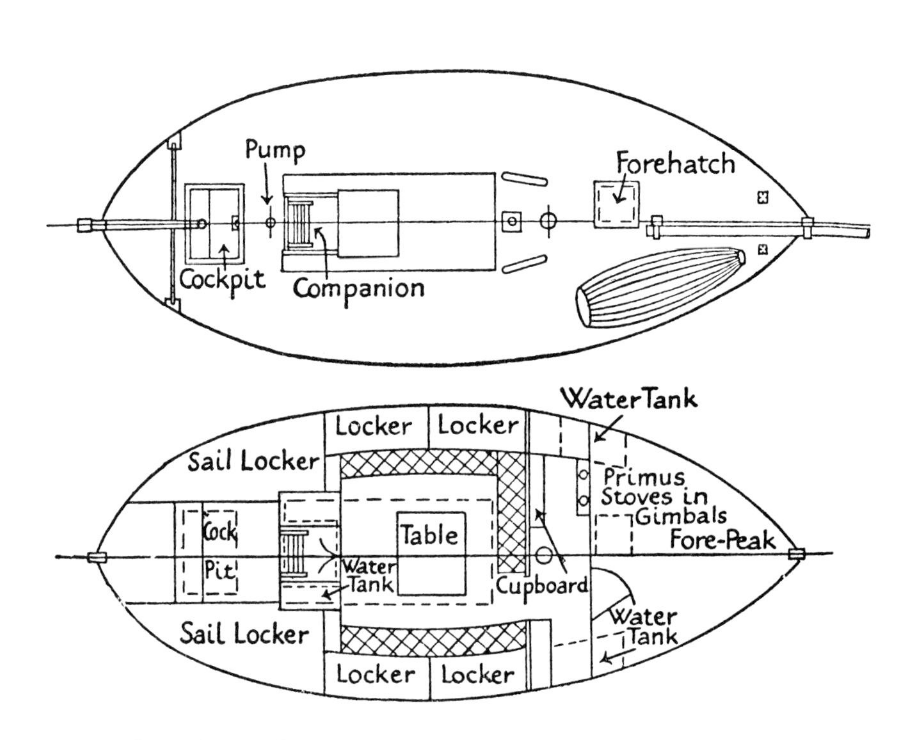

Plans of the Teddy. (The Cruise of the Teddy *by Erling Tambs)*

Challenger Island after many inter-island passages. Tambs and his family survived (a son and a daughter had been born during the cruise), and he went on to write a cruising classic, *The Cruise of the Teddy*.

THE NORTH STAR

Also during the 1920s, many English cruising yachtsmen were becoming increasingly interested in the Norwegian skoite type. In June, 1924, the Norwegian Society for the Rescue of the Shipwrecked sent one of their ketches to participate in the events for the centennial of the British Royal National Lifeboat Institution, which were held on the river Thames in London. Many British yachtsmen were attracted to the redningskoite, and some visited the craft and discussed the boat with her crew. Among these visitors was Michael Tennant, who decided to build a similar yacht in Norway, slightly enlarged to allow for a separate engine room for the auxiliary. She was designed by K. Jekke and was built by Tangens Vaerft Mek Verk at Tvedestrand, Norway. The boat was launched in 1925 as the *North Star.* She was a shapely craft. Here is Tennant's description of her:

> Dimensions are 47 feet, 4 inches by 14 feet, 10 inches and she draws something over 7 feet of water. Though perhaps rather rough, her construction is of great strength, being almost entirely of oak, metal fastened and bolted. This includes 1¾ inch oak planking on massive sawn oak frames closely spaced, in between each of which is a bent timber. The deck is Oregon pine and most of the deck fittings are teak. Some of the beams are fir, but of ample dimensions, and oak where most strain occurs. The ballast is pretty evenly distributed, there being over five tons of iron on the keel and nearly six inside, about two tons of which is lead. At the present moment she is rather clumsily rigged, compared to the usual yacht practice, and several alterations are to be carried out. Being a ketch, as all these Norse lifeboats are, she has a very limited sail plan for anything but ordinary cruising. There are many drawbacks to the rig—its chief advantage, I suppose, being ease of handling, and that is why I had it, for, with a man and a boy, and a trusty 14 h.p. Kelvin to fall back on, we have no difficulty on that score, despite her 36 tons. Had she been a cutter, I am sure we should have given our speedier opponents (in the 1925 Fastnet race) a better run for their money, for these double enders, though they seem rather tubby when afloat, fine down considerably below the W.L.

The North Star. *The wind is abeam, but her sails are trimmed flat, probably for the photographer.*

The *North Star* was entered in many early English offshore events, including the Fastnet. She was slow in light airs, but livened up when the breeze came.

ROCKWELL KENT AND THE *DIRECTION*

There was also contemporary interest in pointed-sterned, Norwegian skoite-type yachts in the United States. Rockwell Kent, the noted American illustrator and author, came to appreciate them. During an eventful life, he had sailed across the Atlantic in a ketch with two others, spent an icebound winter in Alaska seeking artistic and literary material, and, after refitting and strengthening a converted ship's lifeboat for cruising, he voyaged around Tierra del Fuego. After a few years of work and meditation at his studio in New York's Adirondack mountains, the urge to go to sea returned, and in 1929 Kent searched for a vessel fit to voyage to Greenland with a crew of three.

Kent found the perfect boat, newly completed but without an owner, at Miller's Shipyard, Nyack, New York. She was the cutter-rigged *Direction,* which had been designed by M.H. Miner, of whom nothing can be discovered, as an adaptation of the published plans of the 47-foot Colin Archer-designed, Norwegian lifeboat that had also inspired Nutting, Hildebrand, and Atkin. Miner altered the lines and reduced the length to 33 feet for an owner intending to sail her to the South Pacific, perhaps in imitation of Ralph Stock.

The *Direction* was purchased by Arthur S. Allen, father of one of Kent's companions in the venture, and was refitted to sail northern waters. She was built of white oak throughout, and her construction was heavy. Ratlines and a bowsprit net added to her seagoing appearance. An auxiliary engine was not installed, partly from prejudice but also to reduce propeller drag and avoid almost inevitable ice damage to the propeller. With accommodation arranged for three and sturdy gear, she was fit to go almost anywhere within range of her food and water capacity. Arthur S. Allen, Jr., was owner-skipper, Lucian Cary, Jr., was mate, and Rockwell Kent was navigator when the *Direction* sailed for Greenland, without radio or ballast and with little windward ability because of her rig at that time and lack of stability from improper ballasting.

From Baddeck on Cape Breton Island, the *Direction* sailed north through the Gulf of St. Lawrence and the Straits of Belle Isle, up the Labrador coast and then across to Greenland. The ultimate object of the voyage was Godhavn, or farther north if possible. In Greenland she anchored in apparently sheltered Karajak Fjord for the night, but dragged her anchors and was blown ashore by williwaws next morning. The *Direction* pounded on the rocks until she was holed and sunk, but her crew got ashore and salvaged sufficient food and equipment to survive. Rockwell Kent trekked overland for two days and a night to get help. Afterwards he remained in Greenland to paint the rugged scenery he loved. Carey went to Paris and Allen went home, only to be killed in a car accident two weeks later. Kent wrote and illustrated a fine book on the cruise, entitled *N by E.*

The *Direction* was repaired by the Greenlanders and was sailed from Godthaab to Ivigtut, where she was shipped to Philadelphia. Alfred Loomis sailed her from there to Cold Spring Harbor for the winter, and Edward Ayers took her north to Baddeck the following summer, where the senior Allen maintained her until his death in 1945. In the spring of 1946 she was bought by Charles H. Vilas, the indefatigable secretary of the Cruising Club of America. (It is most interesting and speaks well of the skoite type that the Blue Water Medal of the Cruising Club of America has gone to seven yachts of the Norwegian skoite type, and two have been flagships of the club fleet.) The *Direction* had been re-rigged with a Bermudian mainsail set on a hollow wood mast, which, coupled with the addition of stone ballast, increased her stability. In 1966, Carl Vilas wrote of his ownership of the *Direction*:

> "Why would you ever want a boat like *Direction*?" I have been asked by many of my friends. "She's slow to windward, heavier than you will ever have to call for on Long Island Sound, and you can never win a race in her." I find it just as hard to give a consistent and logical reply as did her earlier owner in explaining why he would have neither motor nor radio on board. It is a matter of personality and temperament. Some of the pleasures of yachting are enjoyed vicariously and to own a boat in which you could sail round the world, or to the South Seas, or to Greenland if you had the time and money is a source of satisfaction though you may never leave the waters of Long Island Sound. For twenty years, as a matter of fact, these Promethian chains kept me and *Direction* west of Cape Cod. They were twenty very happy years raising a family, earning a living, sailing *Direction* in the summer and replacing rotten wood in the winter.

Vilas was still happily sailing *Direction* in 1977 and spent much time cruising in his favorite Nova Scotian waters. *Direction*'s story is told in detail in Vilas's book *Saga of Direction,* published in 1978 by Seven Seas Press, New York.

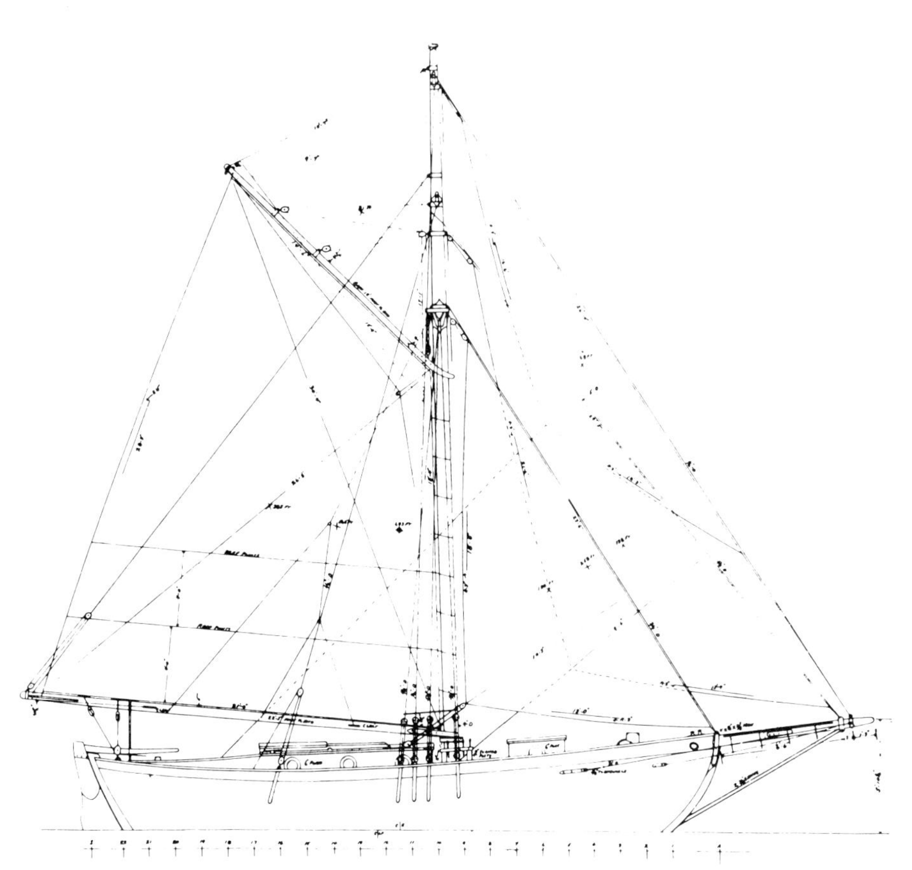

Right: *Original sail plan of the* Direction. (Saga of Direction *by Charles H. Vilas, Seven Seas Press, New York, N.Y.)*
Below: *The* Direction*'s arrangement plan.* (Saga of Direction *by Charles H. Vilas, Seven Seas Press, New York, N.Y.)*

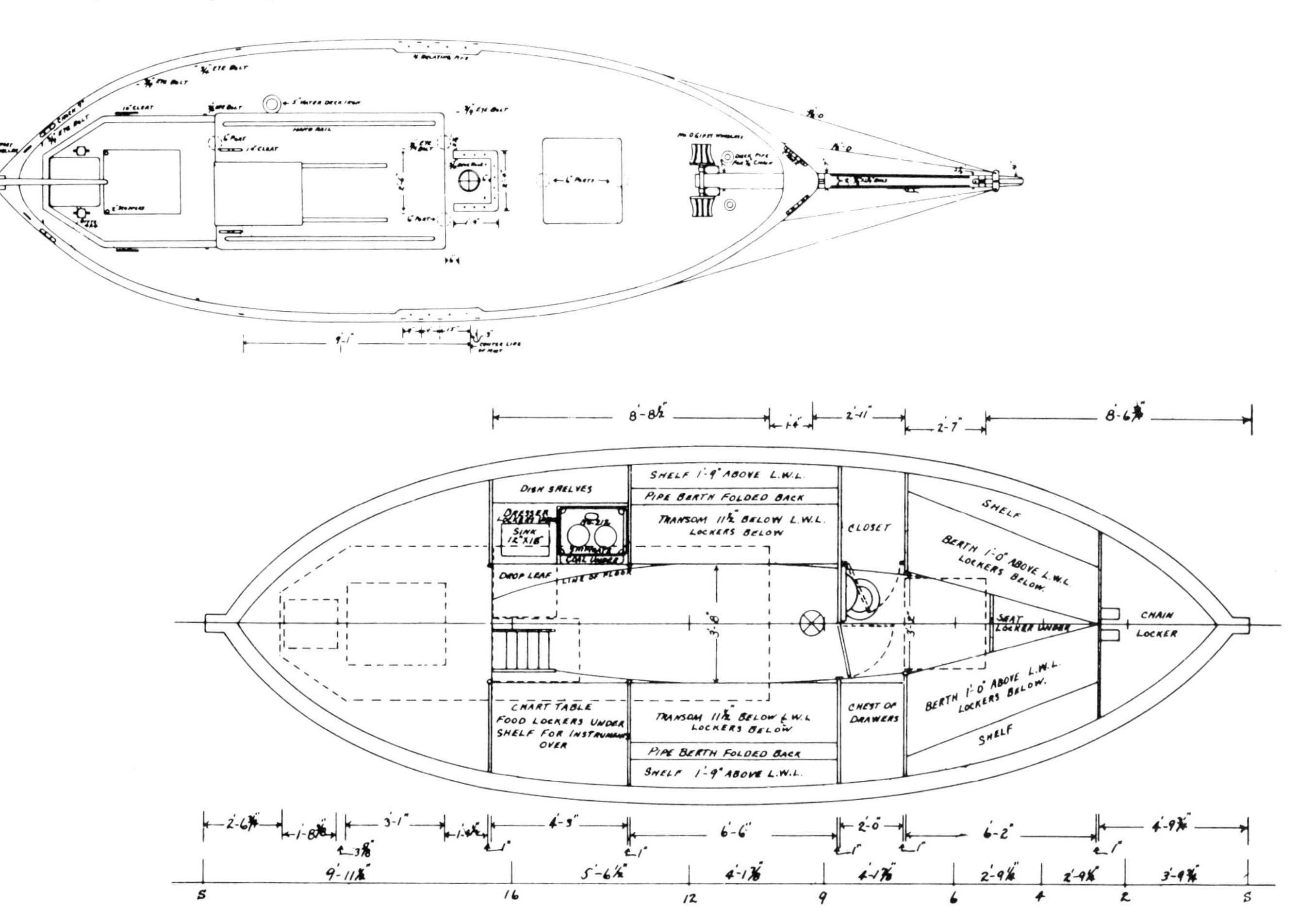

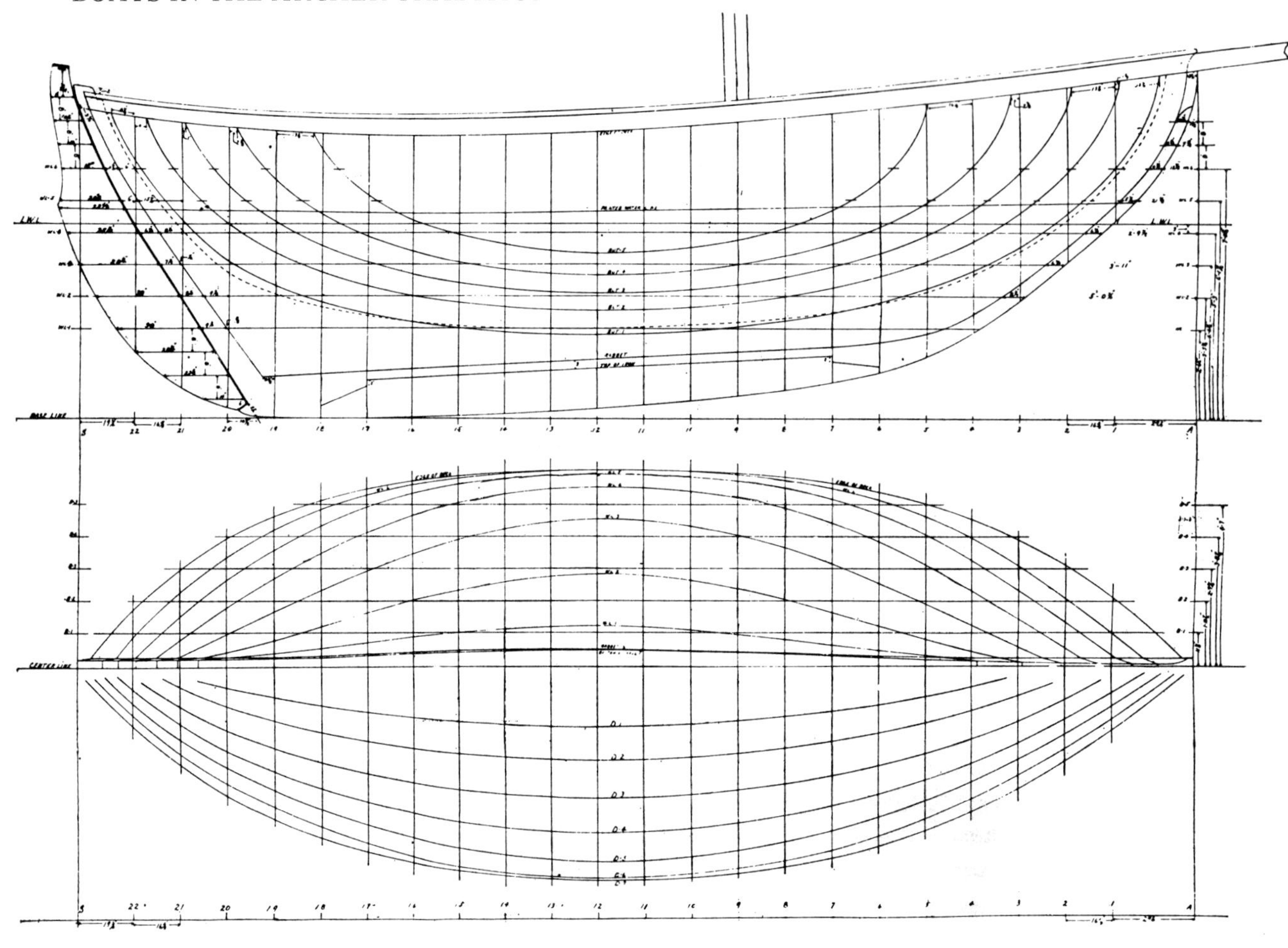

Lines of the Direction. (Yachting, *July, 1929)*

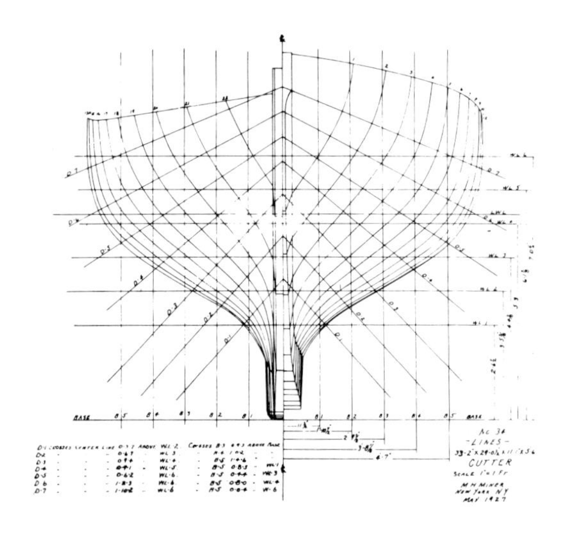

Above: *The* Direction *sailing in Humber Arm, Newfoundland, in 1937. (Photo by Robert Hartwell Moore)*
Left: *The* Direction *with her Bermudian rig in Great Salt Pond, Block Island, in 1964. (Photo by William Hartman)*

WIDENING INTEREST

In the 1930s, adaptations of Colin Archer's work took root in France. During 1931, a craft similar to the Norwegian skoites was built by Jouet of Sartrouville for Alain Gerbault, and reputedly to Gerbault's "design." Gerbault spent a year considering the design and made a model of her to prove she would self-steer. Gerbault had become the third man known to have sailed alone around the world, his predecessors being Captain Joshua Slocum and Harry Pidgeon. He was an amateur tennis champion and eccentric egotist, having, at least at first, little knowledge of seamanship. He circumnavigated the globe in the 39-foot gaff-rigged cutter *Firecrest,* built at Rowhedge, Essex, England, in 1892. He wrote of his sailing, and book royalties enabled him to have a new yacht built.

It seems probable that Gerbault's boat, named *La Blanche Fille de Soleil* (34 feet length overall, 10 feet 6 inches beam), was yet another adaptation of William Atkin's published plans. She was 31 feet long on the waterline and of finer but similar form to Atkin's *Dragon.* She was rigged as a cutter with the mast and boom from the old *Firecrest* put in the new yacht. The foot of the mainsail was angled up sharply at about 10 degrees, and its luff ran on wooden mast hoops to the spreader, above which the luff was hanked to a wire jackstay, drawn taut between the deck and the masthead. The staysail and jib were large, and the jib was set on a bowsprit longer than was even then fashionable on Bermudian cutters. A jib topsail could also be set. For downwind sailing, *La Blanche Fille de Soleil* carried twin spinnakers, which Gerbault considered he had "invented," though they had been used previously by at least one ocean sailor: Otway Waller. After experience at sea, Gerbault decided to elaborate on the rig by devising twin "topsail spinnakers" to be set above the twins, but these were, wisely, to be used only in daylight.

The following year a yard in Boulogne, the Chantiers de la Liane, built a cruising cutter on speculation, to be exhibited at the Paris boat show. This craft appears to have been a modification, by a French naval architect, of one of Atkin's Norwegian-style yachts, whose plans had been published in *Motorboat* magazine, but her sections were fined and beam reduced to that of a contemporary cruising yacht. Her draft was increased over Archer's designs, and a 3½-ton lead keel was fitted. Only the sternpost profile, sheer, and bulwarks resembled Colin Archer's work. While construction was still underway, the noted French marine painter Marin-Marie, a sailor of ability who was seized with the idea of sailing alone across the Atlantic, was seeking a suitable cruiser. He chanced on this boat when she was almost completed at Boulogne and bought her. Re-rigged to his specifications with a jib, staysail, and boomless mainsail,

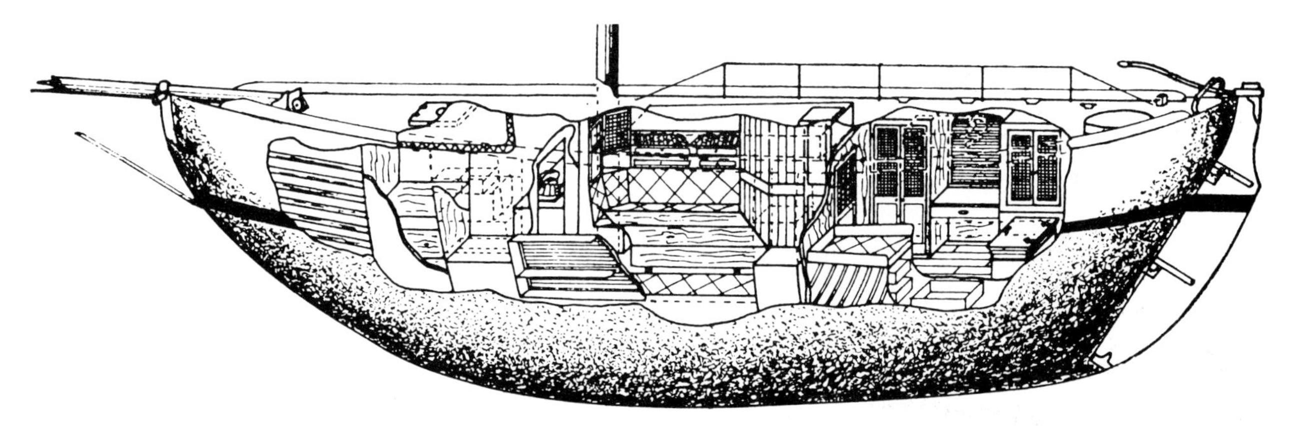

This cutaway drawing of La Blanche Fille de Soleil *indicates that she had a rather lavish interior with many intriguing details, some of which are not self-explanatory.* (Alain Gerbault *by Eric Vibart)*

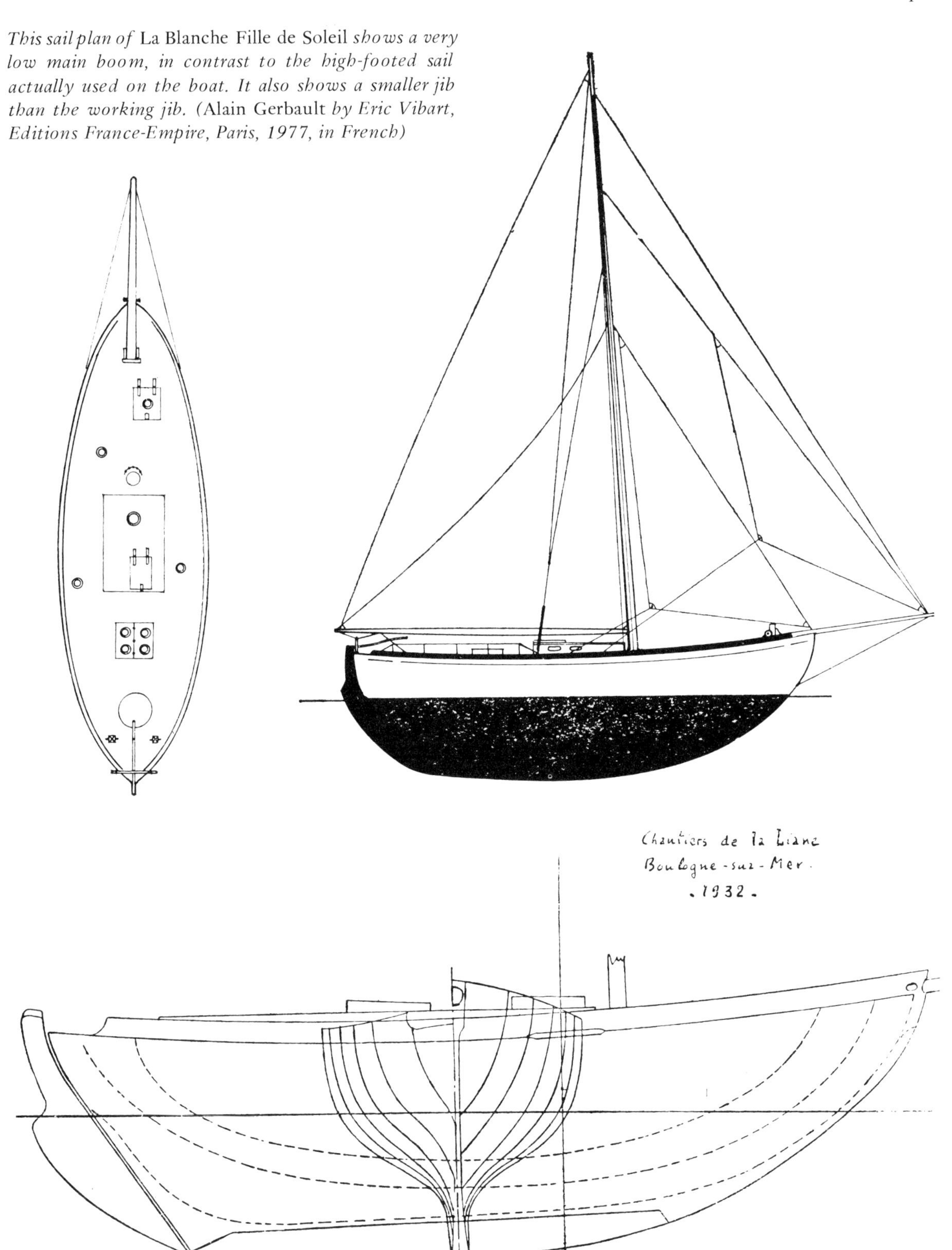

This sail plan of La Blanche Fille de Soleil *shows a very low main boom, in contrast to the high-footed sail actually used on the boat. It also shows a smaller jib than the working jib.* (Alain Gerbault *by Eric Vibart, Editions France-Empire, Paris, 1977, in French)*

Lines of Marin-Marie's Winnibelle. (Wind Aloft, Wind Alow *by Marin-Marie)*

with twin spinnakers for the trade winds, the *Winnibelle,* as she was named, made a notable Atlantic passage, well told in Marin-Marie's book *Wind Aloft, Wind Alow.* Other similar yachts were built in France, where the type became well established and is still being built.

Meanwhile, boats in England based on the Colin Archer type continued to be built. For instance, after cruising many thousands of miles in his 23-ton *Escape,* designed by Colin Archer in 1896 as a lifeboat, David Robertson was convinced that his next yacht should be of the same type. The new boat was conceived as "a home to take to sea," but although larger than her predecessor, she was to have the same hull shape. Robertson commissioned William McC. Meek, a British naval architect, to draft the plans. Robertson had her built in Norway by K. Christensen of Moen, near Risor. She was launched in 1936.

The fame of the Colin Archer type reached New Zealand in the 1930s. A middle-aged New Zealand bachelor, inspired by Erling Tambs's exploits in the *Teddy*, commissioned Arthur Robb, then emerging as a talented young yacht designer, to prepare plans for a 41-foot ketch. The owner planned to live on board all year round, cruise for long periods, and sometimes make ocean passages. Robb modified the Archer style of lines, reducing the beam and fining the forward waterlines in an attempt to increase speed and provide a more comfortable motion than that of the *Teddy,* particularly when going to windward in a seaway. Construction was of New Zealand lumber, and, to reduce the effect of tropical sunlight on the hull, the topside seams

The Winnibelle *in the St. Malo Race in 1934. (Photo by Kirk.* Wind Aloft, Wind Alow *by Marin-Marie)*

Marin-Marie whose full name was Marin-Marie Durand de St. Front. (Wind Aloft, Wind Alow *by Marin-Marie)*

The Winnibelle *running before a squall under her twin staysails and spinnaker, from a watercolor by Marin-Marie.* (Wind Aloft, Wind Alow *by Marin-Marie)*

were splined and the decks covered with canvas and painted. The ketch rig was arranged differently from the usual Archer boats, with the mainmast stepped well aft, allowing a large staysail but resulting in a comparatively narrow and probably inefficient gaff mainsail. The boat carried a jib-headed topsail, and the topsail luff was set on a track on the after side of the mast. The gaff had a metal saddle instead of jaws, and the throat halyard was chain, to combat chafe. The peak halyard was of 2-inch-circumference flexible wire rope, doubled. All halyards had purchases on deck. The mainmast, made in one piece, was supported by a pair of jumper struts at its head and by the forestay and an outer forestay, led to the end of a short bowsprit. The jib hanked to this stay. An ordinary, large, or storm jib could be set.

NOTEWORTHY PASSAGEMAKING

New boats based on the Colin Archer type weren't the only craft receiving attention in the 1930s. Original Colin Archer craft continued to be sold out of service and were modified for cruising purposes. Erling Tambs, of *Teddy* fame, decided to go cruising again. During 1934 he suggested an around-the-world yacht race, which was then regarded as an outrageous idea (as it still is to many sailing people), and challenged anyone to race against him and his crew sailing an ex-redningskoite under the Royal Ocean Racing Club rule. The Royal Norwegian Yacht Club publicized the proposed race, which was to have calls at about five ports en route to increase interest in the progress of the event and allow the race to be covered by contemporary news systems, but nothing came of it.

About that time Tambs bought the ex-redningskoite *Sandefjord* and entered her in the Newport—Bergen race of 1935. However, she did not arrive in Newport until just after the start due to running under and capsizing end for end when running before a gale in the Atlantic.

The *Sandefjord* was running, hard pressed, under a double-reefed mainsail before a gale increasing to almost hurricane strength. The storm staysail had to be repaired, so she ran on under the reefed mainsail with two men at the tiller having difficulty in stopping her from broaching-to. The wind was on the port quarter and the main boom was to starboard. An exceptionally steep sea lifted her stern, the bows plunged deep, and, at the speed she was travelling, the *Sandefjord* turned completely over longitudinally, before apparently rolling upside down, broadside to another wave and righting herself broadside to the sea. During the capsize the chain cable poured from the chain locker and battered at the deck, then fell on to the starboard forecastle bunk as she righted. The mizzen mast, held by one shroud a side, and with the sail stowed, was wrenched out aft during its passage through the water. All the main rigging was strained and the reefed mainsail burst. When the weather calmed, Tambs and his crew repaired damages and limped into Newport 26 days after the incident, which unfortunately caused the loss of one of the crew.

It seems that the *Sandefjord* was running too fast and had run for too long in the storm conditions, and might have been better hove-to, or running under bare poles with a warp or a drogue over the stern. It is interesting that the considerable weight of ballast in her bilge did not burst the sole during the capsize; she would then almost certainly have foundered.

Tambs was reticent on the circumstances of this incident and would not be drawn out by queries about it in the English *Yachting Monthly.* His faith in the type was unshaken: "It must not be inferred, however, that the Norwegian double-enders are particularly apt to act in this manner. On the contrary. They are, in my opinion, the finest type of ocean going small craft existing."

Above: *The* Sandefjord, *ex-R.S. 28.*
Below: *Detail of the* Sandefjord*'s bow. In both mainsail and foresail, a row of eyelets is just visible above the reef points for another deep reef.*

However, it is interesting that Tambs admitted the *Sandefjord* had pitchpoled in a similar way while sailing as a redningskoite. This is the only instance I can discover of this happening in service.

Erling Tambs sold the *Sandefjord* at the commencement of the Second World War to Tilly Penso, a South African yachtsman who owned her until his death in 1958. Afterwards she changed hands several times and eventually was found almost sunk at Durban by Barry and Patrick Cullen, who did considerable rebuilding work on her. In February, 1965, she sailed from Durban with a crew of six for a circumnavigation, visiting the West Indies, the Galapagos, the South Seas, Australia, and Christmas Island, returning to Durban after a year. She sailed in the Cape-to-Rio race, and, after several more owners, again faded to obscurity and disrepair. However, through the efforts of the Norwegian Colin Archer Club, she was purchased by one of their members, Reling Brunborg. After refitting at Mystic Seaport, in Connecticut, the *Sandefjord* sailed for Norway in February, 1974, to have her restoration completed. After several years of refitting, she was sold to an owner in southern Norway and still sails from Oslofjord.

A voyage in the Colin Archer-designed, ex-lifeboat *Vagus* was made during 1939-40 by Edwin John Pratt, who was a commercial artist. The *Vagus* was 42 feet long on the deck, 39 feet on the waterline, and had 13 feet, 6 inches beam. Pratt spent three years refitting her for the voyage; after that time, little that was original remained except for the hull. He installed a new Lister auxiliary engine, which never let him down, and gave her a new mast and rigging.

Shortly before the outbreak of war in 1939, Pratt set sail from Penzance, Cornwall, England with two companions. The *Vagus* put in at numerous French, Spanish, and Portuguese ports, made a stop at Casablanca, and then cruised among the Atlantic Islands—Madeira, the Canaries, and the Cape Verdes. Despite the outbreak of war, Pratt continued his voyage, ultimately crossing the Atlantic to Barbados.

One departure from the traditional rigging on the *Vagus* was the addition of squaresail running gear rigged in England by Pratt before he set out:

> We have two yards, each about 15 feet long, hinged with gooseneck fittings on the mast, the other ends being controlled by lifts to the masthead, forward and after braces.
>
> The two squaresails (which could be laced together) were originally designed to run along the yards on mast hoops, being fixed at the inboard end. While mast hoops are quite satisfactory in a vertical plane, we found they would not work horizontally, and some other method of carrying the sail on the yard had to be devised. We eventually rigged a very taut wire on the underside of each spar, and the sail hung from this on spring hanks. It worked perfectly, the sail sliding easily in and out, controlled by an inhaul and outhaul on each side. When hauled in to the mast the sail could be secured by a brail passing twice round it, this being permanently in position.

Once the *Vagus* was underway on her trade winds passage across the Atlantic, however, Pratt began to wish he had chosen twin boomed staysails for downwind sailing. The starboard squaresail yard broke, and the *Vagus* had to run on under one squaresail and a boomed-out staysail.

Another significant voyage was made in the latter part of the 1930s by J.G. Kuyt, who bought a Colin Archer cutter out of service in Norway and renamed her *De Holland.* Kuyt set out from Zaandijk, Holland, on a voyage to Dakar in West Africa. He then sailed across the Atlantic to Curacao, in the Dutch West Indies, with a companion who was seriously ill for most of the passage. From there, Kuyt sailed *De Holland* to New York, then back across the Atlantic to Holland with a crew of three.

De Holland *reefed down and making knots in a North Sea gale.*

8

THE LEGACY OF INFLUENCE

VITO DUMAS

The Second World War did not stop the sailing or designing of seagoing small yachts inspired by Colin Archer and the Norwegian skoite hull form and rig. Between June, 1942 and September, 1943, Vito Dumas, an Argentinian, made a valiant circumnavigation in his yacht *Lehg II,* whose design was of the Colin Archer type. Dumas was a rancher and farmer of French descent who, during 1931, had sailed from Arcachon, France, to Buenos Aires in a 20-year-old French former 8 meter racing yacht named *Lehg I.* This was believed to be the first singlehanded ocean passage in an International Yacht Racing Union yacht, and at that time was regarded as foolhardy.

In 1933, Dumas decided to commission a design for his ideal ocean cruiser, to be built with the possibility of a future circumnavigation in mind. He approached the Argentinian designer Manuel M. Campos, and the result of their discussion was a pointed-stern ketch having characteristics of Colin Archer's by-then-well-known small craft. Campos was keen on the type, which he considered ideal for running before the wind in bad weather because of its stern shape. He had also designed some other pointed-stern yachts, mainly ketch rigged, developed from the "whaleboat" type used in the River Plate to transport goods and passengers from vessels in the exposed and often very rough anchorage off Buenos Aires before its port was built. These whaleboats were of shallow hull form and had low rigs. They were probably derived from Mediterranean craft. The boats varied from 29 to 50 feet long, and their seaworthiness and the advantage of their pointed sterns impressed Campos.

Campos had also read of the series of small, pointed-stern Norwegian-type yachts William Atkin had designed during the 1920s, inspired by the designs of Colin Archer. Campos researched Archer's designs and compared them with his own experience and the proven ability of the local whaleboats. Dumas was happy to allow Campos expression in the design, and both men were agreed on the necessity for a clean-lined vessel, built and rigged with strength and simplicity, to be constructed of Argentine timbers, of yacht scantlings.

The new boat was to be rigged as a Bermudian ketch, as the Bermudian rig for ocean sailing was then being proved by voyages such as that of the ocean racing yawl *Dorade.* The sail area was to be moderate, with the mainsail and mizzen luffs seized to hoops working on the masts, since track efficient for ocean service had not then been perfected. Campos wished to have all ballast in a cast iron keel bolted on, to ensure self-righting in the event of a capsize and to avoid the possibility of internal ballast shifting when the boat was hove down in storm conditions.

The *Lehg II* was built on the River Tigre by Don Jose Parodi. Her dimensions were 31 feet, 6 inches length on deck; 10 feet, 10 inches beam; and 5 feet, 8 inches draft, loaded. Her displacement was 8.5 tons, and her cast-iron keel weighed 7,700 pounds. Her sail area was 440 square feet and included a jib, storm jib, mainsail, and mizzen. She also carried a storm trysail and a balloon jib for light airs. *Lehg II*'s accommodation was conventional. She had a small steering cockpit in the manner of the Norwegian pilot boats, which, with her long, low cabin house, the *Lehg II* greatly resembled. Her only auxiliary

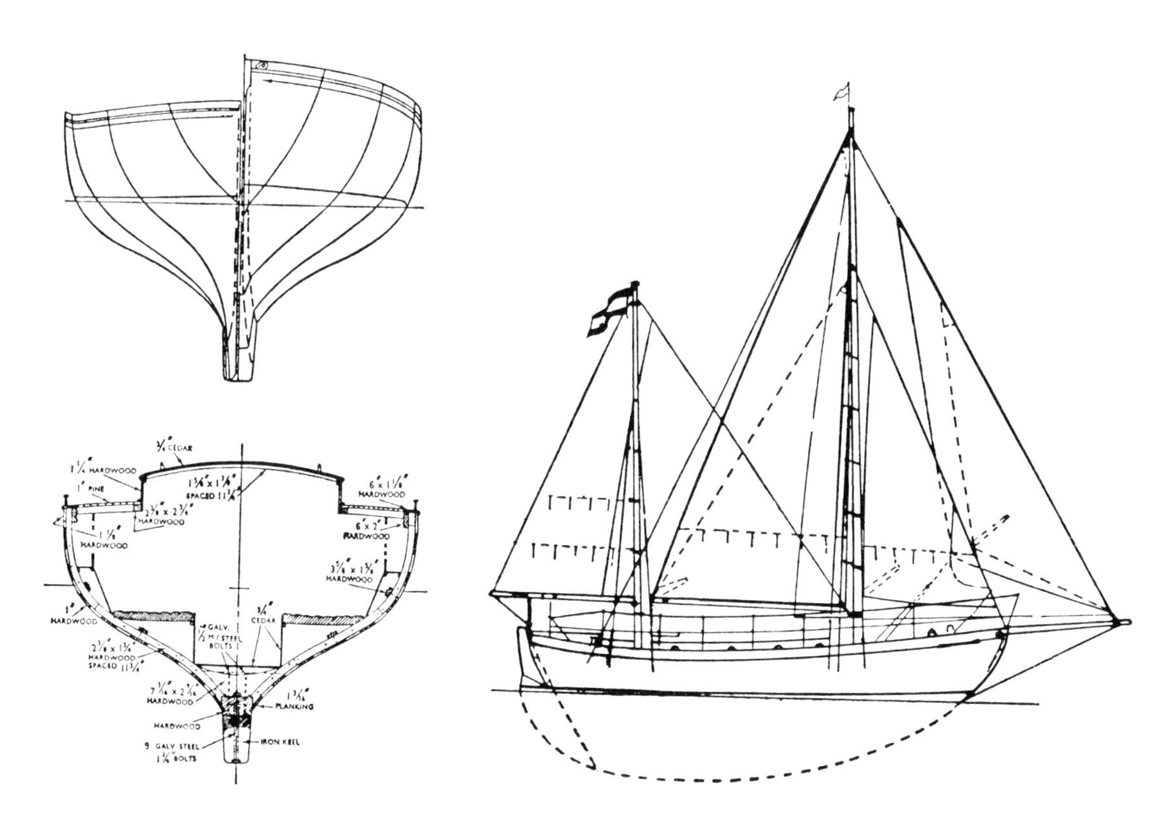

Sail plan and sections of the Lehg II. (Alone Through the Roaring Forties *by Vito Dumas)*
The arrangement plan of the Lehg II. (Alone Through the Roaring Forties *by Vito Dumas)*

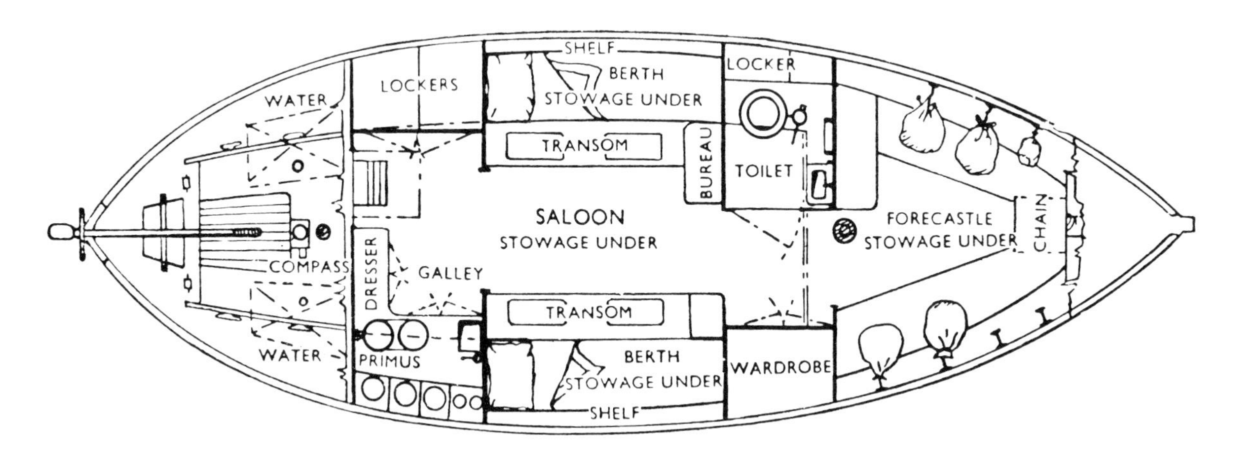

Vito Dumas posing on board the Lehg II *at Capetown. (*Alone Through the Roaring Forties *by Vito Dumas)*

power was a long sweep (Dumas had fixed ideas; besides refusing auxiliary power, he never carried a sea anchor or a bilge pump).

The *Lehg II* proved to be a good ocean passagemaker; she was moderately fast, stable, had a good reserve of buoyancy, and was easy to steer under all conditions. During a cruise to Rio de Janeiro in 1937, Dumas found out how good she was. She capsized in a 60- to-70-knot squall, but righted herself quickly.

Dumas was at first unable to realize his ambition to circumnavigate the globe in the *Lehg II* because of the demands of his ranch. Eventually he had to sell the boat to raise money to buy a badly needed and expensive tractor! After several years, however, the urge to circumnavigate overcame him. He decided to buy back the *Lehg II,* though he had little money available for the enterprise. He was about to sell a herd of cattle to pay for her, when a group of yacht and sporting clubs and friends paid for and provided the yacht, as well as her sails, gear, equipment, food, and medicine.

Dumas commenced his voyage on June 27, 1942 from Buenos Aires in a blaze of publicity inspired by nationalistic fervor. He arrived at Cape Town on August 25; 55 days to sail 4,200 miles. After three weeks in Cape Town he set sail on a 7,200-mile passage to Wellington, New Zealand, which took 104 days. His track was slightly south of the 45th parallel. He then sailed on January 3, 1943, bound for Valparaiso, Chile, where he berthed on April 12th, after sailing 5,400 miles in 38 days. He departed May 30th for Cape Horn, which he rounded in reasonable weather, arriving at Mar del Plata on July 7, 1943, 32 days and 3,200 miles from Valparaiso. Dumas had navigated the earth close to the stormy 40th parallel on a voyage of 20,420 miles and 272 days at sea, accomplished in twelve and a half months and including only three landfalls. His average daily run throughout the

The Lehg II *looking a little forlorn as she nears the end of her circumnavigation. (*Alone Through the Roaring Forties *by Vito Dumas)*

voyage was 74 miles, giving an average speed of three knots. He was the first singlehander known to round the Horn and survive. He was also the first singlehander to circumnavigate in the Roaring Forties.

The *Lehg II* performed admirably. After experiment, Dumas found she would sail herself under mizzen and headsails, which made his passage easier, to say the least. He found her to be a boat that inspired confidence. He wrote, "In waves sometimes exceeding 60 feet and winds up to 70 knots . . . [she] confirmed my belief that a Norwegian, with continuous framing from end to end, had the cohesion to withstand constant terrific shocks. For in my navigation it was no question of a storm here and there, but of an endless succession of dirty weather."

Dumas did not believe in lying-to a sea anchor in bad weather, and this unusual conviction proved the Norwegian-style hull in other ways. He wrote:

> I am convinced that a boat can stand up to any sea, comfortably enough, under sail. She has the freedom of movement and can lift to the seas. Should the wind force exceed 50 knots I would say, contrary to the opinion that following combers can play havoc by breaking on deck, that one of my favorite pleasures was to run through squalls on a mattress of foam. My speed on these surf riding occasions exceeded 15 knots; I then presented the stern to another wave and began this exciting pastime anew when a wave arrives roaring from astern and it seems impossible that the ship could lift, it stands to reason that one is frightened. . . .
>
> . . . In these circumstances many people would lay to; I at once rejected this solution, feeling, as if in my own flesh, the suffering of the boat buried under raging waves. Whatever the hurricane it never compelled me to strike all sail; my mainsail has no reef points. The old saying which prescribed a salute to squalls by taking in sail was never adhered to in the course of my voyages; when I did take it in it was in order to get some rest."

A BRIGANTINE-RIGGED REDNINGSKOITE

Just after the Second World War, a most interesting boat, based on the Colin Archer type, was designed and built. Named the *Mary Fortune II,* she was basically a redningskoite with a brigantine rig, rather than the usual fore-and-aft ketch or cutter rig favored by Archer for this type of boat. Because of the uniqueness of the *Mary Fortune II,* we will go into her particulars in some detail.

Her owner was P. Dalzel Job, an experienced British yachtsman who had cruised extensively along the Norwegian coast from 1934 to 1939. He lost his yacht to the Nazis during the war, so commissioned Greville S.R. Le Poer Trench in 1946 to design a new boat.

Job had admired the Norwegian redningskoites during his pre-war cruises, so the hull of his new boat basically followed that of a Colin Archer rescue ship, except she was larger and had a small raised quarterdeck to permit a stern cabin. Her dimensions were 53 feet, 4 inches length on deck; 45 feet, 2 inches waterline; 16 feet beam; and 7 feet, 9 inches draft. Her displacement was 39 tons, with 14,000 pounds in an external ballast keel. Her profile greatly resembled Colin Archer's craft, but the sections were much less beamy, with a slacker bilge and a very steep rise of floor. Altogether the *Mary Fortune II* was intended to have a much easier motion than the Archer types and had a greater displacement. The long keel made her steady on the helm, so she was to be fairly easy to work with one man on deck.

The *Mary Fortune II*'s brigantine rig was derived from Job's previous yacht. Her working sail area was 1,567 square feet in the forestaysail, jib, forecourse, fore topsail, mainsail, and main topsail. The staysail was hanked to an extra-stout forestay and had two rows of reef points. The jib was set at the end of a well-steeved bowsprit on which it was sent out on a traveller. The jib was furled by the invaluable Wykeham-Martin gear, which enabled it to be sent out or brought in as a controllable sausage instead of a thrashing fiend.

The lower masts were comparatively short and well raked. The forecourse of 443 square feet was hauled out to the ends of the yard on slides and sail track. The foretopmast was set in irons on the after side of the masthead, in the manner of many small square-rigged craft

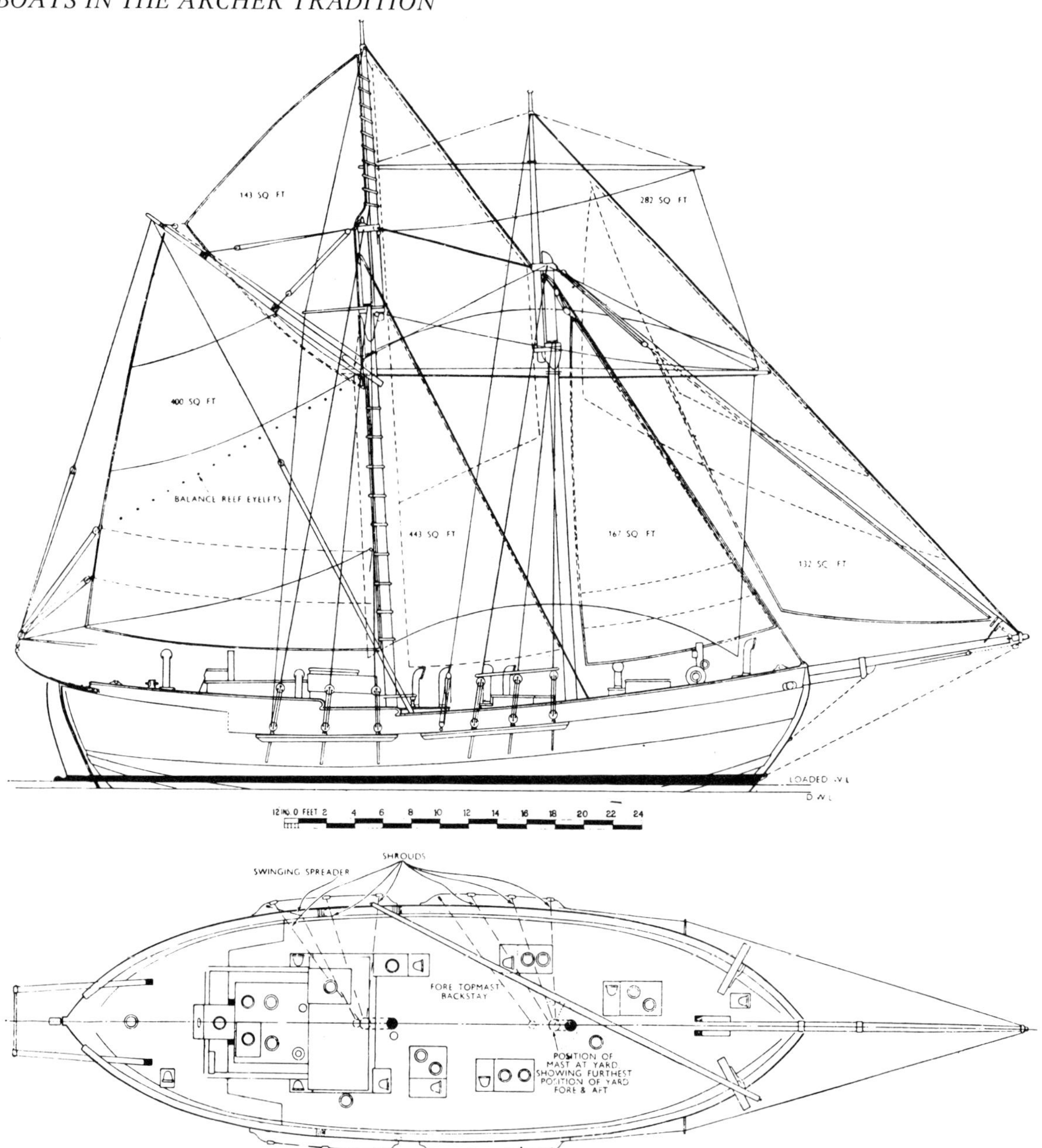

Above and right: *Plans of the* Mary Fortune II. (Motor Boat and Yachting)

of a century ago. This enabled the eyes of the forestays and the lead of the staysail and jib halyards to be clear of interference, and made lowering the topmast perhaps slightly easier, especially in combination with the well-raked mast. The foretopsail was set flying, sent up by halyards and outhauls and, like the fore-course, was cut with a deep roach to its foot.

The boomless gaff mainsail was sheeted to a rather flimsy looking bumkin, and the sheeting arrangement was unusual for a gaff sail. The sheet led from the clew, through a multiple sheave block on the horse to two blocks on the clew and another on a pendant from the gaff end. This arrangement was an attempt to reduce twist on the sail and was

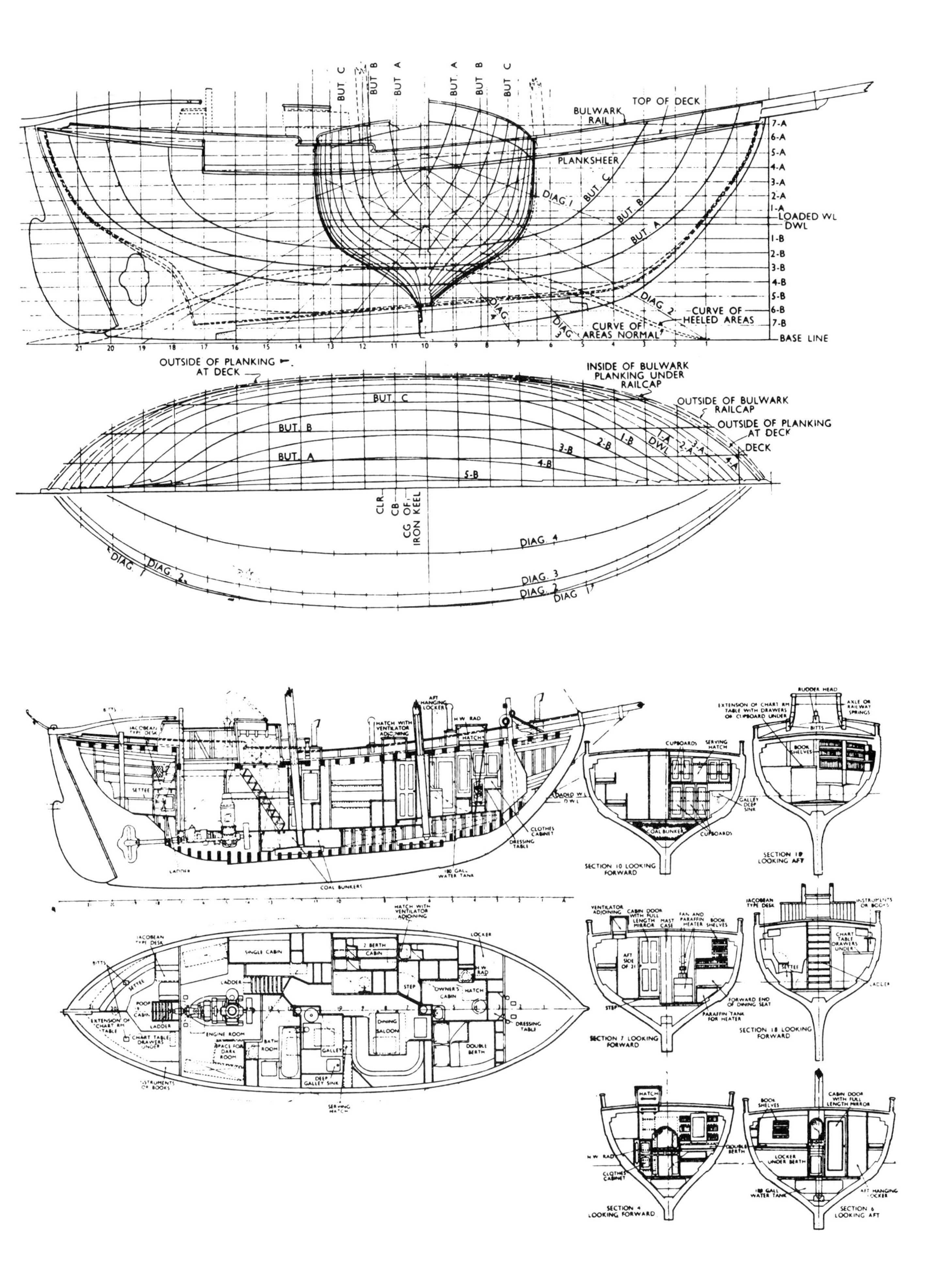

BUT C
BUT B
BUT A
TOP OF DECK
BULWARK RAIL
PLANKSHEER
DIAG 1
LOADED WL
DWL
DIAG 2
CURVE OF HEELED AREAS
CURVE OF AREAS NORMAL
BASE LINE
OUTSIDE OF PLANKING AT DECK
INSIDE OF BULWARK PLANKING UNDER RAILCAP
OUTSIDE OF BULWARK RAILCAP
DECK
CLR
CB
CG OF IRON KEEL
DIAG 4
DIAG 3
COAL BUNKERS
SECTION 10 LOOKING FORWARD
SECTION 18 LOOKING AFT
SECTION 7 LOOKING FORWARD
SECTION 18 LOOKING FORWARD
SECTION 4 LOOKING FORWARD
SECTION 6 LOOKING AFT
SINGLE CABIN
2 BERTH CABIN
OWNER'S CABIN
ENGINE ROOM
DINING SALOON
GALLEY
DOUBLE BERTH

aided by vangs port and starboard, set up abreast the foot of the mainmast. The vangs were also used to steady the gaff when the mainsail was furled by brails—one was rigged to the luff, one to the throat, and one to the gaff.

The jib-headed main topsail ran on hoops on the topmast, which was set in irons on the forward side of the mainmast head. A disadvantage of this arrangement was that the topsail had to be stowed aloft and, apart from the work and sometimes difficulty of stowing it, the windage of the stowed sail was serious in such a small vessel in strong winds. A large or small jib-topsail could be set, hanked to the topmast forestay, and a main topmast staysail added area for reaching. The mainsail had two rows of reef points, coinciding with the mainsheet blocks on the leech. A diagonal row of reef eyelets from the throat to the leech provided a balance reef for extreme conditions. The shrouds were set up by deadeyes and lanyards to channels, and the main topmast was stayed aft via well-swept spreaders. The foretopmast was stayed by a running backstay set up with a purchase to the channels, enabling it to clear the yard when braced on the wind.

The *Mary Fortune II* was built at Newfoundland Shipyards Ltd., Clarenville, Newfoundland. The stem and sternpost were of greenheart, sided 6 inches, and the greenheart keel was 12 inches square. Floors were juniper, sided 3½ inches and of grown shapes where possible. Frames were sawn oak or juniper, molded 3 inches at the head and 5 inches at the heel, double sided 3½ inches and spaced 12 inches between centers. Planking was 2-inch-thick pine above the waterline and fir or crabwood below; the hull was sheathed additionally below the waterline with ½-inch-thick greenheart.

In accordance with Maritime Provinces tradition, the hull was "salted"; plywood salt stops were fitted between the frames, and the enclosed spaces were filled with rock salt through holes in the covering board. Builders claimed that salting would add years of life to a wood hull and would prevent mildew (but from experience I believe it to be bad practice, leading to deterioration of the structure). For cruising in northern waters, the underside of the deck and inner side of the planking to the waterline were covered with a layer of bituminous paper and a ½-inch-thick layer of insulating board. Ordinary deck beams were sided 5 inches and molded 6 inches at the center; they were decreased to 4½ inches at the ends. Heavy deck beams and those in way of the mast were sided 6 inches and molded 5 inches at the ends and 6 inches at the centerline. The deck planking was 2-inch pine, riftsawn. All fastenings were galvanized steel. A single cylinder 29/36 hp Rapp diesel engine with a reversible propeller was installed.

The *Mary Fortune II* was truly a seagoing vessel. She had the capacity for 500 gallons of fuel oil, 450 gallons of fresh water, two tons of coal, and half a ton of food. With 20 percent of her stores, water, and fuel on board—as at the end of a long passage—she floated about six inches higher than with a full load.

There is an inspiring boldness and lift about the *Mary Fortune II*'s sheer and sail plan. She is an admirable design for a seagoing home. My major criticism of the design, however, is the tiller steering, which, on long sea passages, could be wearing on the crew. A modern wheel and rod gear mounted in a more protected position, such as the cockpit, would be preferable.

The brigantine rig is now little understood, though interest in it is growing as ocean passagemaking in small cruising yachts has again become common. The rig should be seriously considered by offshore voyagers who are not in a hurry.

POST-WAR DESIGNS

The Second World War proved to be a turning point for Colin Archer-type yachts. There was a limited revival of interest in the type, after the War, but the surviving craft Archer had designed and built were scattered about the world and were becoming old and unsound. Colin Archer's fame among yachtsmen persisted, but the term "Colin Archer type" was often distorted and was used to refer to many beamy, pointed-stern craft that had few of the characteristics of the vessels Archer designed. They were usually rather beamy cruising yachts with little flare amidships, shortened keels, fine bows, and varying stem and stern shapes; they only vaguely followed Colin Archer's work.

Some vessels were built after the war, however, that are good examples stemming from the Colin Archer tradition. Let's take a look at some of them.

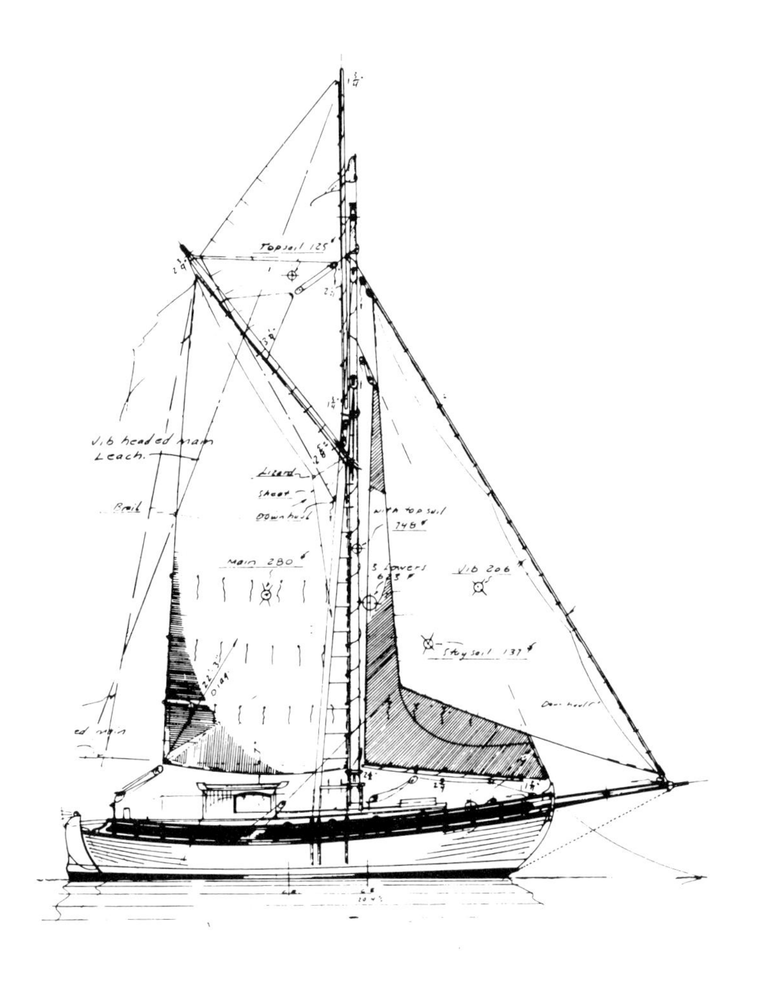

BULLFROG

In 1947, William Garden, the Seattle naval architect, designed a 30-foot cutter influenced by the redningskoite type. The *Bull Frog* was built for Robert Ellis of Los Angeles by Lester Franck of Seattle. Her dimensions are 30 feet long on deck, 26 feet waterline, 10 feet beam, and 5 feet, 4 inches draft. Her displacement is 18,000 pounds, and she has a sail area of 526 square feet. The *Bull Frog*'s cutter rig

Above, below, and next page: *Plans of the* Bull Frog. *(*Yachting, *August, 1947; and* Yacht Designs *by William Garden, International Marine Publishing Company, Camden, Maine, 1977)*

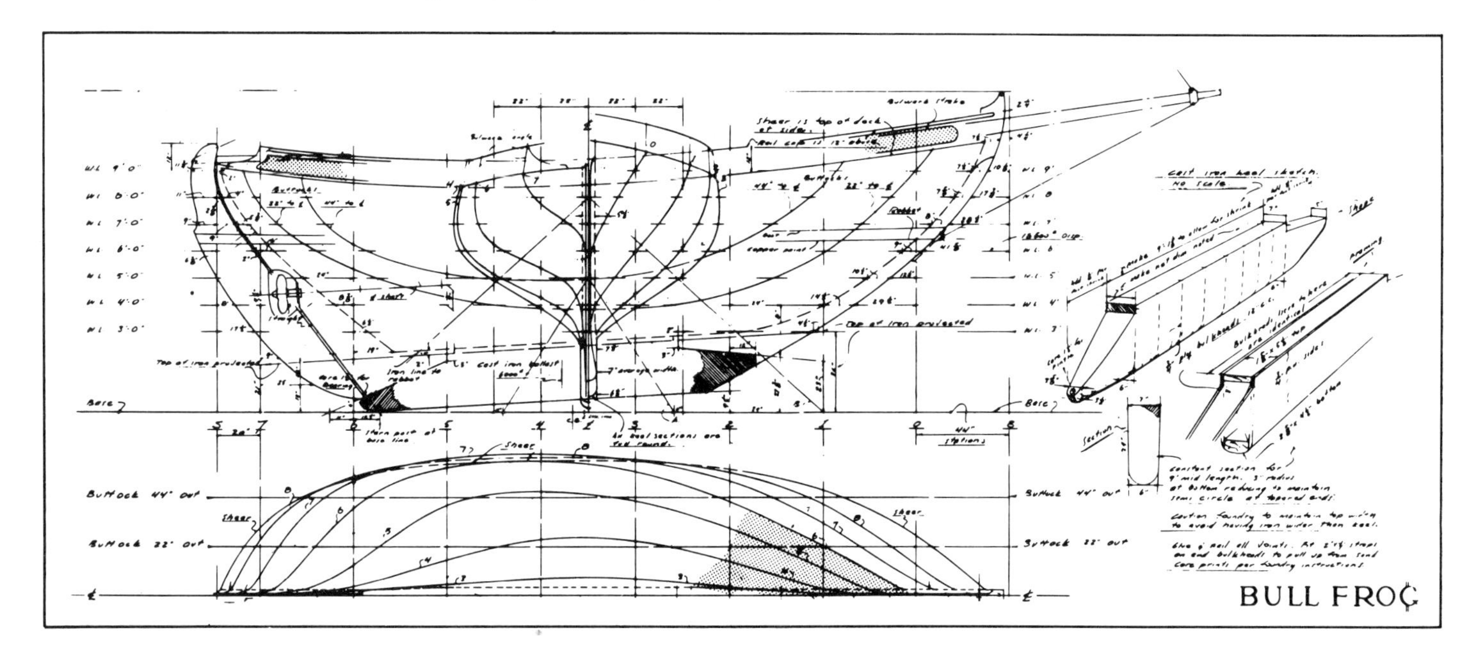

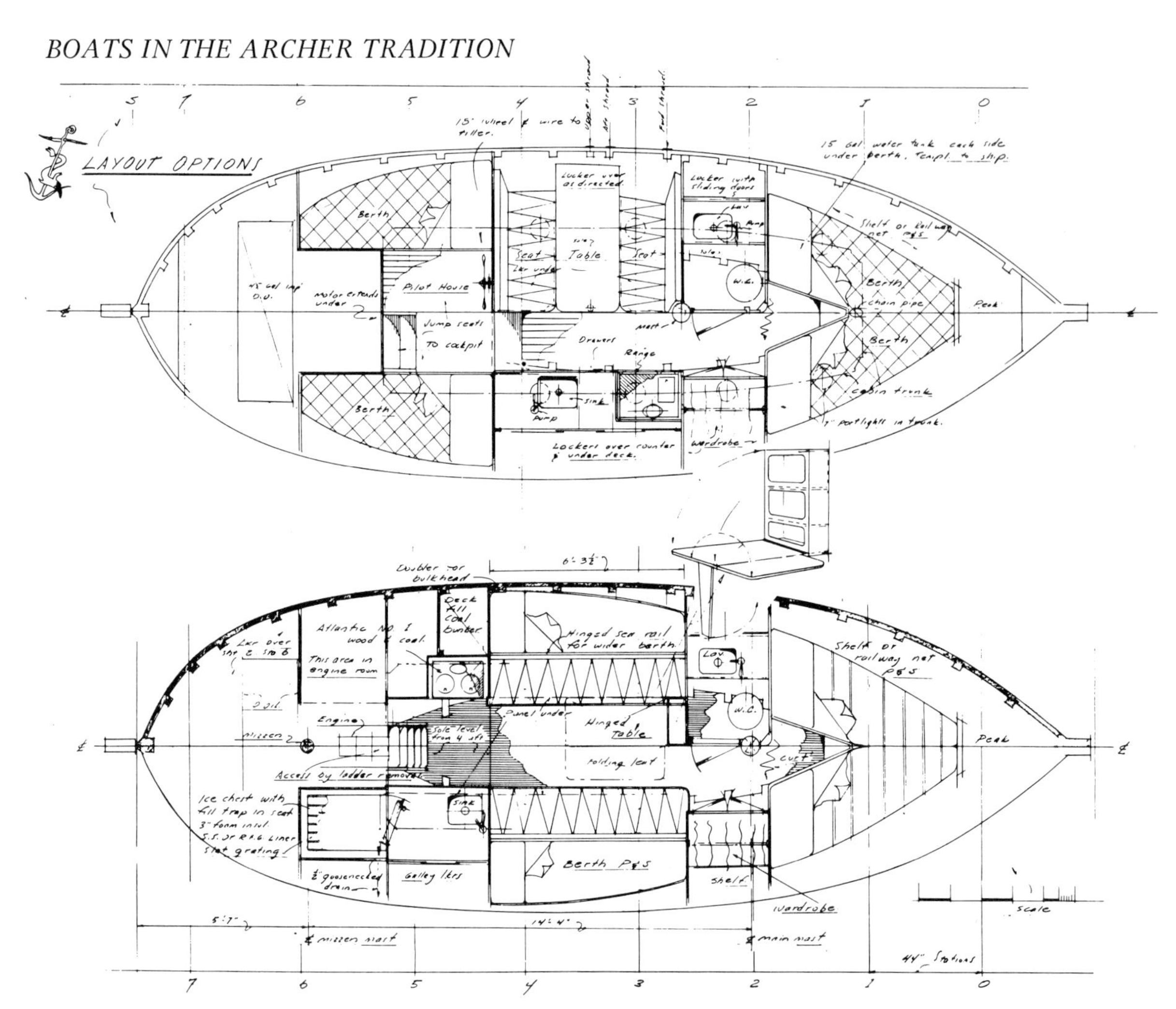

has a short gaff and a bowsprit of moderate length. Construction was of local timbers and to commercial rather than yacht standards. She has tankage for 44 gallons of fuel for her auxiliary engine and for 40 gallons of water, which gives her a good cruising range. The *Bull Frog*'s accommodation is practical and is arranged with two berths in the forecastle, and a settee berth and a seat in the main cabin, with the galley and toilet adjoining.

ALAN BUCHANAN'S COLIN ARCHER

During the early 1950s, the English yacht designer Alan H. Buchanan owned the Swedish-built cutter *Karin III*, an ocean-voyaging yacht 41 feet, 6 inches long that had the beam and characteristics of the Norwegian skoite type. In 1955, he designed a 41-foot, 3-inch cruising ketch that he named *Colin Archer* as a tribute to his source of inspiration. Alan Buchanan wrote of the design:

> We were asked to produce a vessel with ketch rig capable of long ocean passages as she was intended as a floating ocean cruising home and the accommodation had to be suitable for living on board for long periods in harbour as well as being practically laid out for deep water cruising. The main requirement was to produce a seaworthy hull which would run well in the trades and yet have a good windward performance. With these requirements in mind we set off to produce the lines. The vessel is roughly the same size as the *Karin III* and the experience gained in sailing this vessel was of enormous help in designing the new ship. The hull form is very different and all the ballast is outside. Scantlings . . . are heavy by modern-day practice. The ketch rig has been selected as being the most suitable for deep water cruising, cutting the sail area up into easily-handled units.

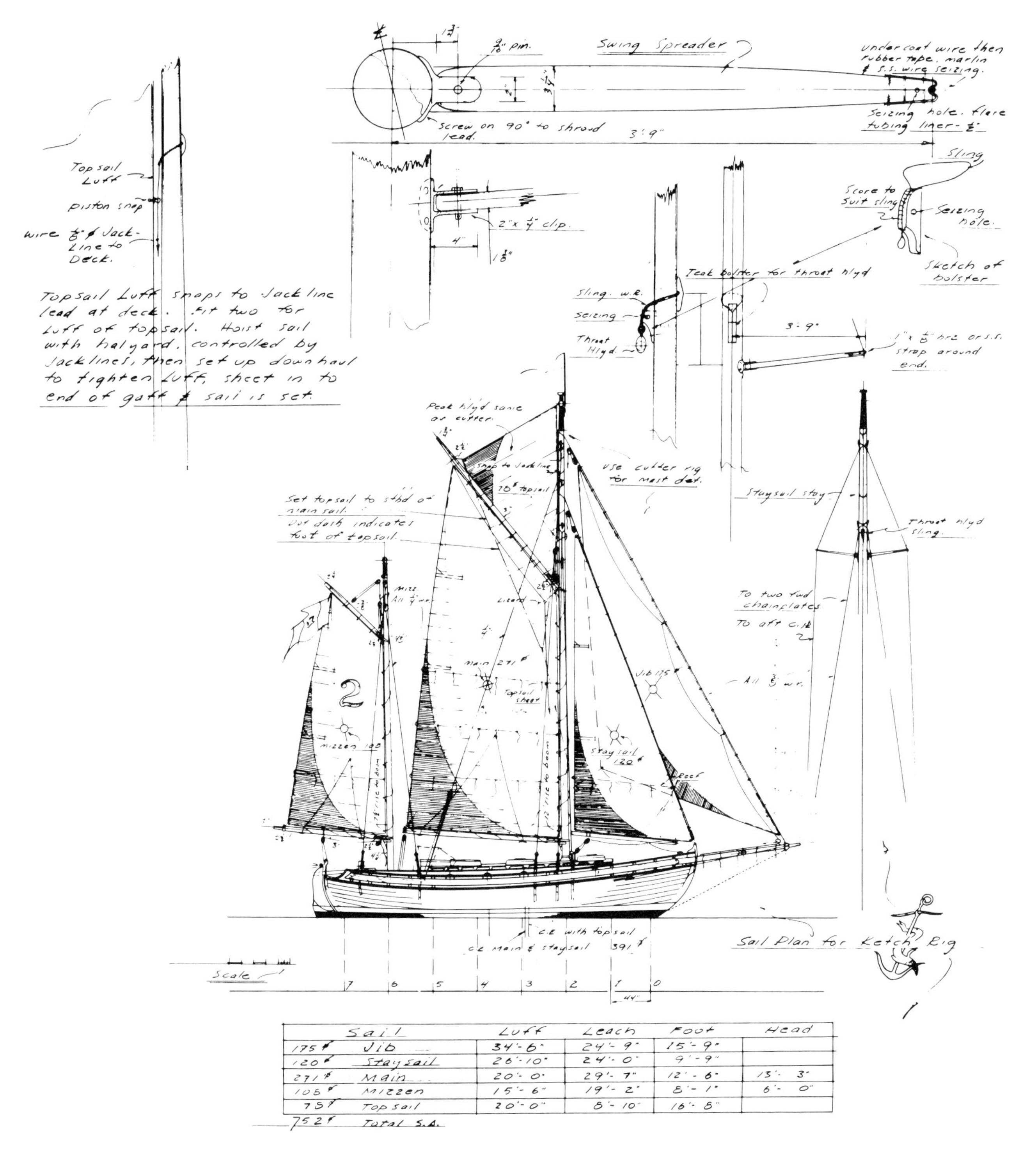

Sail		Luff	Leach	Foot	Head
175#	Jib	34'-6"	24'-9"	15'-9"	
120#	Staysail	26'-10"	24'-0"	9'-9"	
271#	Main	20'-0"	29'-7"	12'-6"	13'-3"
105#	Mizzen	15'-6"	19'-2"	8'-1"	6'-0"
75#	Top sail	20'-0"	8'-10"	16'-8"	
752#	Total S.A.				

William Garden designed alternate rig and cabinhouse arrangements for the Bull Frog: *shown is a ketch rig with a long trunk cabin.* (Yacht Designs *by William Garden)*

The hull of Buchanan's *Colin Archer* has less beam than the skoite type of similar length, has less flare in the sides, but retains the atmosphere of her prototypes. Her dimensions are 41 feet, 3 inches length on deck; 35 feet, 10 inches waterline length; 12 feet, 6 inches beam; and 6 feet, 4½ inches draft. Her displacement is 18.2 tons, of which 7.4 tons are in the lead keel. There is no internal ballast. The rig is lofty with a narrow mainsail and large staysail. The Bermudian mizzen is an improvement over the lower, gaff mizzens of the Norwegian type and allows the setting of a mizzen staysail, in practice a sail seldom set in my experience. The yard topsail is a doubtful advantage except off the wind. Smaller jibs and a staysail can be set. The *Colin Archer*'s sail areas are: 330-square-foot

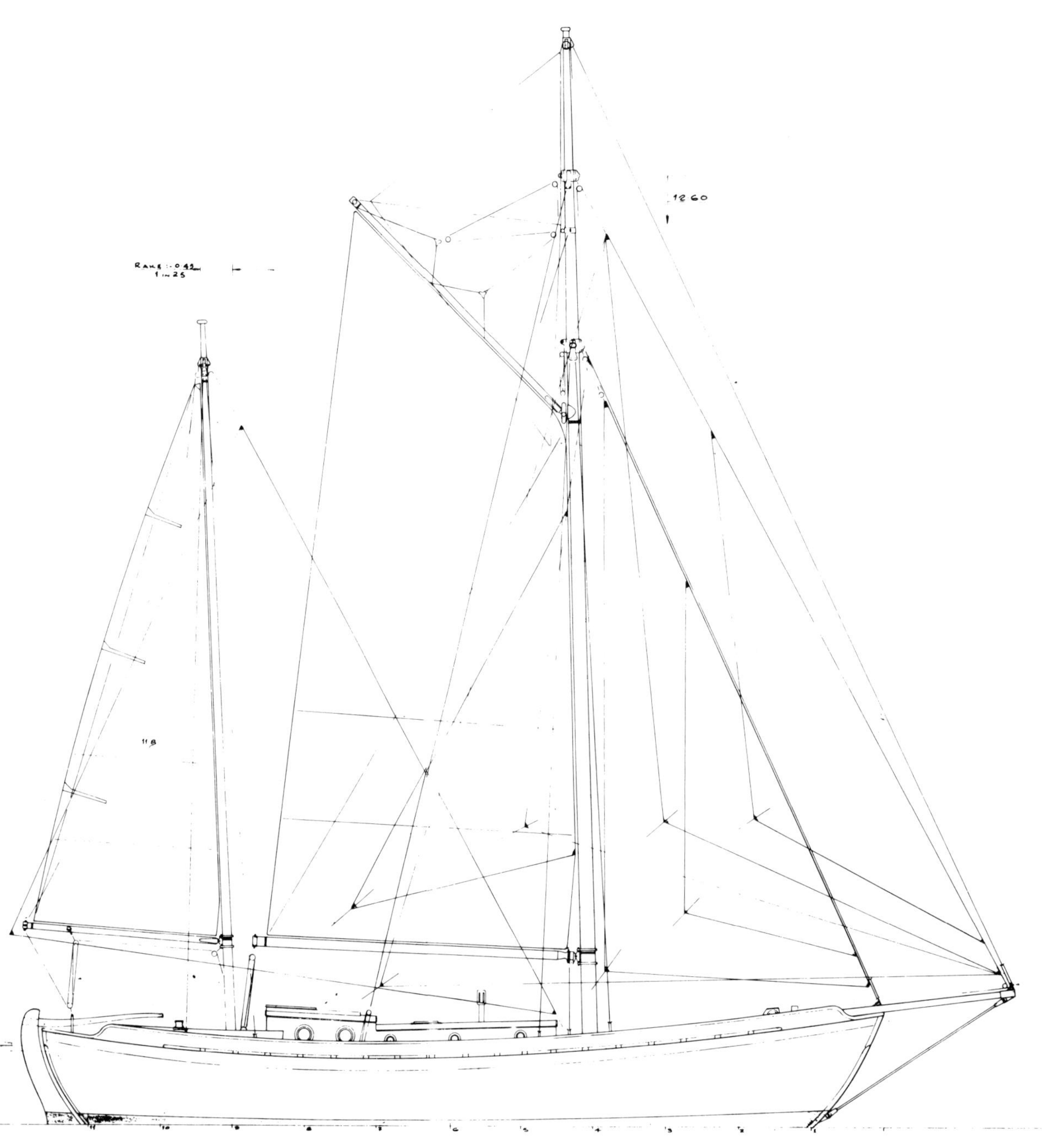

Above and next two pages: *Plans of Alan Buchanan's* Colin Archer.

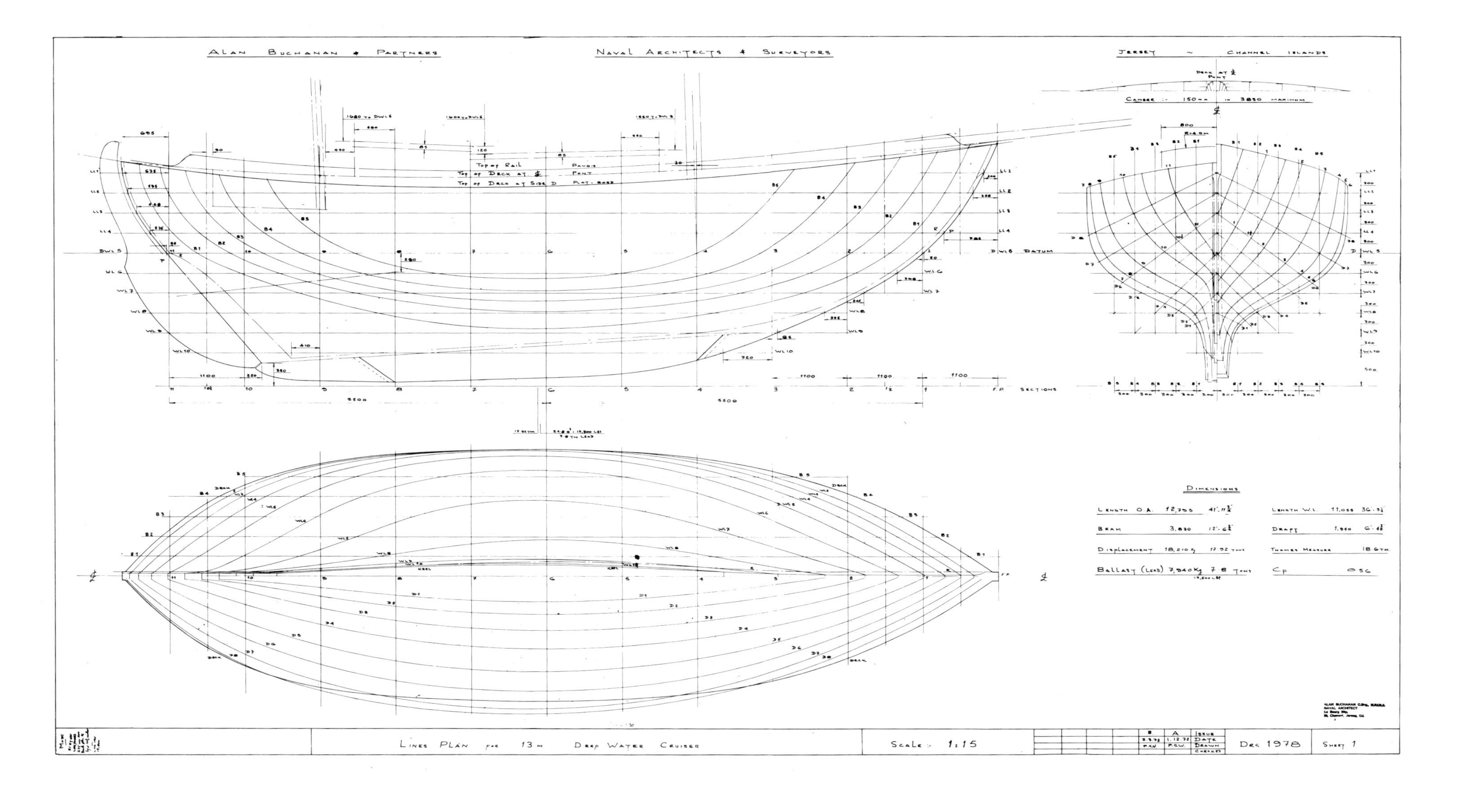
Alan Buchanan & Partners
Naval Architects & Surveyors
Jersey ~ Channel Islands
Deck at ℄ Pont
Camber :- 150mm in 3830 maximum
Top of Rail
Top of Deck at ℄
Top of Deck at Side D
Pavois
Pont
Plat-bord
DWL 5 Datum
Sections
Dimensions
Length O.A. 12,755
Length W.L. 11,055
Beam 3,830
Draft 1,940
Displacement 18,210 Kg 17.92 Tons
Thames Measure 18.6 T.M.
Ballast (Lead) 7,940 Kg 7.8 Tons
17,500 LBS
Cp 0.56
Alan Buchanan C.Eng., M.R.I.N.A.
Naval Architect
Lines Plan for 13m Deep Water Cruiser
Scale :- 1:15
Issue
Date
Drawn
Checked
Dec 1978
Sheet 1

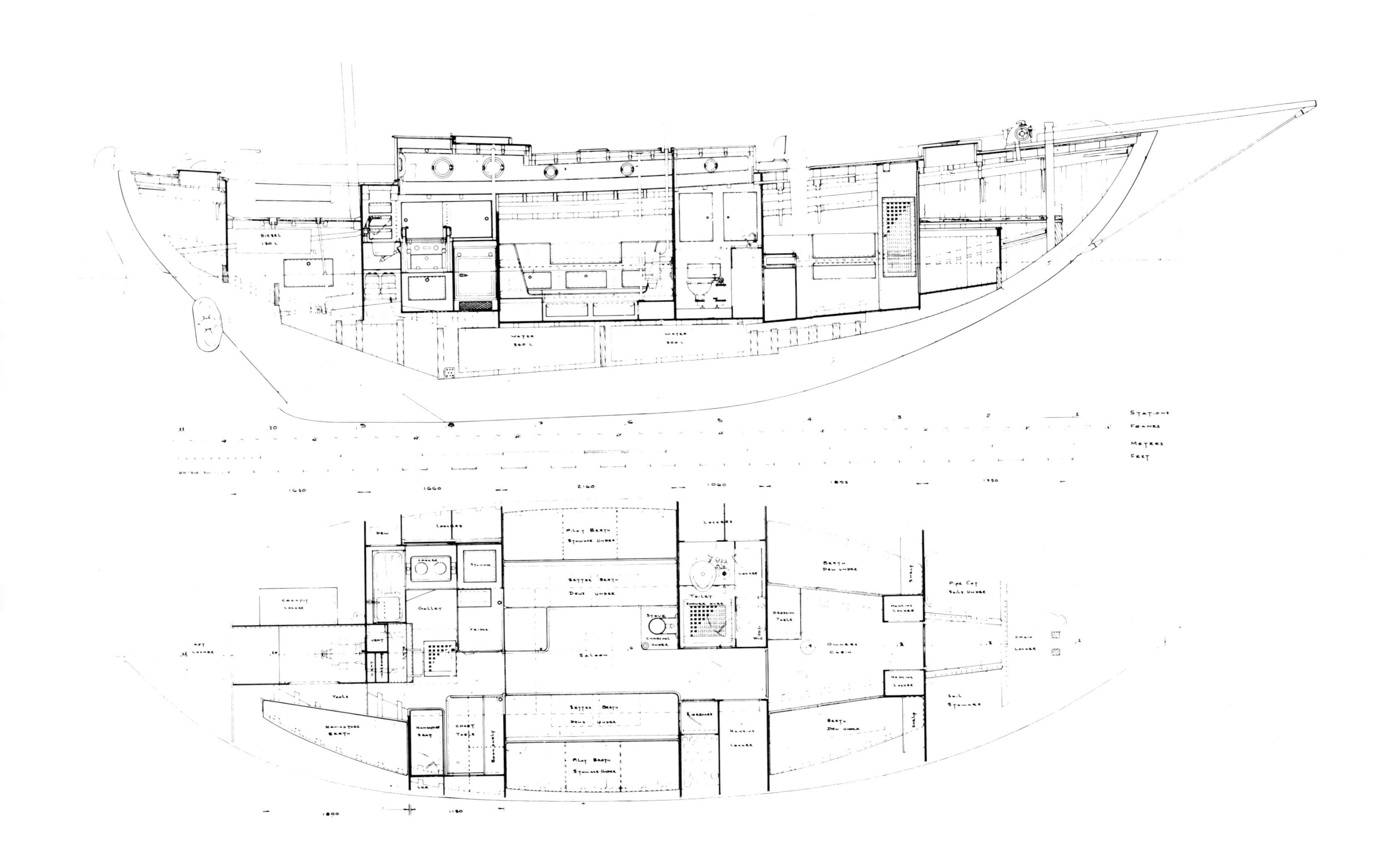
Diesel
130 L
Water
360 L
Water
300 L
Stations
Frames
Meters
Feet
1630
1660
2160
1060
1895
1750
Lockers
Pilot Berth
Stowage Under
Settee Berth
Drws Under
Galley
Cockpit
Locker
Aft
Locker
Vent
Saloon
Stove
Charcoal
Under
Toilet
Dressing
Table
Berth
Drw Under
Owners
Cabin
Hanging
Locker
Pipe Cot
Sails Under
Chain
Locker
Sail
Stowage
Navigators
Berth
Chart
Table
Hanging
Locker
1800
1150

mainsail, 175-square-foot staysail, 171-square-foot jib, and 128-square-foot mizzen. Her accommodation is arranged for five, but she was intended to be a comfortable cruising home for two or three. The first boat to this design was built in Canada and a second in the West Indies for Caribbean cruising.

Alan Buchanan's *Colin Archer* is altogether a practical and interesting design. She should go to windward better than most yachts designed with Colin Archer influence.

KURUN

The French cutter *Kurun* was among the most noted craft designed after World War II with considerable influence of the Colin Archer type. Her owner, Jacques-Yves le Toumelin, sought a craft fit to brave "any sea, anywhere" and knew his business, thinking of a hull of 30 to 38 feet, with good proportions of beam and freeboard, and with short overhangs. He was appreciative of the need for an external ballast keel for stability and the desirability of an externally hung rudder. Le Toumelin had a predilection for the pointed-stern Norwegian type and for the work of Colin Archer. He particularly admired the pilot cutter *Teddy* and wisely sought a professional designer, choosing M. Dervin, a noted French cruising-yacht designer who also sailed and owned small craft and had run his own yard. However, Le Toumelin did not disclose his world-cruising intentions, so Dervin entitled his lines plan "fishing vessel."

Between them, Le Toumelin and Dervin designed a pointed-stern cutter with the following dimensions: 33 feet length on deck; 27 feet, 10 inches waterline; 11 feet, 10 inches beam; and 5 feet, 9 inches draft. She had 8.5 tons displacement and a 1.87-ton cast-iron ballast keel. The boat exhibited Norwegian characteristics but had marked French influence in the heavily raked sternpost and cutaway underwater profile. The lines suggest a craft that would sail well. The hull is powerful, with great initial stability and a good reserve of buoyancy. She has proved to be stiff under sail and has easy motion. The long keel and the balance of her hull lines make her comfortable at sea.

Le Toumelin insisted that the *Kurun* have no cockpit in order to maintain the strength of her deck, though, as a sizable deckhouse was fitted, the reasoning was inconsistent. The helmsman sat on a bench across the after end of the deck, between the bulwarks, in the manner of some French fishing and pilot boats. The long tiller thus swept a large part of the after deck, where the dinghy and the yacht's legs (for supporting her upright when grounded) were stowed at sea.

Kurun was intended to be her owner's home for several years. She had a forecastle with racks for boat's gear, sails, tools, spares, and materials for repairs. A hatch led to the deck. The head was placed just forward of the mast, facing forward. The main cabin had two bunks, a table, chart table to port, and a galley to starboard. There was an after compartment. The stone ballast was stowed below the cabin sole, with the anchors and chain cables on top of it.

Kurun's gaff cutter rig had a short pole mast, extending only 30 feet above deck, but having four shrouds on each side and two stays for twin staysails for running, in addition to the forestay proper. In the manner of pole-masted working craft, runners were not fitted. The jib was set on an unstayed bowsprit extending 10 feet outboard. Occasionally Le Toumelin lashed a bamboo pole to the bowsprit, setting the jib 20 feet outboard so that, when sheeted flat, it kept the *Kurun* on course with her tiller lashed in a quartering breeze, apparently in the manner of the extremely long bowsprits of some old working craft.

Le Toumelin was concerned that the *Kurun* be able to steer herself as well as possible for his singlehanded ocean sailing, and the length

The Kurun *sailing herself with the tiller lashed while Le Toumelin clears his flag halyard. (*Kurun in the Caribbean *by Jacques-Yves Le Toumelin)*

of her keel and the balance of her lines were intended to make her steady on the helm. She proved a good course keeper but was not infallible. She was docile when sailing close-hauled or reaching, and would steer herself if the sheets and tiller were adjusted to suit the state of the wind and sea. With the wind on the quarter in light airs and a smooth sea, *Kurun* steered herself with the mainsheet well off the jib sheeted flat, but as the wind increased, the jib-boom was used to shift the jib tack 20 feet outboard; then she continued to steer well. Running before the wind for long periods, Le Toumelin set twin staysails to the bowsprit end and guyed them aft.

The *Kurun* was a successful example of a craft inspired by Colin Archer's work, even though she emerged in a country and for a purpose well removed from the original environment of the Norwegian pilot boats and redningskoites.

VIXEN

A designer who has gained considerable fame since World War II with his designs based on the Colin Archer type is John Atkin, the son of William Atkin. Actually, for many years the father and the son worked side by side, collaborating on many designs. John Atkin has worthily carried on the design of seaworthy, practical small yachts and boats of various types, and it is natural that he should continue the development of the pointed-stern yachts his father had evolved. Forty or so boats have been built to John Atkin's Colin Archer-type designs, ranging from 25 to 44 feet long, each refined from the previous one. Atkin reduced rocker in the buttock lines, altered overhangs, improved the balance of the ends, and made many other changes to produce able and reasonably fast cruising yachts. Some of his boats were gaff rigged, others Bermudian to suit the owners' preferences.

One interesting design was the 34-foot gaff cutter *Vixen,* designed in 1950, representing the experience of 35 years of development of the Colin Archer theme for yacht use. The design was the result of collaboration between William and John Atkin for James Stark, and she was built at Black Rock, Connecticut, by Joel Johnson. The *Vixen* gave no trouble in hull or gear during a subsequent circumnavigation. Her dimensions are 34 feet, 7½ inches length on deck; 32 feet waterline length; 10 feet beam; and 5 feet draft. She is a husky craft, with a displacement of 26,000 pounds and a lead keel of 9,490 pounds. Her sail area is 585 square feet. John Atkin had this to say about *Vixen*'s conception and use:

It is my feeling she possesses most of the attributes desirable in a vessel intended for offshore voyaging

The Vixen *with a bone in her teeth. (John Atkin)*

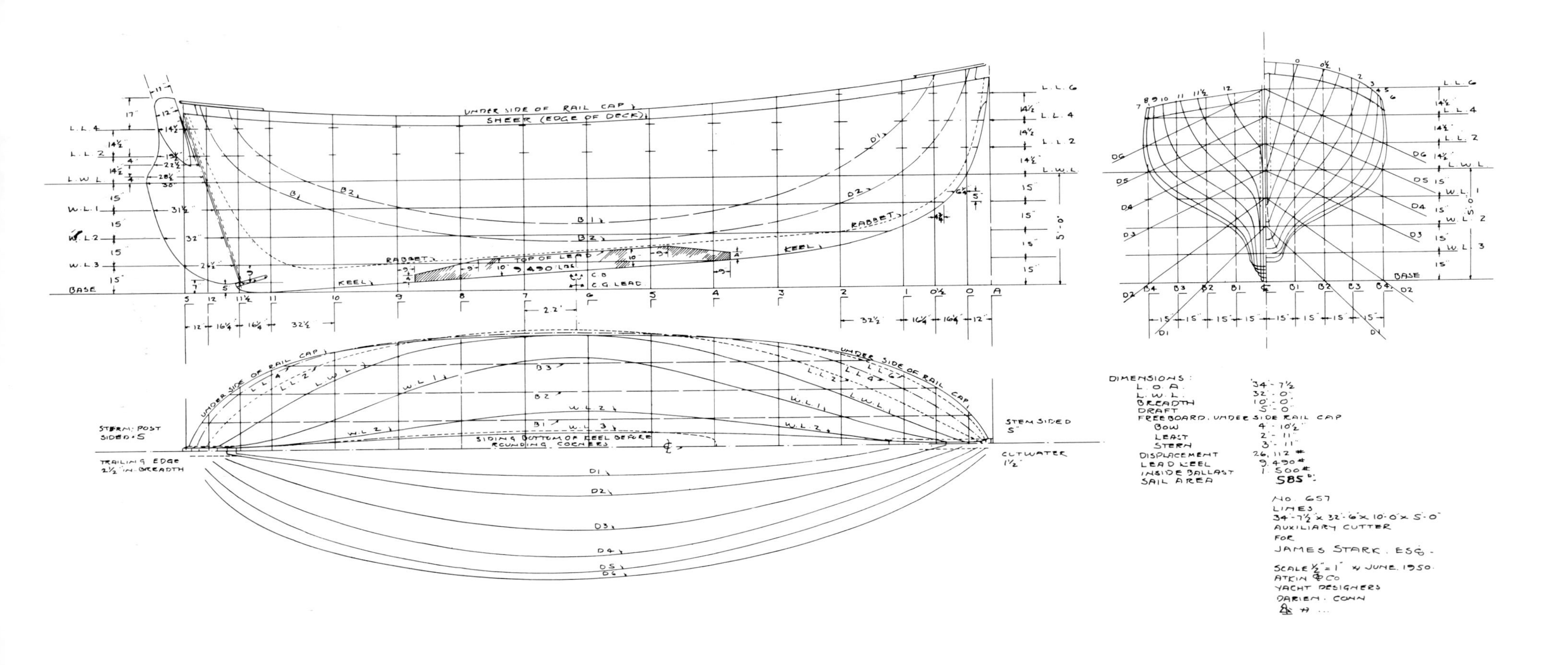

Lines of the Vixen *(John Atkin)*

and extended passages in safety and comfort. While conceivably based on the original *Eric,* Stark's *Vixen* embodies most of the desirable characteristics and has eliminated most of the undesirable ones. She is fast, extremely able and entirely capable of going almost anywhere. *Vixen*'s design is based on tradition, accumulating the best that was proven in the past for use in the present. A study of her lines shows well balanced ends; her load waterline, for example, is only slightly more full aft than forward. Her buttock lines show a desirable degree of flatness very nearly full length, tending to reduce the uncomfortable hobby-horsing experienced in the much earlier *Eric.* She is wide through the garboards, far wider than a vessel with the conventional on-edge keel, a highly desirable feature in achieving great speed. The short ends are in keeping with proven behavior in a sea, with sufficient flare to provide dryness and offering reserve stability to prevent violent motion or pitching. The balanced ends combined with adequate flare enable the hull to ease down in a sea rather than to take up quickly as is likely to be experienced with a hull embodying excessively long overhangs. The long drag of her straight keel and relatively deep forefoot allows her to hang on to the wind in fine fashion and eliminates the need for constant steering, for *Vixen* will sail herself on any point for hours on end. The modern racing-cruising yacht with her extreme cutaway forefoot necessitates the use of various complicated self-steering devices observed on a number of contemporary singlehanders. Properly designed and balanced, the need for such delicate, though often ingenious, devices is completely unnecessary. In keeping with a proper seagoing vessel the *Vixen* is fitted with outside lead ballast as well as sufficient inside ballast. The proper distribution of weight inside and outside in a true cruising yacht is a desirable feature. It tends to ease the motion to a comfortable degree and tends to eliminate the quickness or violent motion often encountered in racing-cruising yachts carrying all of their ballast outboard. It has been said many times that the development of any vessel involves numerous compromises and this is surely true. The elimination of compromises tends to enable a better vessel to be created. *Vixen* was developed, as I have mentioned previously, for the purpose of offshore cruising, without any regard for racing rules! Her highly successful circumnavigation under the hands of Jim Stark and his wife Jean rather conclusively illustrated that *Vixen* more than fulfilled the expectations of her designers, skipper and crew. Some 38,000 miles without a hitch!

Vixen is arranged in a rather unusual manner, but quite in accordance with her intended function. To be sure, her arrangement would hardly be in accordance with normal cruising, but it must be kept in mind that this was not the purpose for which she was developed. Her arrangement plan shows the galley aft at the companionway in quite a conventional manner, with a sink and gimballed Primus stove fitted to port and ice box and lockers opposing. The main cabin is fitted with a settee and box berth to port, and a better, more practical shipmate would be hard to find indeed. An extension berth is to starboard with a proper seafixed table tucked in the L shaped portion of the berth. Her chart table and navigation gear are just forward of amidship as requested by Stark. While there are those who feel the chart table might better be located aft, possibly atop the ice chest, Jim Stark reasoned he could as easily time himself from the point of taking a sight to reaching the working area forward as if the area were aft. And he further reasoned he would be out of the way of his crew in the galley. A chest of drawers and a particularly large hanging locker is opposite.

The yacht's head is tucked just forward of the chart table bulkhead, again quite intentionally. While the entire forepeak may be closed off for the delicate members aboard, the position of the head has indeed a great deal to be said for it. There is scarcely anything more uncomfortable than a tiny, enclosed toilet room with inadequate space to properly hoist one's trousers and be otherwise confined in undertaking the daily toilet!

Lockers for the yacht's spare sails and the entire forepeak, other than the head, were given over to stowage space. All quite in keeping for a little vessel conceived for world cruising.

Arrangement plan of the Vixen. *(John Atkin)*

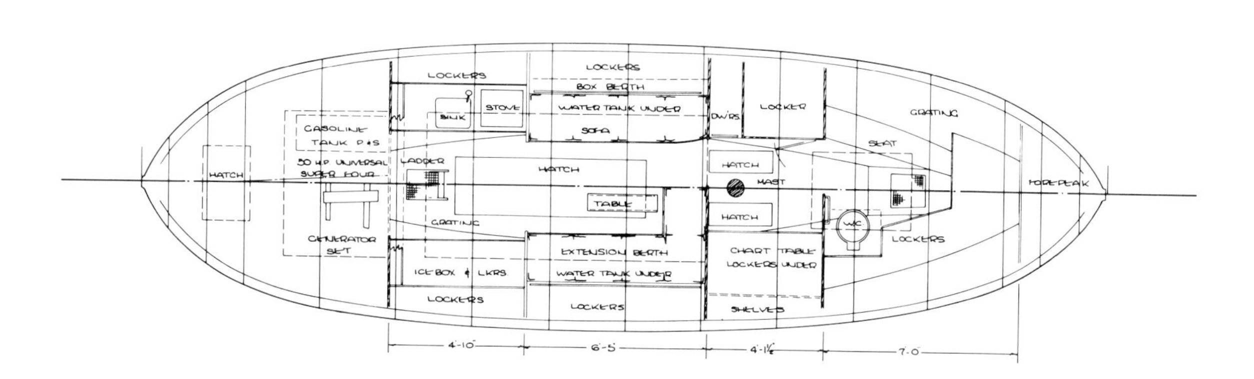

The gaff-head cutter rig, in a vessel just under thirty-five feet overall is equally in keeping with the intended task. There are those who consider the ketch rig as ideal for offshore, and quite possibly this is so. The matter is one of those unresolved subjects which can wear well into the night, with staunch advocates of either school presenting sound arguments. It is my feeling that the cutter, possibly under forty feet, is perhaps superior in many respects, as the areas of the sails are not too great to handle, yet are sufficiently large to be reasonably efficient. A ketch, on the other hand, of the same principal dimensions, is likely to find her cockpit far too busy for comfort, and the areas of the individual sails a bit on the small side. So much depends on overall design that it is a problem, quite obviously, most difficult to solve. It is quite evident, however, that a low aspect ratio rig, for a vessel of powerful proportions and heavy displacement, is far superior than the higher, spindly jib-head rig of the lighter displacement racing-cruising yacht developed to conform, or circumvent to advantage, the current racing rule! Whether this be cutter, ketch or schooner is unquestionably a problem which will continue to be discussed for years stretching off to windward. In any event, *Vixen* is rigged as a gaff-head cutter and, quite obviously, with a low aspect ratio.

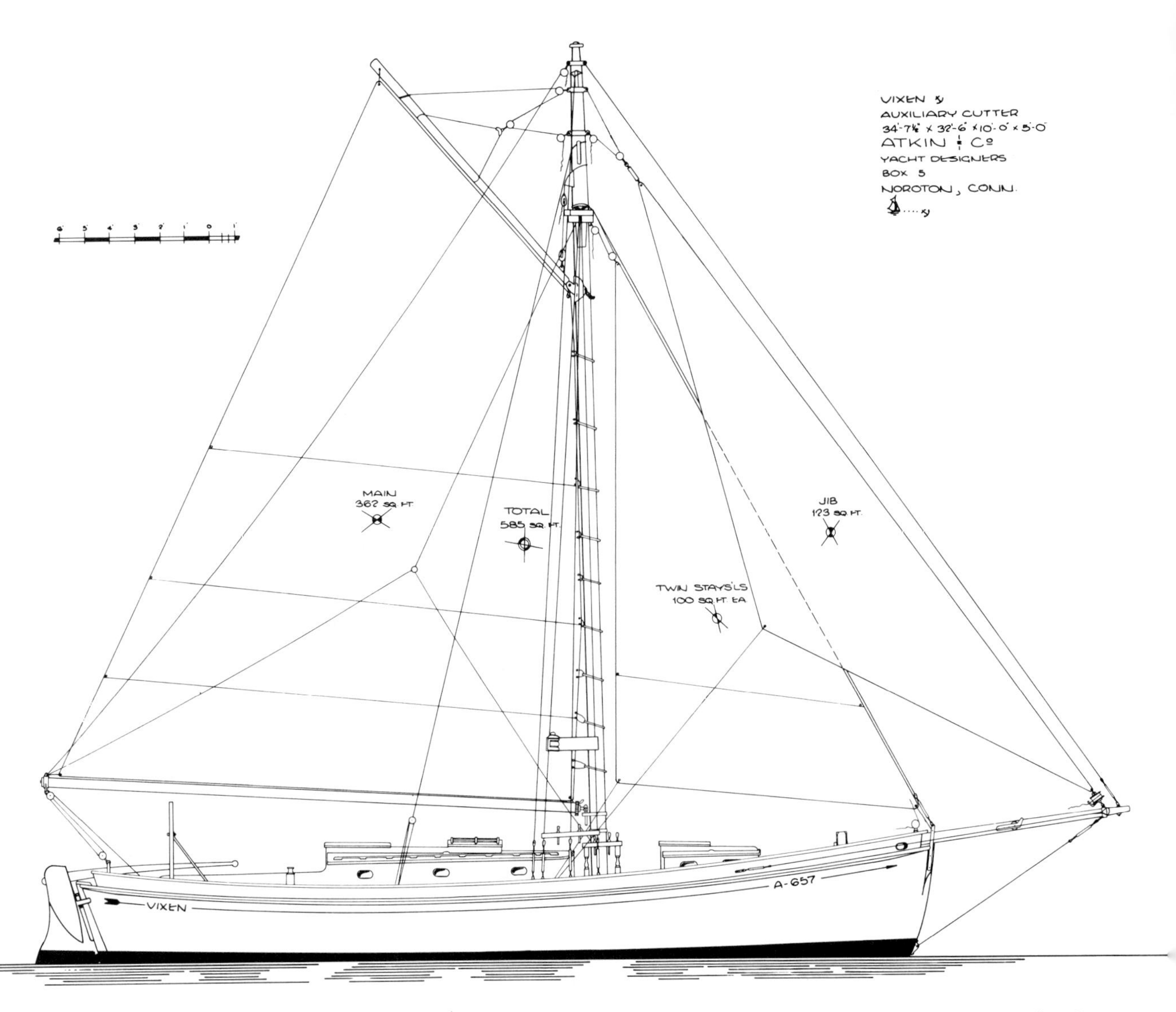

Above and opposite: *Sail plans of the* Vixen *showing her as a gaff-headed cutter and as a Bermudian ketch. (John Atkin)*

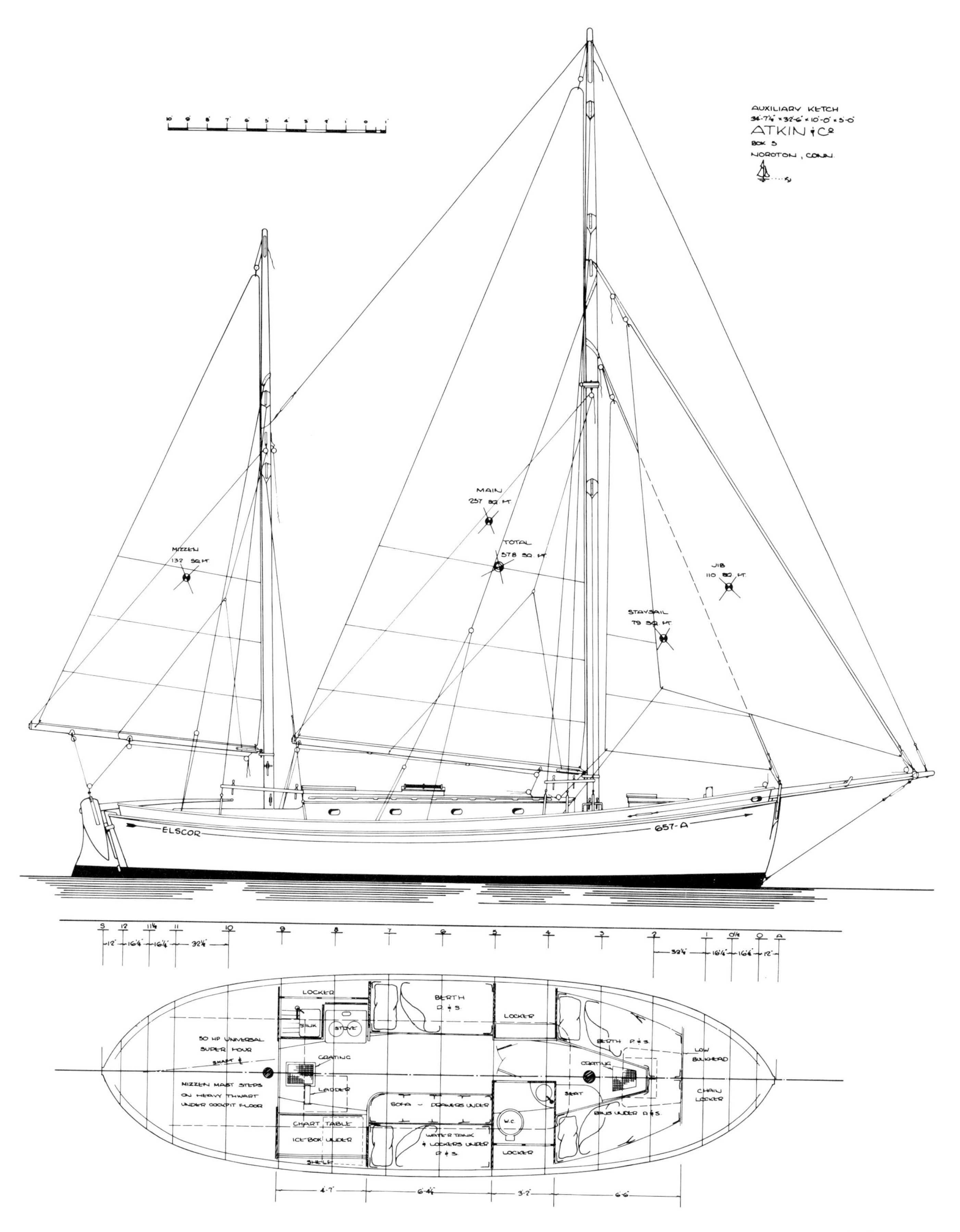
AUXILIARY KETCH
34'-7¼" × 32'-6" × 10'-0" × 5'-0"
ATKIN & Co
BOX 5
NOROTON, CONN.
MAIN
257 SQ. FT.
TOTAL
578 SQ. FT.
MIZZEN
132 SQ. FT.
JIB
110 SQ. FT.
STAYSAIL
79 SQ. FT.
ELSCOR
657-A
LOCKER
BERTH P. & S.
LOCKER
SINK
STOVE
50 HP UNIVERSAL
SUPER FOUR
SHAFT ℄
GRATING
LADDER
MIZZEN MAST STEPS
ON HEAVY THWART
UNDER COCKPIT FLOOR
BERTH P. & S.
LOW
BULKHEAD
GRATING
SEAT
CHAIN
LOCKER
SOFA - DRAWERS UNDER
W.C.
BINS UNDER P. & S.
CHART TABLE
ICE BOX UNDER
SHELF
WATER TANK
& LOCKERS UNDER
P. & S.
LOCKER
4'-7"
6'-4¼"
3'-2"
6'-6"

Her gaff is of Sitka spruce, hollow in section and light in weight, and sets with the peak and throat halyards handed at the same time. The mainsail may be roller-reefed and the area reduced to a considerable degree by taking several turns in the reefing gear. Twin staysails proved invaluable, according to Stark, and the little vessel ran down the trades in grand fashion!

Her jib is also fitted with roller furling gear, thus there is no particular need to venture forth on her bowsprit. There is a total of 585 square feet of sail area, divided into 362 in her main, 100 in her staysail, and 123 in her high cut furling jib. The modern yachtsman frowns on running backstays, yet gladly accepts the Herculean task of trimming a huge genoa, which I find often confounding. *Vixen,* with her gaff head rig, is fitted with running backstays to maintain her headstays in reasonable tautness—as they should be. Perhaps, once again, it must not be forgotten that in *Vixen* we are discussing a vessel developed for extended voyages, not a light displacement day sailer conceived for a brief flirtation with the sea, or with a rule beating, ocean racing vessel to be manned by a highly trained, physically fit group of daredevil young stalwarts driven by a keenly competitive minded skipper, whose primary desire involves winning the game at any cost, come spinnaker, hell or high water! There is a world of difference. . . .

. . . *Vixen* as has been mentioned, and perhaps as should be stressed, was conceived and grew into a mature, wholesome, modestly fast and able vessel, aboard which one might venture forth and return from the unknown in safety and comfort. While all manner of opinions come to mind involving just what constitutes the ideal world cruiser, it is my opinion that *Vixen,* considering her size and overall characteristics, comes pretty close to fulfilling most of these requirements in a highly satisfactory manner. And she, as well as several sister ships, including the Emmerson's *Mariboma,* fairly conclusively indicate that there is a lot to be said for vessels based on tradition—accumulating the best, proven in the past, for use in the present.

SYLTU

In 1959, American yachtsman George Berry commissioned John Atkin to prepare a design for a 36-foot, pointed-stern, ketch-rigged cruising yacht for sailing the American east coast, but to be capable of ocean passage-making if it were possible for him to give time to it. Her keel was laid in April, 1960, and she was launched in July, 1962, as the *Syltu.* John Atkin developed the yacht from another design for a similar ketch for the late W.G. McCullogh. The buttock lines were flattened compared to those of the *Faith, Hope,* and *Charity,* with which William Atkin commenced the line in the 1920s. The waterlines are almost symmetrical. As draft was to be restricted to under 5 feet, the rig is of moderate height and area, so she is at her best in a breeze, like the original Norwegian boats.

The dimensions of the *Syltu* are 36 feet, 5½ inches length on deck; 31 feet waterline length; 10 feet, 6½ inches beam; and 4 feet, 6¾ inches draft. Her displacement is 20,500 pounds, of which the lead ballast keel is 8,200 pounds. Her sail area is 488 square feet in mainsail, staysail, and mizzen. The modest draft allows her to enter interesting places, not just deep-water harbors and planned marinas, but little creeks, coves, and rivers that are the stuff of cruising. She is maneuverable enough to enter and leave confined waters with certainty. She can carry all sail, including the genoa, in winds of 30 knots with her lee deck just awash and making about 8 knots. In bad weather, her owner reports that she has a comforting feeling below decks, where her sturdy wooden hull damps sea sounds and the heavy displacement gives a reassuring motion.

The *Syltu* was built by C.A. Harrington at Bradford, New Hampshire. Here is what John Atkin has to say about her:

> *Syltu* should be a good cruising boat in all kinds of weather. In addition, her modest sail area should make her easy to handle by two people. In light weather a masthead Genoa greatly increases her sail area and can be carried effectively. Both main and mizzen mast are set in tabernacles to enable these spars to be lowered and removed for winter storage without disturbing wedges or the watertight deck.
>
> *Syltu* was designed for comfortable cruising accommodations for four persons. By today's standards a 31-foot-waterline boat sleeps nearly twice that number with resulting crowded conditions. *Syltu* was not designed with any racing rule in mind. Her owner does not intend to race and therefore he does not

Below and next two pages: *Plans of the* Syltu. *(John Atkin)*

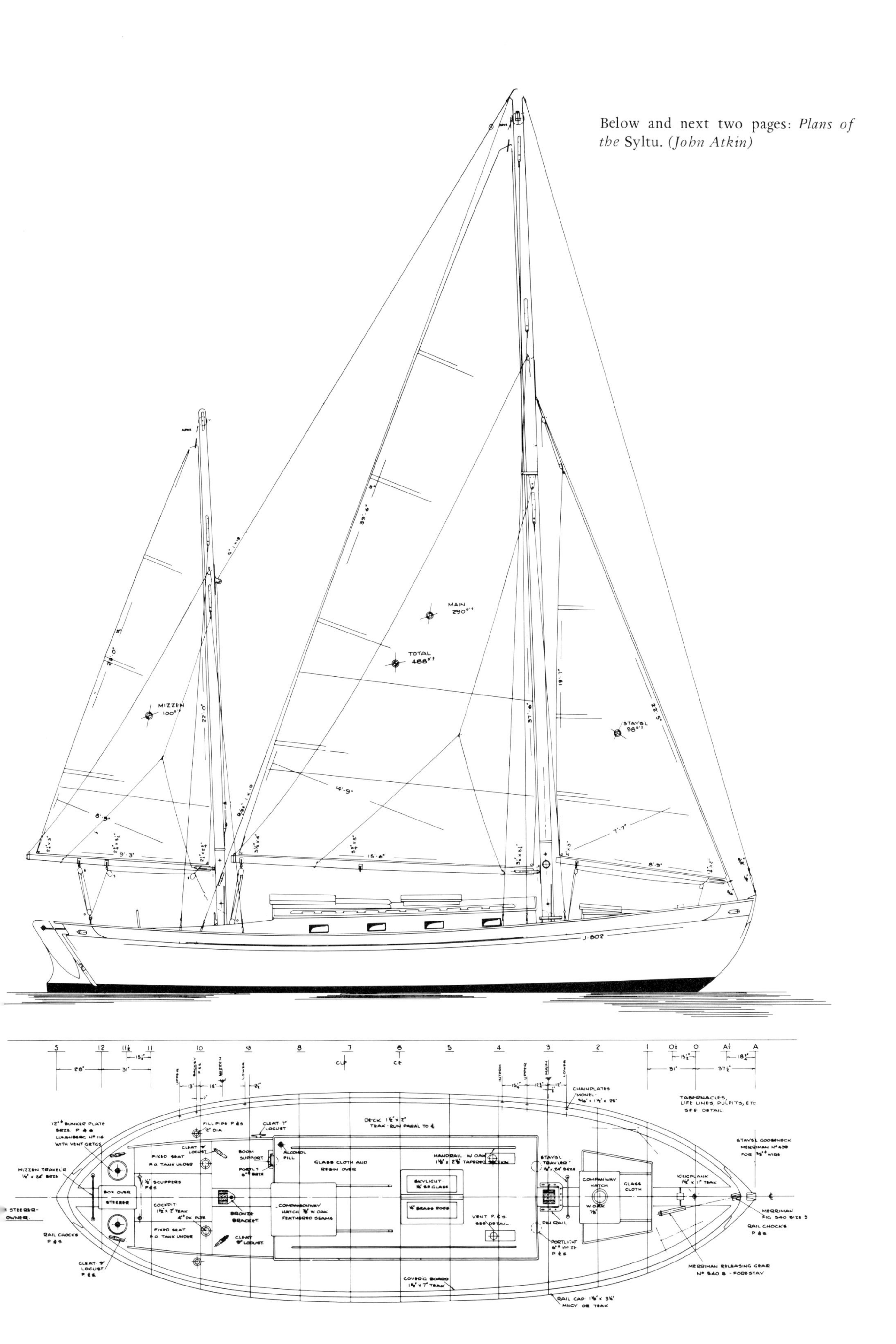

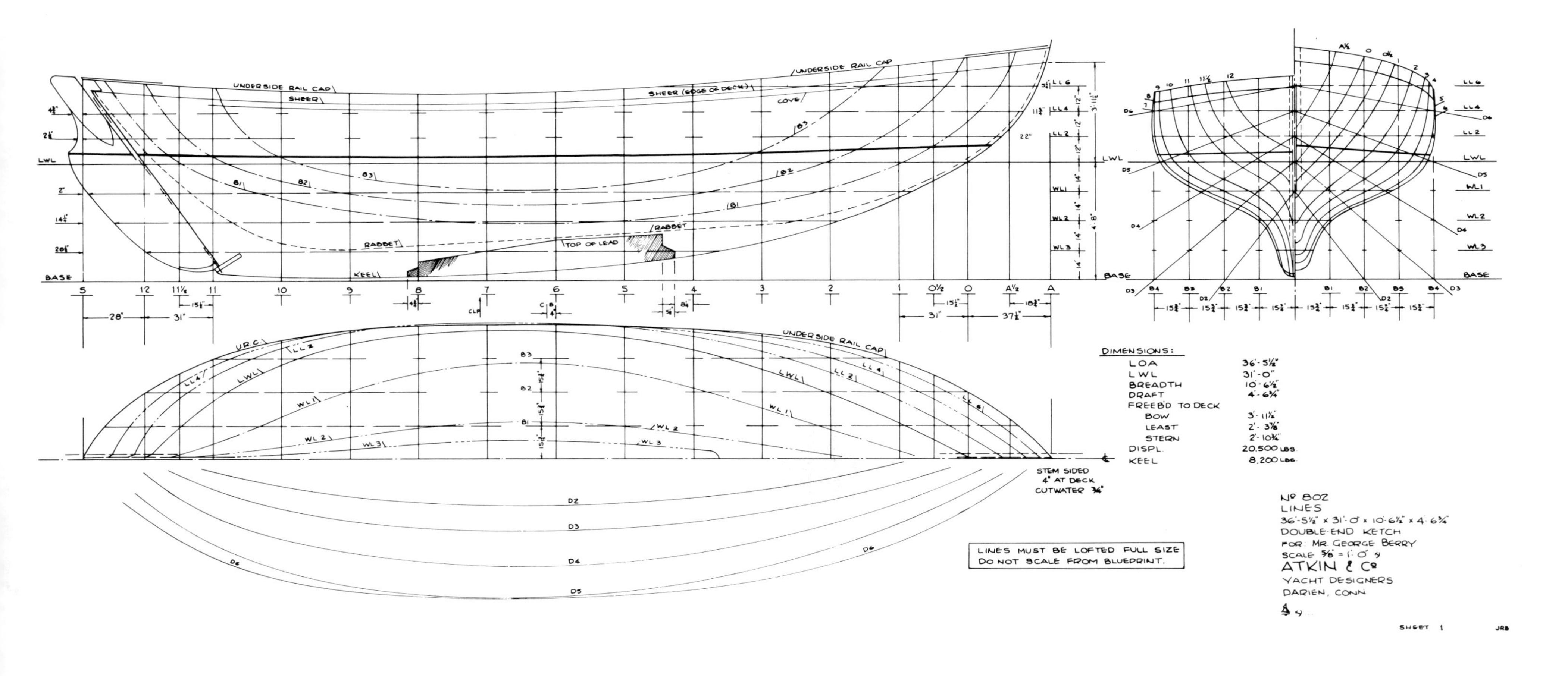
UNDERSIDE RAIL CAP
SHEER
SHEER (EDGE OF DECK)
COVE
RABBET
TOP OF LEAD
KEEL
LWL
BASE
LINES MUST BE LOFTED FULL SIZE
DO NOT SCALE FROM BLUEPRINT.
STEM SIDED
4" AT DECK
CUTWATER 3/4"
DIMENSIONS:
LOA 36'-5½"
LWL 31'-0"
BREADTH 10'-6½"
DRAFT 4'-6¾"
FREEB'D TO DECK
BOW 3'-11½"
LEAST 2'-3⅞"
STERN 2'-10¾"
DISPL. 20,500 LBS.
KEEL 8,200 LBS.
Nº 802
LINES
36'-5½" x 31'-0" x 10'-6½" x 4'-6¾"
DOUBLE-END KETCH
FOR MR GEORGE BERRY
SCALE ⅝" = 1'-0"
ATKIN & Cº
YACHT DESIGNERS
DARIEN, CONN.
SHEET 1
JRB

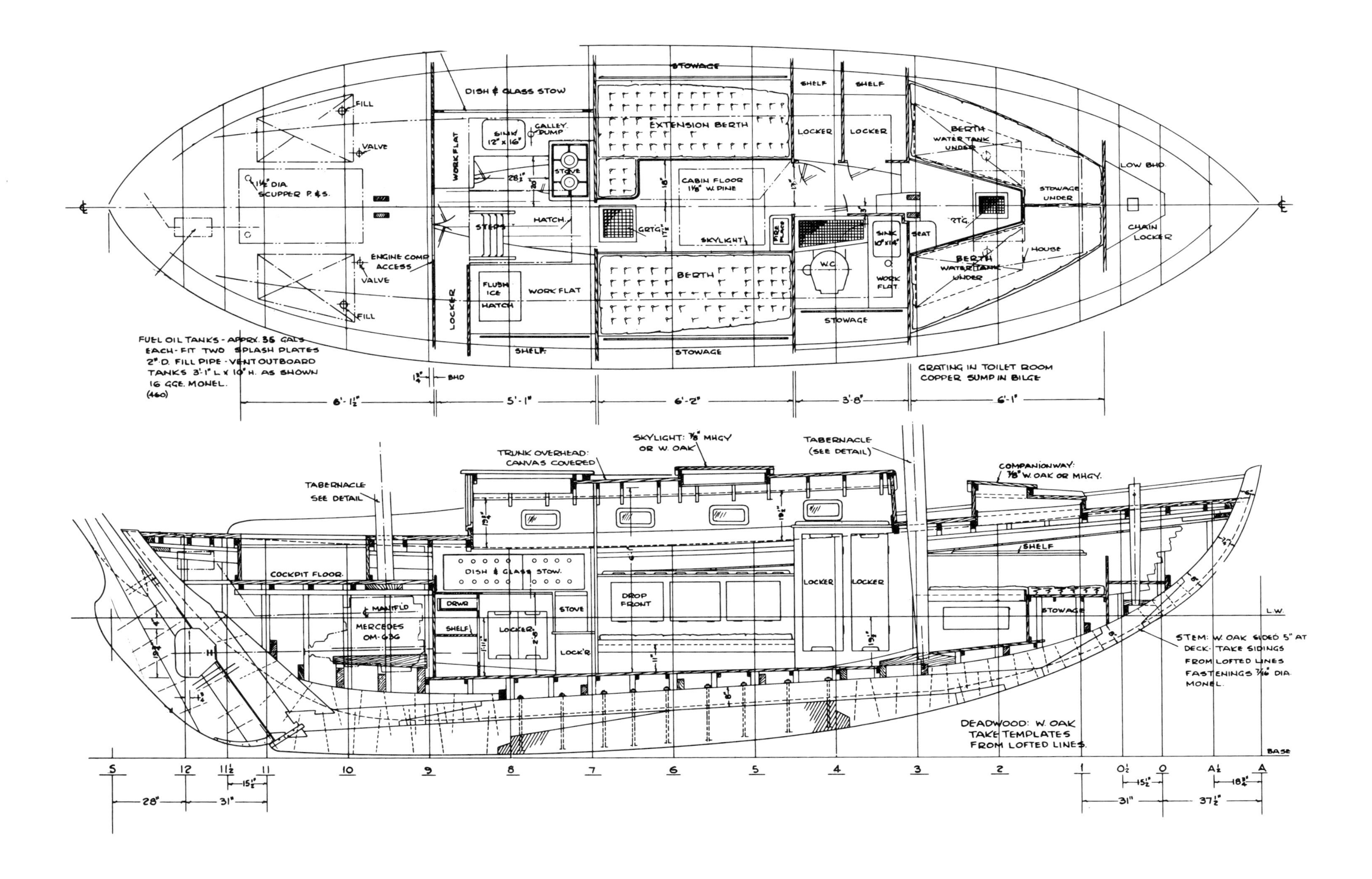
STOWAGE
SHELF
SHELF
DISH & GLASS STOW
EXTENSION BERTH
LOCKER
LOCKER
BERTH
WATER TANK UNDER
LOW BHD.
SINK 12" x 16"
GALLEY PUMP
WORK FLAT
STOVE
CABIN FLOOR 1 1/8" W. PINE
STOWAGE UNDER
1 1/2" DIA SCUPPER P. & S.
FILL
VALVE
HATCH
STEPS
GRTG.
SKYLIGHT
FIRE PLACE
SINK 10" x 14"
SEAT
RTG.
CHAIN LOCKER
HOUSE
ENGINE COMP ACCESS
W.C.
BERTH
WATER TANK UNDER
FLUSH ICE HATCH
WORK FLAT
LOCKER
WORK FLAT
STOWAGE
SHELF
STOWAGE
FUEL OIL TANKS - APPRX. 35 GALS EACH - FIT TWO SPLASH PLATES 2" D. FILL PIPE - VENT OUTBOARD TANKS 3'-1" L x 10" H. AS SHOWN 16 GGE. MONEL. (460)
BHD
GRATING IN TOILET ROOM COPPER SUMP IN BILGE
6'-1 1/2"
5'-1"
6'-2"
3'-8"
6'-1"
SKYLIGHT: 7/8" MHGY OR W. OAK
TABERNACLE (SEE DETAIL)
TRUNK OVERHEAD: CANVAS COVERED
COMPANIONWAY: 7/8" W. OAK OR MHGY.
TABERNACLE SEE DETAIL
SHELF
COCKPIT FLOOR
DISH & GLASS STOW.
LOCKER
LOCKER
DROP FRONT
STOWAGE
L.W.
℄ MANIFLD
MERCEDES OM-636
DRWR
SHELF
LOCKER
STOVE
LOCK'R
STEM: W. OAK SIDED 5" AT DECK. TAKE SIDINGS FROM LOFTED LINES FASTENINGS 7/16" DIA. MONEL.
DEADWOOD: W. OAK TAKE TEMPLATES FROM LOFTED LINES.
BASE
5
12
11 1/2
11
10
9
8
7
6
5
4
3
2
1
0 1/2
0
A 1/2
A
15 1/2"
28"
31"
15 1/2"
18 3/4"
31"
37 1/2"

have to berth and feed a large racing crew. With this in mind her accommodations for only four makes sense and more enjoyable cruising conditions are gained thereby.

Her New Hampshire building has accomplished a first class construction job in all respects. Planking is white cedar and fastenings monel screws. Tanks, tabernacles and chainplates are also of monel. Decks and outside trim are of teak and the cabin top is covered with fiberglass. Her interior joinerwork is oiled pine paneling with mahogany trim.

Syltu is powered by a four cylinder Westerbeke diesel (though a Mercedes is shown on the drawings, it wasn't used) driving through a 2:1 reduction gear.

Her owner has reported, "I've sailed her a little over 1500 miles and have only been (a little) disappointed in her windward ability—but that stems from the fact that I've been sailing a light displacement I.O.R. boat that points so high your teeth would itch. I've grown used to this, however, and find her more weatherly than other vessels of her displacement. . . . We left Cuttyhunk and sailed through Woods Hole and out along the Cape then off to Nantucket. That was the finest sailing day of my life. *Syltu* clocked a constant 7 knots and kept bending the knot meter past 8, she really had a bone in her teeth and we let her go. . . . We have weathered a nor'easter off the Vineyard, against a foul tide running against winds of 35 with gusting to 45 with nary a worry about how she would hold up. She brings comments in every harbor she enters and we always have a crowd aboard if we pull into a dock. To put it simply—I love her."

Syltu is relatively shoal, as desired by her owner, and this influences her accommodations in the forepeak, which are a bit crowded in my opinion. She could use additional horsepower to push her 20,500 pounds along at a more realistic speed. But the yacht does tend to "inspire" a sense of security, which I feel is important.

Four sisterships of the *Syltu* have been built. The design has considerable appeal for cruising and is an interesting example of the enduring legacy of Colin Archer's influence on the design of small yachts.

The Syltu *working to windward in a fresh breeze. (Photo by Morris Rosenfeld, courtesy John Atkin)*

THE COLIN ARCHER TYPE TODAY

The popularity of the Colin Archer type continues to this day. A renaissance of heavy-displacement cruising yachts has been gathering momentum for several years. For many sailing people the type has never lost its spell, and the explosion of sailing craft since the early 1960s has brought more owners seeking some consummation of a voyaging dream or owning a craft capable of cruising the oceans, even if they get no farther than the English Channel, Long Island Sound, or Baja California. As we have seen, this mystique of far wandering has for three-quarters of a century attracted owners to the Norwegian-style cruising yacht.

Feeling that many Colin Archer-style cruising yachts became floating homes, American designer Nelson Zimmer set out to design one—the sturdy 42-footer named the *North Sea Ketch.* She combines the heavy displacement and wide beam of the type, with a tall Bermudian rig, well-rockered keel profile, and comfortable, if unusual, accommodation. Her principal dimensions are 42 feet length on deck, 36 feet waterline length, 14 feet beam, and 6 feet draft. Her displacement is 55,000 pounds, of which 18,000 pounds is in the ballast keel. Her sail area is 1,116 square feet, and a 72-hp Volvo Penta diesel engine provides auxiliary power. She has a deep hull and a flush deck, with the hatch to the accommodation amidships, well away from the cockpit, which could be a disadvantage in rough conditions.

Below deck she is designed to accommodate two with comfort and has space for two guests. There is a spacious owner's cabin aft, with a large double berth, a comfortable settee, a fireplace, and a door to the single toilet, which can also be entered from the main cabin. The galley is amidships and has the entrance door to the after cabin opening from it. There is generous stowage space on the starboard side amidships, and the roomy main cabin has a table and settee, and a fireplace. The fore cabin has two berths, a head, and washbasin. This ketch has much to offer a retired couple or dedicated cruisers, and should sail well.

Many desire a smaller cruising craft in the skoite tradition, a boat requiring less expense in construction and maintenance, yet still capable of seagoing, and, if well equipped and resolutely sailed, of making ocean passages. To meet these needs, the author designed the 21-foot *Pilot Boat* as a versatile cruiser for two. Her principal dimensions are 21 feet length on deck, 18 feet waterline length, 7 feet, 3 inches beam, and 3 feet draft. Her displacement is 5,050 pounds, and her sail area is 150 square feet in the sloop rig, or 230 square feet as a cutter. The jaunty sheer and profile are in character, and the hull sections are developed from other similar-size yachts to my design that have made long ocean cruises.

The choice of rigs is intended to suit the various uses to which owners might put the boat. Those keen on sailing and passage-making will prefer the gaff-cutter rig, which allows considerable adjustment of the sail area to suit conditions from light airs to gales. Those wishing to potter or gunk-hole, often under power, or power and sail, may prefer the gaff-sloop rig, with its staysail set to the stemhead, a sail plan reminiscent of the Norwegian motor-sailing lifeboats. The low bulwarks blend with the cabin top arrangement, provide a secure foothold on the foredeck, and give added protection to the cockpit. The mast is stepped in a tabernacle, allowing it to be lowered for maintenance—a helpful feature when fitting out or laying up. The mast is well supported by a pillar under the deck.

Below deck the *Pilot Boat* has two comfortable berths, a good galley, a table, and plenty of stowage. There is a bridge deck over the engine, which may be a Sabb 8-, 10- or 18-hp diesel, or some other make comparable in type and power. The cockpit is arranged for two or more, and on deck she is laid out in a simple manner, well proved in practice. This craft can be built in any small yard, or

Above and opposite: *Sail plan and lines of the North Sea Ketch. (Nelson K. Zimmer)*

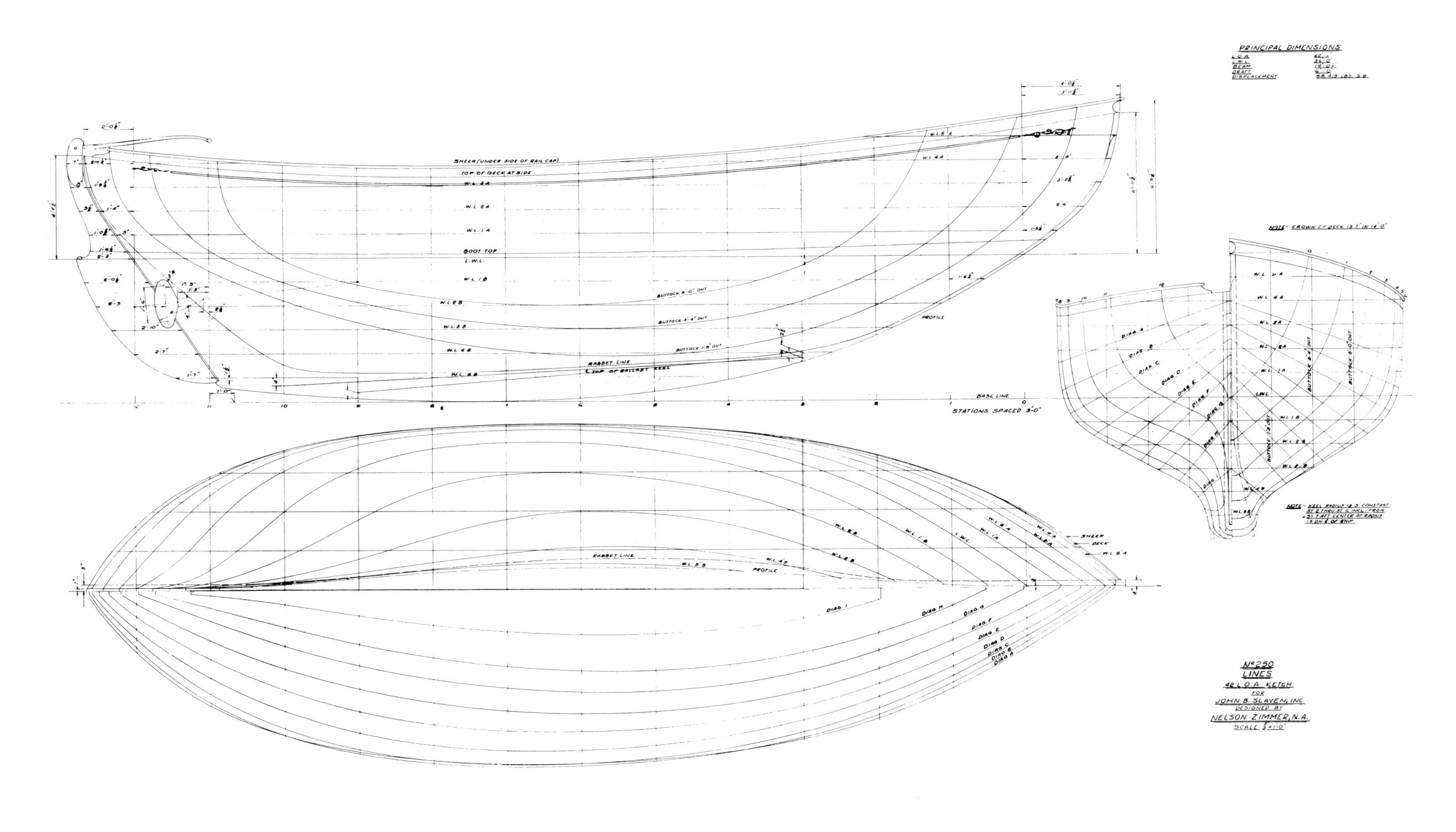
PRINCIPAL DIMENSIONS
L.O.A. 42'-1"
L.W.L. 36'-0"
BEAM 14'-0½"
DRAFT 6'-0"
DISPLACEMENT 58,419 LBS. S.W.
NOTE - CROWN OF DECK 13" IN 14'-0"
NOTE - KEEL RADIUS IS 3 CONSTANT - ST. 2 THRU ST. 6 INCL. - FROM ST. 7 AFT CENTER OF RADIUS IS ON ℄ OF SHIP
SHEER (UNDER SIDE OF RAIL CAP)
TOP OF DECK AT SIDE
BOOT TOP
L.W.L.
RABBET LINE
TOP OF BALLAST KEEL
PROFILE
BASE LINE
STATIONS SPACED 3'-0"
Nº 250
LINES
42 L.O.A. KETCH
FOR
JOHN B. SLAVEN, INC.
DESIGNED BY
NELSON ZIMMER, N.A.
SCALE ¾" = 1'-0"

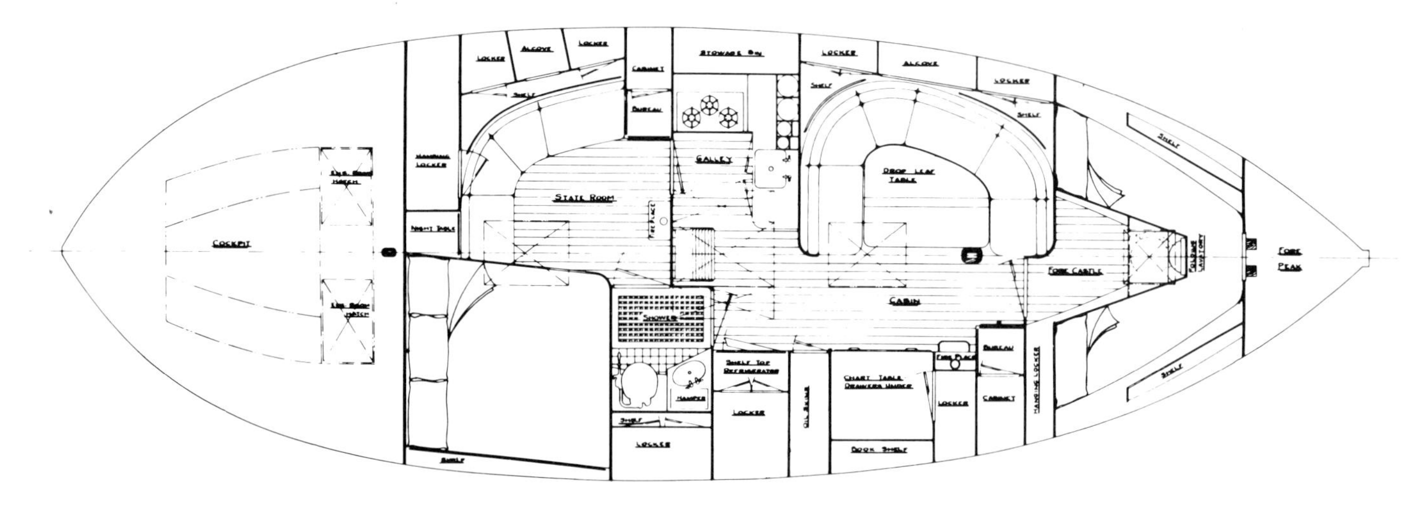

Accommodation plan of the North Sea Ketch. (Nelson K. Zimmer)

by the owner. The construction allows a wide choice of woods, and she can be planked carvel, strip, cold-molded, or lapstrake.

Cruising yachts having characteristics of the skoite type are being built in glass-reinforced plastic. Among the most popular of these boats is the *Westsail 32,* with a hull form drafted from a design by William Atkin and adapted for plastic construction at the Westsail yard in Costa Mesa, California. Dimensions are 32 feet length on deck; 27 feet, 6 inches waterline length; 11 feet beam; and 5 feet draft. Displacement is 19,500 pounds, and ballast is a mixture of lead and iron weighing 7,000 pounds, fitted into the keel shape. The hull form is typical of William Atkin's work of the 1930s, influenced by Colin Archer designs, but the rig is a long-luffed Bermudian cutter with 303 square feet in the mainsail, 149 in the boomed staysail, and 172 in the jib, which is set at the bowsprit end. The aluminum mast is stepped on deck and has a standing backstay. The shrouds lead to chainplates outside the hull, unusual in modern construction, but very practical.

The low plastic deckhouse has strong, round portlights. Below deck the layout from forward includes a two-berth forecastle, a head to port, and hanging lockers to starboard. The main cabin has a dinette to port, which can be converted to a double berth, and a single upper berth to starboard with an occasional lower berth extending from the locker seat. The galley is to port of the companion ladder, and the chart table is to starboard. A narrow bridge deck divides the main hatch from the cockpit. Internal joinery is teak and mahogany. A 25-hp Volvo Penta diesel is installed for auxiliary power, with a 35-gallon fuel tank giving a 450-mile range.

Boats built to the *Westsail 32* configuration have made many long passages. As a result of its success, a 28-foot version is now being built.

The latest development in the enduring influence of Colin Archer's work is the formation of the Colin Archer Club in Stockholm, Sweden, and a similar club in Norway. Both are associations of people interested in sailing and restoring craft of Archer's design and construction, and in collecting information on them. The Swedish club is particularly concerned with collectively ordering and completing the hull and deck moldings, fittings, and equipment for a plastic-hulled, 39-foot, 4-inch craft molded to the lines of a redningskoite designed by Colin Archer. The club

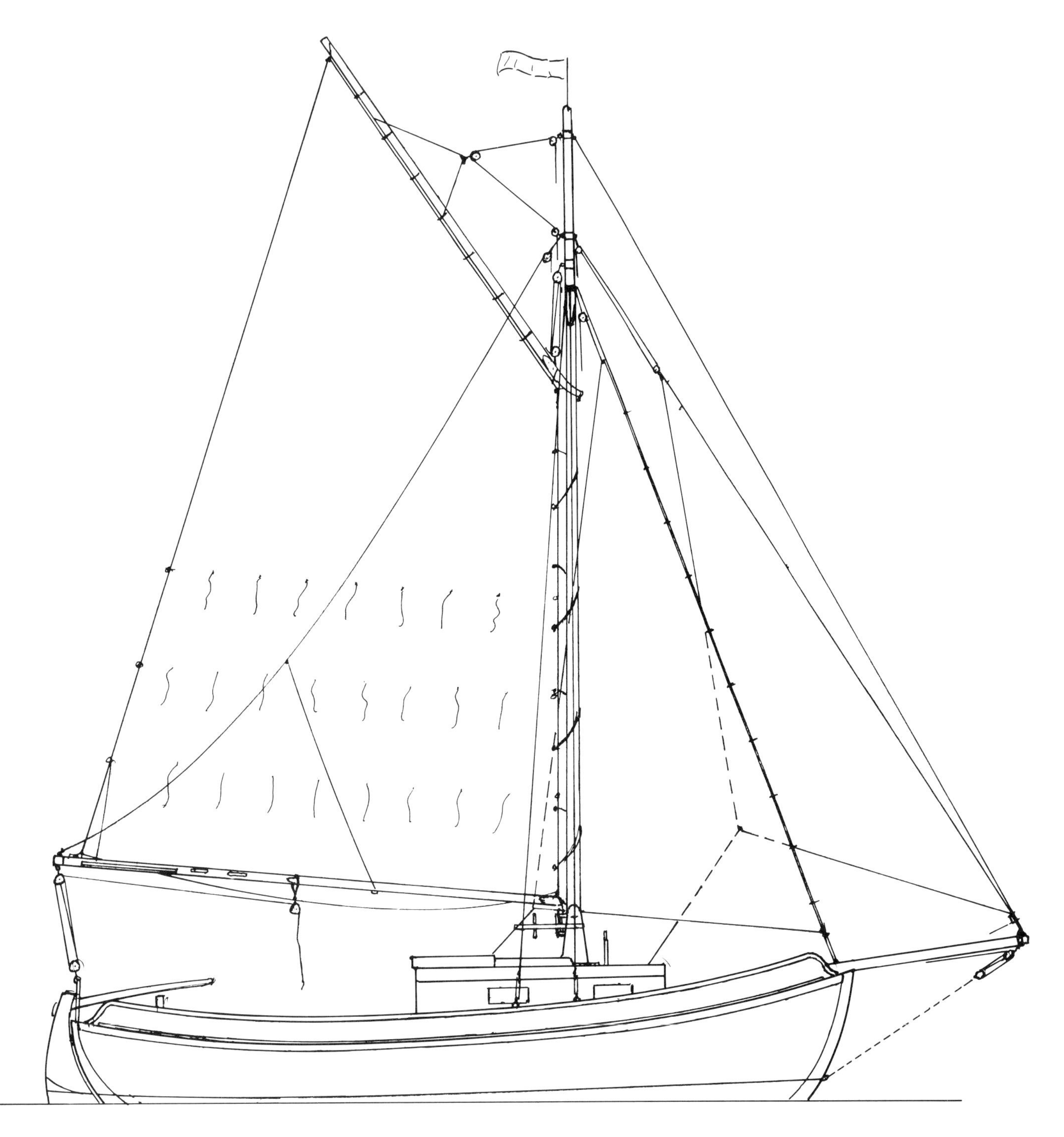

Above and next page: *Plans of the* Pilot Boat, *designed by the author.*

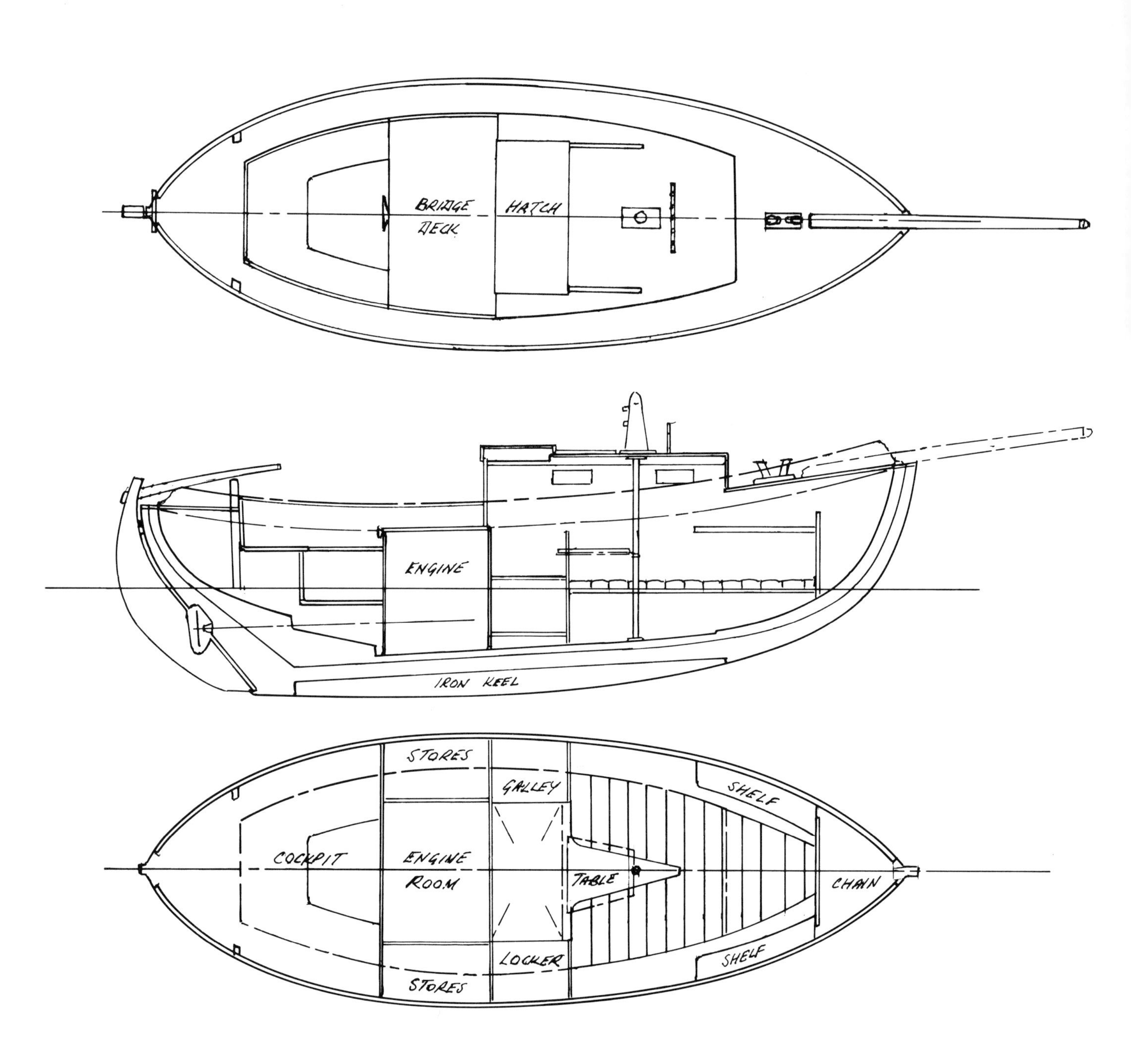
BRIDGE DECK
HATCH
ENGINE
IRON KEEL
STORES
GALLEY
SHELF
COCKPIT
ENGINE ROOM
TABLE
CHAIN
LOCKER
SHELF
STORES

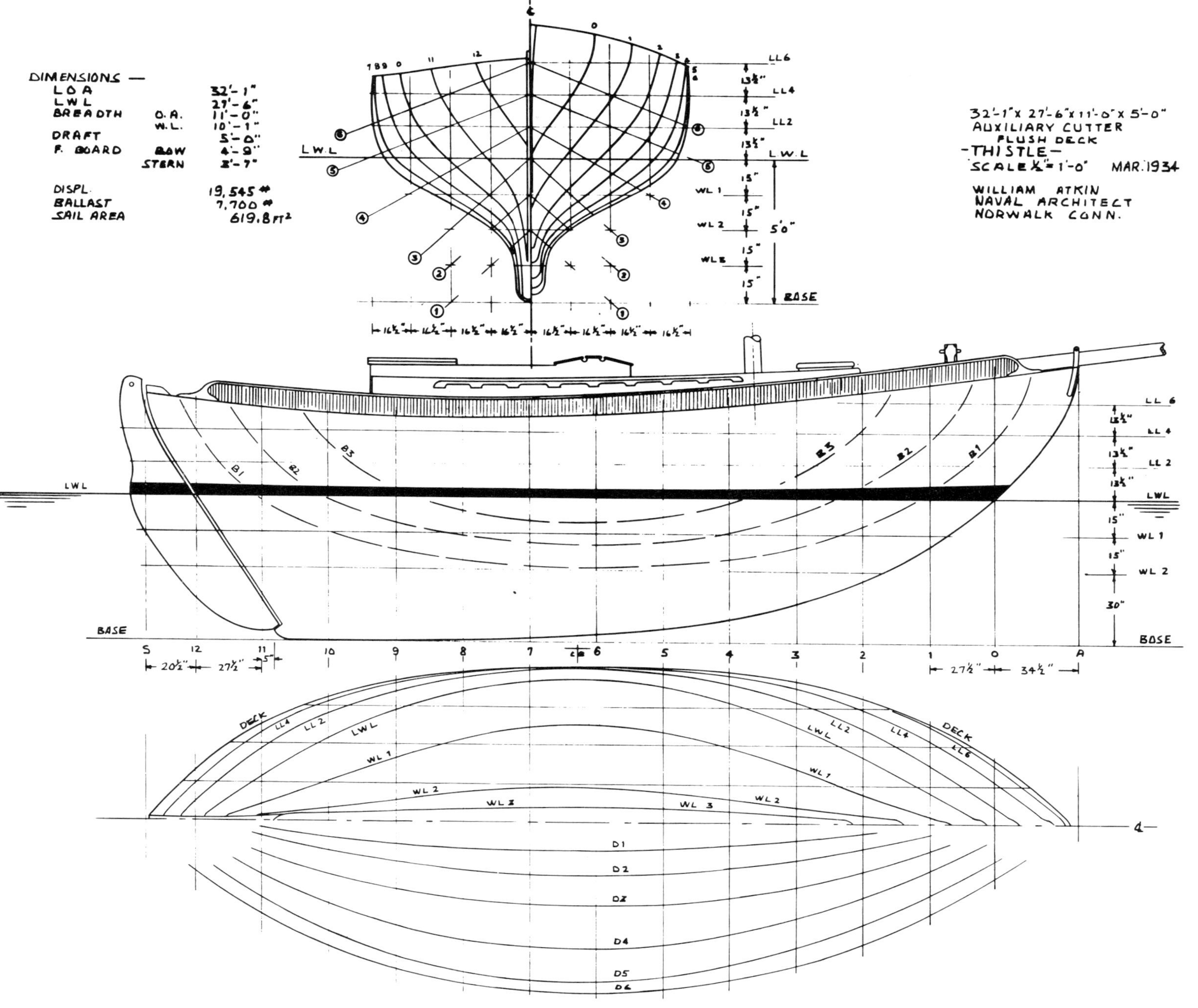

Lines of the Westsail 32 were from a William Atkin design.

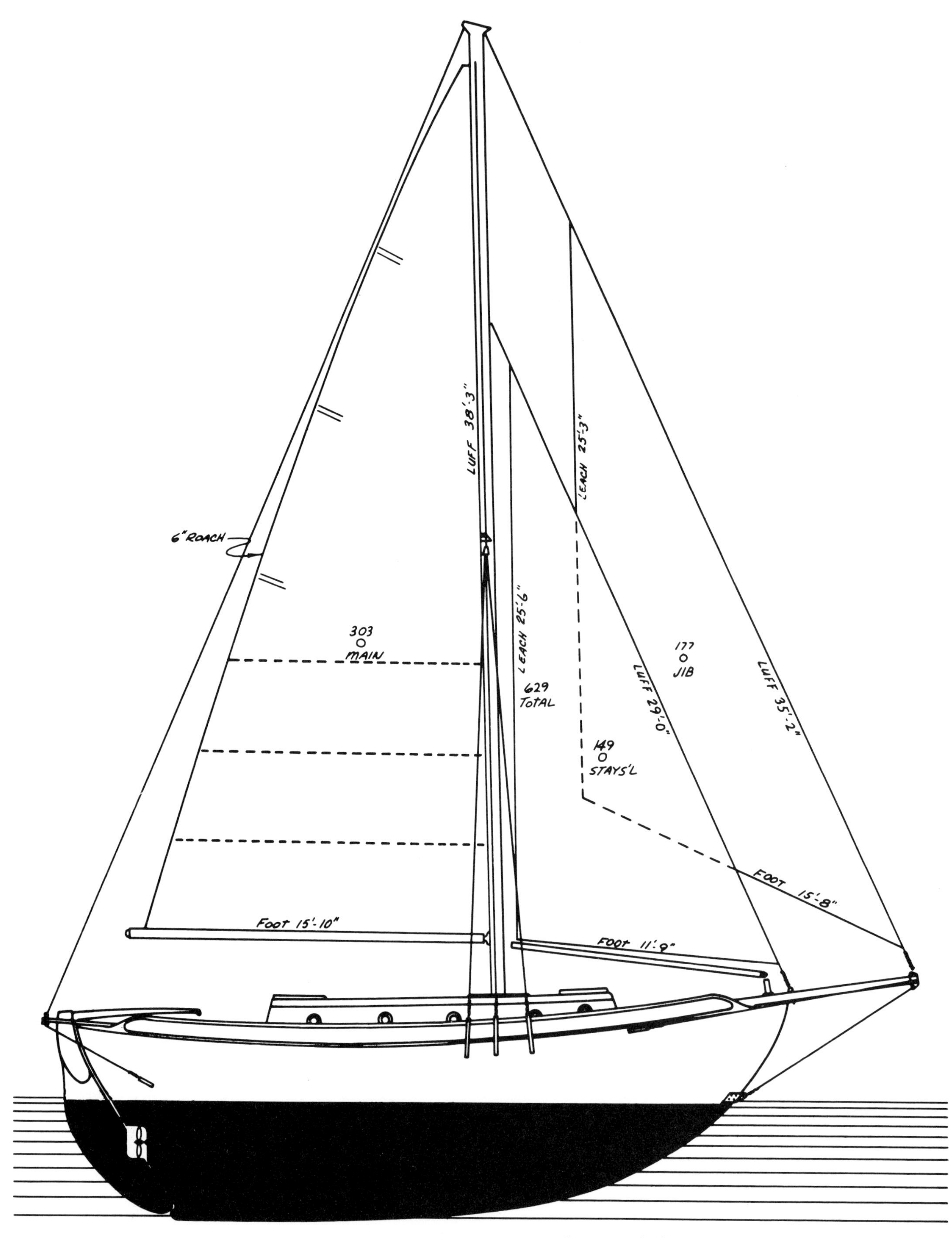

Sail plan of the Westsail 32. (Westsail Corporation)

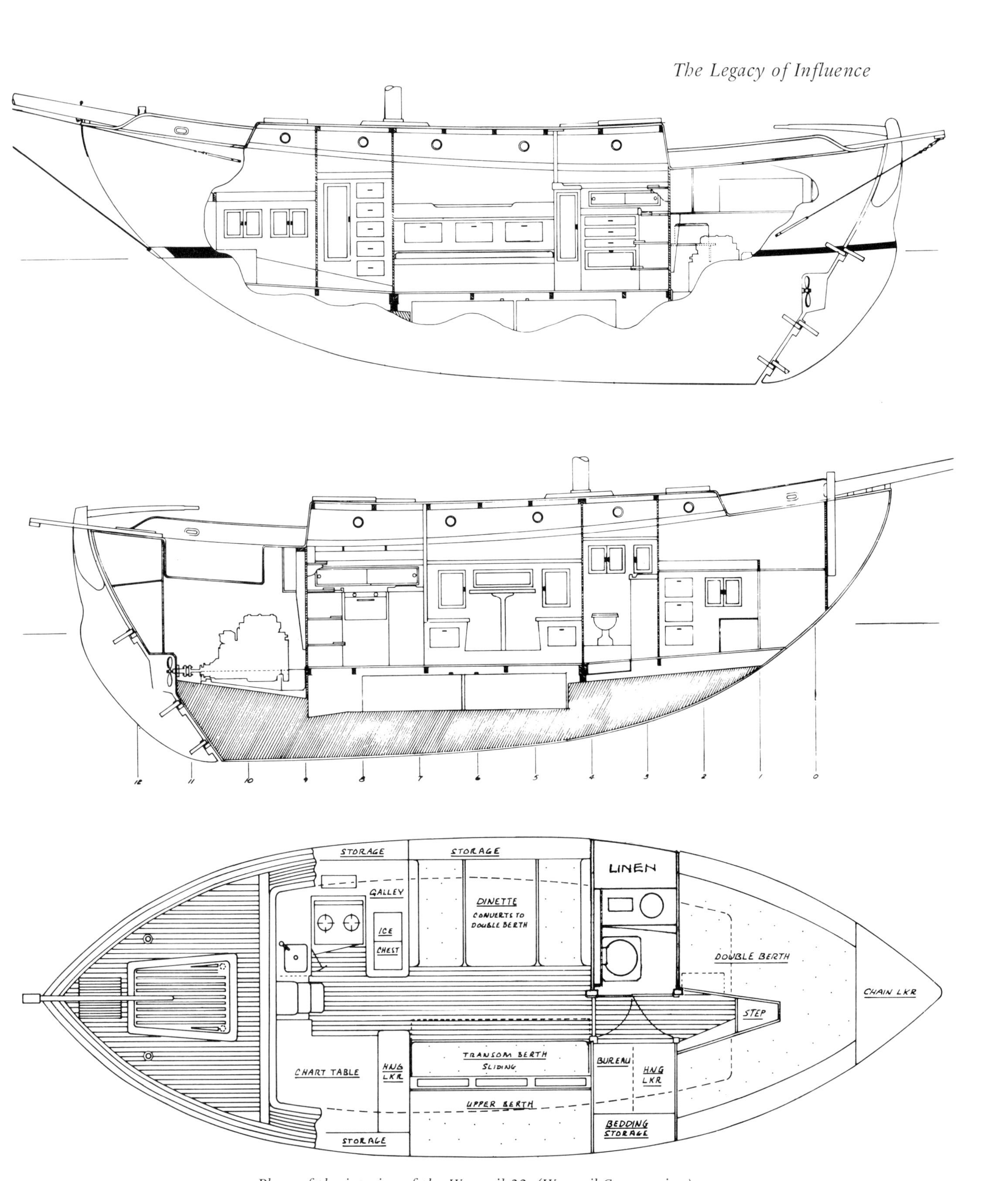

Plans of the interior of the Westsail 32. (Westsail Corporation)

attempts to purchase fittings, rigging, sails, engines, and sterngear for members at advantageous prices. During 1973 and 1974, plans of the selected craft were used to construct a wooden plug from which the mold was taken, and from this the plastic hulls are laminated. Principal dimensions of the boat are 39 feet, 4 inches length on deck; 34 feet, 5 inches waterline length; 13 feet, 8 inches beam; and 6 feet, 3 inches draft. Displacement is 18 metric tons, and 6 metric tons of ballast are fitted internally.

The hull of the Swedish club's redningskoite is a polyester molding stiffened with longitudinal framing and structural transverse bulkheads. The deck is of two skins of plywood with a balsa wood core between. Some owners will prefer to sheath it with teak. The cockpit is a separate plastic molding, bolted to the deck to allow removal of the engine for serious overhaul. The ballast is internal, of iron pellets and bars set in cement and glassed over. Fresh water, fuel oil, and sewage tanks are molded into the bottom, below the cabin soles, with suitable cofferdams and access manholes. The traditionally shaped rudder is also made of plastic, with bronze fittings.

The sail is 1,500 square feet, and alternative rigs are offered—gaff ketch, as the original; gaff cutter, with a short boomed mainsail; Bermudian ketch; and Bermudian cutter. All these rigs have a bowsprit of moderate length. A further unusual rig option is a wishbone ketch, with a quadrilateral mainsail and topsail in one, spread by a wishbone gaff; the boomless foot is sheeted to either quarter, and the gaff to the mizzenmast

The Westsail 32 Lezarder *shortened down and punching into a gale off Catalina Island, California. (Westsail Corporation)*

head. A large balloon foresail and a big jib topsail are also carried with the wishbone rig, which is of doubtful value in such a small craft. Alternatively, the boomless Bermudian mainsail can be set in place of the wishbone sail.

On the Swedish club's boat there is 6 feet, 6 inches clear headroom below the flush deck, and the accommodation has berths for up to ten people, though this crew would only be practical for a very short time, as apart from over-crowding she could not carry water and stores for that number for long voyaging. Up forward is the chain locker, badly placed at the top of the stem (this locker would have been better below the cabin sole at the after end of the forecastle, with the chain fed up through a chainpipe to the deck

A Westsail 32 off Anchorage, Alaska. (Westsail Corporation)

The plug for the Colin Archer 40 nearly finished. (Swedish Colin Archer Club)

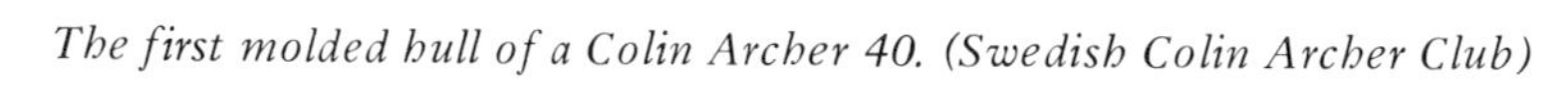

The first molded hull of a Colin Archer 40. (Swedish Colin Archer Club)

and leading forward to the windlass). A transverse store locker for paints, ropes, and similar items lies between the locker and the forecastle, which has four single berths and a ladder to the forehatch. A transverse washplace with toilet, washbasin, and shower to port and hanging cupboards to starboard is abreast the mainmast. Abaft this is the main cabin, with four high pilot berths outboard, U-shaped settees and table, and a settee opposite them when the table flap is extended. The galley is immediately below the main companion hatch. Opposite, where one would expect to find a large chart table is a small table top and a double quarter berth. A diesel engine of 36 bhp at 1,800 rpm is recommended. The cockpit as designed cramps the engine, which is far too close to the sternpost. Necessary maintenance will be very difficult and attention to the sterntube gland almost impossible. If these criticisms are rectified, this new Colin Archer-type will be a fine craft for those who dream of distant sailing.

The pointed-stern Norwegian lifeboats, pilot boats, and fishing boats developed by Colin Archer remain some of the most intriguing sailing craft and continue to be admired by cruising yachtsmen and those who choose to live as "ocean tramps." These boats are sturdy, seakindly, well-proved in hull form, and driven by an economical rig, one that is readily repaired if damaged.

Boats influenced by Colin Archer's designs are slow and unhandy by modern yacht standards, but they are comparatively comfortable at sea. Since they now represent a well-tried tradition, they will undoubtedly continue to be built and sailed, and will justifiably perpetuate the ability and name of Colin Archer.

Appendix A

PRINCIPLES OF DESIGN

In 1872, Colin Archer published an elementary paper entitled "Directions for Designing Yachts and Boats." Archer included in his paper an appreciation of some of the work of the noted Swedish naval architect Fredrik Henry Chapman (1725-1802), who was born in Sweden of English parents and became an officer in the Swedish Navy. Chapman studied the design of ships and craft of many types, and recorded the lines, construction, and technical characteristics of as many as possible, from diverse sources. He was always searching for improvements in speed under sail and other desirable seagoing qualities for vessels.

Chapman became a leading authority on the design of ships based on scientific theories and evolved a system as an aid to successful designing known as the curve of cross-sectional areas, which is still in use. The waterline length of a vessel is divided into stations at which the area, or more usually one-half area, of a transverse section across the shape of the hull, below the waterline, is calculated and then erected at the relevant station to a suitable scale. The spots are joined by a curved line—the curve of areas—rising from nothing at each end of the waterline to follow the various scaled area spots in what should be a fair, flowing curve. Chapman used the principle of this curve of areas to facilitate calculations of a ship's displacement, or the mass of water the ship displaced when floating at a certain waterline, and in determining her stability.

The aspect of Chapman's work that particularly interested Colin Archer was Chapman's comparison of the curves of areas of the fastest frigates of the time, in attempts to establish the relationship of form with speed. Colin Archer's paper recommended the use of the curve of immersed cross-sectional areas as a means of comparing the forms and performances of various sailing craft and as an aid in the development of improved vessels.

Although seeking to establish a factual basis for ship design, Chapman and his contemporaries had little knowledge of the laws governing the resistance of vessels moving through water. These laws received considerable attention after the British naval architect and engineer John Scott Russell (1808-1882) published the conclusions of his research into the formation of waves and their effect on the resistance of ships in motion. Much of Russell's work was directed toward the advancement of the then rapidly improving steamship, but it was to have considerable influence on designers of fast sailing craft and other naval architects, including Colin Archer.

Scott Russell's theory was basically that waves of two distinctly differing types are created at the bow and stern of a moving vessel. He observed and calculated their curves and proposed that if the resistance arising from wave-making were to be reduced, the entrance, or shape of the bow waterlines, should correspond with the form of a bow wave and the after end waterlines with the shape of the stern wave. He advocated the shaping of the forward and after end waterlines to this "wave line theory," which was adopted in or influenced the design of many notable steamships of the mid-nineteenth century, including the huge *Great Eastern,* the conception of the eminent British engineer I.K. Brunel, with whom Russell collaborated on her design.

Russell published the results of his research and conclusions in *The Modern System of Naval Architecture.* About 1876, this book was read by Colin Archer, who was impressed by Russell's investigations and conclusions on the relationship between wave-making and the speed of ships, a subject that had fascinated Archer for some time.

Colin Archer was unable to make a systematic scientific study of the motion of craft, but he was a shrewd observer of the behavior of all types of vessels underway and particularly of those built from his designs. The wave line theory appealed to him as a new aspect of the puzzle that makes the design of sailing craft so fascinating.

Colin Archer did not fully accept Scott Russell's conclusions and gradually thought of modifying them and allying them to the curve of immersed cross-sectional areas, which he was recording and examining for his own and other designs and lifting from successful existing craft, most of which had been designed by traditional, elementary, practical methods. Archer considered that Russell's theory of relating the wave line form to the waterlines was wrong and that instead the wave line form should be applied to the form of the curve of immersed areas.

Archer wrote a paper that was read before the Institution of Naval Architects in London on April 13, 1878, entitled "The Wave Principle Applied to the Longitudinal Disposition of Immersed Volume." It discussed the two causes of resistance arising from the formation of waves. Archer stated that waterlines did not follow the flow of water along a ship's bottom and that they were no criterion of resistance experienced. He illustrated this by citing that the cutting away of a vessel's forefoot, thus removing the waterlines of the "entrance," often reduced resistance and improved speed:

> When a vessel is propelled through the water it is found that the water forced out of her—or a like quantity—rises above the surface of repose and forms a wave or waves which assume a particular shape. If the vessel's entrance is of an unsuitable shape, and if she is propelled with considerable force, the water is displaced in a form which is not that of a natural wave; and it will then after a time, besides the principal wave of displacement, break up into a series of smaller residuary waves; and these residuary waves may be looked upon as representing the force wasted. We may therefore infer that the most suitable form of entrance is one which displaces the water in such a way that a wave of the natural form will be fully supplied at every stage of its formation, and will at the same time absorb all the water displaced, so that no residuary waves will be thrown off.
>
> In order to fulfill this condition, it is necessary first to ascertain what shape the bow wave of displacement takes, and then to construct the entrance so as to throw off water at a rate sufficient for supplying the wave, and no more. And it is evident that the rate at which water is thrown off is best determined, not by the shape given to any set of lines whatever, but by the rate of increase in area of the transverse sections.

He concluded that, for the after end, ". . . the rate at which the solid contracts should correspond at every point with the rate at which the following wave naturally grows. . . ." He referred to Scott Russell's pioneer work but continued his interpretation of the observations:

> The eminent author seems not to have succeeded in devising the best means for transferring the wave properties to his solid structures; and, if there is any force in what I have submitted in the early part of this paper, this want of success may probably be ascribed in a great measure to his having adopted a system of construction by waterlines.
>
> But, whatever may be the defects of the "Waveline system," I am not aware that the accuracy of the observations of wave motion as recorded in the *Modern System of Naval Architecture* has been impugned; and a study of these records, coupled with my own observations on the performances of ships, has led me to adopt Mr. Scott Russell's wave of the first order, or wave of translation, represented by the curve of versed sines, for the bow wave of displacement; and the wave of the second order, or the oscillating sea wave, cycloidal in form (a trochoid) for the wave of replacement aft.
>
> But what is of more value than any conclusion of a speculative nature is the fact that the peculiar form of the wave of the first order is found more or less accurately expressed in the entrances of some of the fastest sailing vessels of their size known. . . .

Colin Archer described the simplest effective method of designing a craft to suit his interpretations of wave form theory and outlined its application to craft of various sorts, emphasizing that, "the constant nature of the curve adopted for the fore body precludes all discussion as to the fullness to be given to the entrance." However, this was not intended to apply to the after end, for which formulas were given to decide the radius of the generating circle for the trochoid to suit the type of craft intended.

He concluded his paper by stressing the importance of the subject to the practicing designer and hoping that further research would be carried out, intimating that Professor William Froude, who undertook research for the British Admiralty, might be interested.

Scott Russell joined the discussion that followed and, although naturally critical of Colin Archer's interpretations, was appreciative that his work had attracted notice from overseas. Dixon Kemp, a leading English yachting author and observer who was also yachting editor of *The Field,* joined in and afterwards generally accepted Colin Archer's views, incorporating a short analysis of the wave-form theory in his book *Yacht Architecture,* first published in 1885.

The publication of Colin Archer's version of the wave-line theory in *The Field* and the Institution of Naval Architects' transactions brought him considerable correspondence—some critical, but much of it requesting further information and guidance in interpretation of his design principles. In May, 1878, Archer recieved a letter from John H. Hyslop of New York, a well-known amateur yacht designer and a student of yacht development, who later was measurer for the New York Yacht Club. He had studied Scott Russell's wave-line theory and had also modified it in a similar manner to Colin Archer, after experimenting with models. Hyslop noted Archer's *Field* articles and sent copies of his own articles on his conclusions, then being published in America. This initiated a correspondence between Hyslop and Archer that lasted for many years and covered many yachting subjects: rating, design, and the *America*'s Cup challengers and defenders.

In a letter to Hyslop in 1878, Archer wrote:

> The conclusion I have formed that the shape of any particular set of lines is of subordinate importance has probably been derived from seeing clumsy, bluff bowed boats with absurd waterlines performing remarkably well under favorable conditions as compared to boats with wave-formed lines, and finding that these boats very often have a very good curve of sectional areas. . . . I may mention that I have now built nearly a dozen boats of various sizes on the system we have adopted, and I have every reason to believe that it is far superior to any I have used before, and I have tried the usual ones. I also use a modification of it for merchant ships. No very marked improvement on the best existing boats is, however, to be expected, since as you remark, builders have intuitively found out the best form without the aid of science; in fact, science must

probably here, as so often, be content to generalize the teaching of practical experience.

Surprisingly, Colin Archer's exposition of his wave-form system of design continued to have impact for many years. In September, 1898, the naval architect of the Dutch shipbuilding company Fijenoord, of Rotterdam, Mr. D. Croll, wrote of his intention to embody the wave-form principle in the design of several new steamships. In 1907, Croll sent Archer a photograph of the *Grotius*, Fijenoord's latest steamship, which was designed on the principle. Archer's reply summarized his feelings:

> It is very gratifying to me to find that the principle—which I have reason to believe has been used largely, though without acknowledgement, in the designs of yachts—can also be applied with good results to merchant steamers. As far as I am aware your firm is the first and only one (besides myself) who has had the pluck to make the attempt. . . . The ships I have designed on this plan have, I believe, all been successful and fast for their type, and I attribute the fact that the system has not been more generally adopted largely to my want of energy in not pushing it into notice.

Colin Archer was then 75 years old. He continued to be interested in the development and application of the wave-line theory as a guide to design until the end of his life. When 80 years old he corresponded with Johan Anker, referring to Anker's mention of the wave-form theory in a lecture to the Norwegian Engineers and Architects Society during 1911. Archer said, in part:

> . . . In my exposition of the wave theory I have neither prescribed nor mentioned any fixed degree of fullness for a boat's after body. On the contrary I consider it an advantage of the system that it gives the designer a free hand to decide on the fullness (displacement) of the after body in the light of his own experience. As regards the after body the function of the waveline—the displacement having been determined—is to indicate the most advantageous way in which to distribute the boat's mass longitudinally; in other words, it prescribes the rate at which the sectional areas diminish in relation to the area of the midship section as they recede from it. To be of any value a comparison between a given boat's after body and a wave form must necessarily be based on fixing for both boats the same value for the three factors—length, area of midship section and displacement. But the degree of fullness in the wave form depends on the size of the construction circle, and when these three factors are given, its radius,
>
> $$r = \frac{4d}{M} - \frac{2L}{\pi},$$
>
> where d is the displacement of the after body, L the after body's load waterline, and M the area of the midship section. By using a generating circle of this size a wave curve is obtained which indicates very nearly the actual displacement of the boat with which the comparison is made, though the lines do not necessarily coincide.
>
> You say, "It has been seen that it [Archer's theory] does not cover all forms and circumstances." This assertation is clearly undeniable. My claims do not extend so far. But when you say that "the reason for this is to be sought in the role played by the hull above water and in the influence of the stability moment," it appears to be that insofar as you refer to modern [sic] fast sailers, these can hardly be the right grounds. The wave theory, as far as I have understood it, applies only to the immersed portion of the hull. But, as it indicates no prescribed form for any one line—certainly for no waterline—but gives the designer all possible freedom here also, it must be an easy matter to adapt these lines in complete conformity with the requirements of the hull above water, so as to create a harmonious whole. . . .

This last paragraph reveals the wisdom of Colin Archer.

Colin Archer's wave form theory has since been discredited by many naval architects, but he designed successful craft and derived inspiration from it, and it was used by other designers, particularly of yachts.

Archer's best-known designs—the pointed stern pilot, rescue, and fishing vessels, and some of his yachts—had sections varying from a veed "peg top" form to a "wineglass" shape. These sections are easily driven at moderate angles of heel, and the forward and after bodies being similar, the fore and aft trim should be constant and the steering easy at all angles. Some had slightly harder bilge sections than others, with considerable beam, which exaggerated the section shape. Strangely, this type of craft was relatively easy to build.

Colin Archer also applied his theory to sailing merchant ships. For instance, during the 1880s, he was commissioned to design some sailing ships for the trade in mahogany from Minatitlan, Mexico, where it was necessary to negotiate a bar at the river entrance and other shallows. The load draft could not exceed 13 feet. Naturally, the owners wished the ships to carry the largest possible load on the draft and dimensions that would produce about 500 tons register, consistent with good handling characteristics. Archer based the form of the ends on the wave-form principle and inserted a suitable midship section. The *Scott* was the first of this type to Archer's design, built at Arendal and rigged as a bark. Her success led to the construction of many similar ships, some of which were built at the Raekevik yard, down the fjord.

Appendix B

COMPREHENSIVE LIST OF REDNINGSKOITES, 1893-1940

Number	Name	Builder	When Built	Remarks
1	*Colin Archer*	Colin Archer	1893	Sold 1933
2	*Langesund I*	Porsgrunn	1893	Sold 1913
3	*Tordenskjold*	Skipsbygger Rolfsen Bergen	1893	Sold 1905
4	*Feie*	Colin Archer?	1894	Sold 1905
5	*Liv*	Porsgrunn Batbyggeri	1894	Sold 1932
6	*Nordland I* (later *Havskaaren I*)	Colin Archer	1894	Lost 1900
7	*Bergen I*	Skipsbygger Rolfsen Bergen	1895	Lost 1907
8	*Oscar Tybring*	Colin Archer	1895	Sold 1937
9	*Stadt*	Skipsbygger Rolfsen Bergen	1895	Sold 1931
10	*Christiania*	Carl Arnold Christiania Batbyggeri	1896	Sold 1932
11	*Tromso* (later *Havskaaren II*)	Carl Arnold Christiania Batbyggeri	1897	Sold 1937
12	*Svolvaer*	Colin Archer	1897	Sold 1938
13	*Trondhjem*	Colin Archer	1899	Sold 1934
14	*Stavanger*	Colin Archer	1901	Sold 1939
15	*Langesund II*	Colin Archer	1901	Sold 1938
16	*Christiansund*	Porsgrunn Batbyggeri	1901	Sold 1921
17	*Christian Bors*	Skipsbygger Chr. Dekke Bergen	1904	Sold 1936

Number	Name	Builder	When Built	Remarks
18	*William Eger*	Colin Archer	1904	Sold 1934
19	*Halten*	Colin Archer	1907	Reserve 1940
20	*Bergen II*	Colin Archer	1907	Sold 1940
21	*Solli*	Colin Archer	1907	Reserve 1939
22	*Vardo* (later *Colin Archer*)	Colin Archer	1910	Reserve 1940
23	*Nordland II*	Brodrene Marcussen Lyngor	1910	Reserve 1940
24	*Risor I*	Brodrene Marcussen Lyngor	1911	Lost 1913
25	*Namsos*	Brodrene Marcussen Lyngor	1912	Motor installed 1935
26	*Bergens Kreds*	Brodrene Marcussen Lyngor	1912	Reserve 1939
27	*Vadso* (later *Oscar Tybring*)	Brodrene Marcussen Lyngor	1913	Reserve 1940
28	*Sandefjord*	Jens Olsen and Risor Batbyggeri	1913	Sold 1934
29	*Arne Fahlstrom*	Jens Olsen and Jebsen Risor Batbyggeri	1913	Motor installed 1935
30	*Risor II*	Jens Olsen and Jebsen Risor Batbyggeri	1914	Sold 1937
31	*Kristiansand* (later *Haugesund*)	Jens Olsen and Jebsen Risor Batbyggeri	1914	Sold 1938
32	*Kragero*	Lindstol and Son Risor	1920	Motor installed 1934
33	*Larvik*	Lindstol and Son Risor	1920	Motor installed 1934
34	*Haugesund* (later *Kristiansand*)	Lindstol and Son Risor	1921	Motor installed 1931
35	*Johan Bruusgaard*	Tangens Mek Verksted, Tvedestrand	1924	Motor installed 1933
36	*Andreas Aaro*	Knut Christensen and Co. Moen, pr. Risor	1930	
37	*Catherine Booth*	Colin Archer	1901	Purchased 1931 Sold 1938
38	*Biskop Hvoslef*	Brodrene Lovfald, Rosendal	1932	
39	*Erik Farup*	Knut Christensen and Co. Moen, pr. Risor	1933	Dims: 55′ 3″ x 17′ 2″ x 8′ 4″ draft 70/90 H.P. Winchmann diesel
40	*Frithjof Wiese*	Knut Skaaluren Rosendal	1935	70/90 H.P. Winchmann diesel Dims: 56′ 5″ x 17′ 2″ x 8′ 4″ draft
41	*Christian Bugge*	Knut Christensen and Co. Moen, pr. Risor	1935	40/60 H.P. Winchmann diesel Dims: 58′ 7″ x 17′ 2″ x 8′ 4″ draft

Number	Name	Builder	When Built	Remarks
42	*Storebrand*	Knut Christensen and Co. Moen, pr. Risor	1936	90/140 H.P. Winchmann diesel Dims: 60′ 8″ x 17′ 10½″ x 8′ 6½″ draft
43	*Astrid Finne*	Anker and Jensen	1937	90/140 H.P. Winchmann diesel Dims: 60′ 8″ x 17′ 10½″ x 8′ 4″ draft
44	*Idun*	Knut Christensen and Co. Moen, pr. Risor	1937	90/140 H.P. Winchmann diesel Dims: 60′ 8″ x 17′ 10½″ x 8′ 6½″ draft
45	*Christian Bors II*	Gravdals Skibsbyggeri og Trelast forretning	1937	100/140 H.P. Union Diesel Dims: 61′ 8½′ x 17′ 10½″ x 8′ 6½″ draft
46	*Thomas Fearnley*	Knut Christensen and Co. Moen, pr. Risor	1938	90/140 H.P. Winchmann diesel Dims: 60′ 8″ x 17′ 10½″ x 8′ 6½″ draft
47	*Ragnhild Schanche*	Lindstols Skibsbyggeri, Lindstol, pr. Risor	1938	90/140 H.P. Winchmann diesel Dims: 62′ 4″ x 17′ 10½″ x 8′ 6½″ draft
48	*Gustav B. Bull*	Lindstols Skibsbyggeri, Lindstol, pr. Risor	1939	90/140 H.P. Winchmann diesel Dims: 62′ 4″ x 17′ 10½″ x 8′ 6½″ draft
49	*Willie Wilhelmsen*	Knut Christensen and Co. Moen, pr. Risor	1939	90/140 H.P. Winchmann diesel Dims: 64′ 0″ x 18′ 4½″ x 8′ 6½″ draft
50	*Osloskoyta*	Knut Christensen and Co. Moen, pr. Risor	1940	90/140 H.P. Winchmann diesel Dims: 62′ 4″ x 17′ 10½″ x 8′ 6½″ draft
51	*Fredrik Langaard*	Knut Christensen and Co. Moen, pr. Risor	1939	90/140 H.P. Winchmann diesel
52	*Ole O. Lian*	Lindstols Skibsbyggeri, Lindstol, pr. Risor	1940	100/140 H.P. Union diesel

Appendix C

SCANTLINGS FOR SECOND SERIES REDNINGSKOITES

THE KEEL

Pitch pine or good Norwegian pine in one piece. It should be cut along the sides to a thickness of 6 inches. It should fit the iron keel and should have 6⅝-inch transverse clinked bolts. The iron keel is about 5-6 tons, and should be fastened with two iron screw bolts to each frame 1½-1¼ inches. The iron keel could consist of two horizontal layers. The fillings at the end of the iron keel should be made of hard wood.

THE STEM

The stem should be cut along the sides to 6 inches, decreasing from the waterline to about 4 inches at the keel. In the longitudinal plane, it should be 7 inches at the upper end, and about 10 inches at the keel.

THE STERNPOST

The sternpost should be 7 inches sidecut, and in the longitudinal plane as the stem. Both the stem and the stern should be made of oak.

DEADWOOD KNEES

For both stem and stern, the deadwood knees should be 10 inches in the center and fastened with ⅝-inch through bolts.

FRAMES

The frames are mostly pine, but also some oak. They should be sidecut to 3½ inches with the exception of those frames where the bolts for the iron keel come through; they should be 5 inches thick. The frames are built in two rings that should be compact bolted together. Between the rings it should be lubricated with carbolineum [carbolineum is an old type of wood impregnation/primer]. Double floors, deadwood, should be pointing in the opposite direction of each other at the top of the timber, tie plates 1½ inches by ¼ inch should be fastened with through bolts or iron nails that should be bent. The frame spacing should be 0.60 meter. The frames should be fastened (before the planking is started and before the iron keel is installed) to the wooden keel with one through bolt in each frame.

THE KEELSON

The keelson should be made of oak, from the frame in front of the mast to the pump, about 12 inches by 4 inches in the middle, more narrow toward the ends. All the bolts for the iron keel run through the keelson.

THE OUTER PLANKING

The outer planking should be made of 1½-inch oak, approximately 20 planks. The planks should not be wider than 6 inches. Each plank is fastened with a wooden nail (made of juniper) and a 5-inch nail to the frames.

OAK RIBS (BENT TIMBERS)

The ribs should be made of 3-inch by 1-inch oak, and there should be one between each frame. They should be plugged into the wooden keel and fastened to each plank in the outer planking with a clinker nail.

CLAMPS

The clamps are about 8 inches by 2 inches amidships, the thickness decreasing toward the stem and the stern; should be fastened with nails, and should be connected to the stem and the stern by knees.

HEADLEDGES

2½-inch oak. Under all the headledges, carlings are placed.

THE DECK

To be made of pine, the planks 2 inches thick and not wider than 4 inches. To be fastened to the beams by two nails. The deck planks should have smooth sides and should be caulked.

THE WATERWAYS

5 inch by 3 inch. Made of oak, and should have a rebate [rabbet] for the deck. They should be fastened to the frames by holdfasts.

THE BOLLARDS

5-inch by 5-inch oak, the lower end to be fastened to a frame.

BULWARK STANCHIONS

3-inch by 3-inch oak, should be fitted into the waterways. Screw bolts are placed under, running through the pillars.

THE "BEKKEN"

To be built as shown, the upper plate made of 4-inch oak. [It is not known what bekken means.]

THE RUDDERSTOCK

10-inch by 4-inch oak, decreasing from the waterline downwards. It should have three rudder irons.

THE FLOOR CEILING

Should be laid upon beams that are fastened to the frames. Should be made of 2½-inch pine, and it should have watertight hatches amidships to take in ballast. The floor ceiling should be fastened to the pillars.

THE CLOSE CEILING

1¼-inch pine to go from the clamps to the floor ceiling. It should be caulked watertight.

THE TRANSVERSE BULKHEADS

In the hull, four watertight bulkheads will be placed. They are made of 2-inch tongued and grooved planks, and will divide the hull into three, plus the ends.

NOTE

The floor ceiling, the close ceiling and the bulkheads will form an inner hull that will keep the boat afloat if the outer planking is damaged.

BLOCK LIST

Throat halyard patent block; one, 8 inch, double, with shackle and becket.

Throat halyard patent block; one, 8 inch, double, with shackle. The lower peak halyard patent block; five, 8 inch, single, with vacant hooks.

Main sheet, iron; one, 8 inch, double, on the horse with kevels [clamps].

Main sheet, iron; one, 8 inch, double, under the boom with shackle and becket.

Jib halyards; one, 6 inch, single, with stiff hook and becket. Upper.

Jib halyards; one, 6 inch, single, with stiff hook. Lower.

Jib sheets, iron; two, 7 inch, single, with ordinary vacant hooks.

Jib sheets, iron; two, 7 inch, single, with long vacant hooks.

Outer jib halyards; one, 6 inch, single, with stiff hook. Lower.

Outer jib halyards; two, 6 inch, single, with vacant hooks. On the mast.

Reefing block; one, 6 inch, single, with becket and stiff hook.

Reefing block; one, 6 inch, double, with stiff hook.

Tack block; one, 5 inch, double, with rope strop.

Tack block; one, 5 inch, single, with stiff hook and becket.

Tack block; ½-inch Bullseye fairlead to be bent on the upper part of the boom.

Mizzen sheet; one, 5 inch, single, at the horse with shackle and becket.

Mizzen sheet; one, 5 inch, double, with shackle under the boom.

Mizzen throat and peak halyards; 2.5 inch, single, with rope strop.

Topsail sheet; one, 5 inch, single, with rope strop.

Topsail halyards; one, 5 inch, single, with rope strop.

Topsail halyards; one, 5 inch, single, with stiff hook.

Outer jib stretch block; one, 5 inch, single, with stiff hook.

Outer jib stretch block; one, 5 inch, single, with rope strop.

Outer jib sheets; two, 6 inch, single, with rope strop.

Deadeyes; 12 units, 4 ¾ inch, single, ⅞-inch holes. Notch for iron 1½ inches by 3⁄16 inch.

Bullseye fairlead; 6 units, 1½ inch, single, outer jib sheets, main sail tack, topsail sheet, topsail downhaul.

Bullseye fairlead; 6 units, 5⁄4 inch, single, flag halyards and so on.

Bullseye fairlead; 6 units, 1 inch, single.

INDEX